L. Malloch

A HARVEST-FLY OF THE DAY SALUTES A KATYDID OF THE NIGHT

OUR INSECT FRIENDS *and* FOES *and* SPIDERS

A series of fascinating stories of Bee, Ant, Beetle, Bug, Fly, Butterfly, Moth, and Spider life

WITH SIXTY-FOUR PAGES REPRODUCING OVER 500 INSECTS AND SPIDERS AND THEIR HABITS IN THEIR NATURAL COLORS

Foreword *by Dr. Gilbert Grosvenor, President of the National Geographic Society;* Exploring the Wonders of the Insect World, and Insect Rivals of the Rainbow, *by William Joseph Showalter, Chief of the Division of Research, National Geographic Magazine;* Man's Winged Ally, the Busy Honeybee, *by James I. Hambleton, Senior Apiculturist, Bureau of Entomology and Plant Quarantine, U. S. Department of Agriculture;* Stalking Ants, Savage and Civilized, *by W. M. Mann, Director, National Zoological Park, Washington, D. C.;* Living Casks of Honey, *by Jennie E. Harris;* Strange Habits of Familiar Moths and Butterflies, and Where Our Moths and Butterflies Roam, *by William Joseph Showalter;* Afield with the Spiders, *by Henry E. Ewing, Entomologist, U. S. Department of Agriculture;* California Trapdoor Spider Performs Engineering Marvels, *by Lee Passmore.* Paintings of Life Habits of Insects, *by Hashime Murayama, Staff Artist, National Geographic Magazine.*

PUBLISHED BY

THE NATIONAL GEOGRAPHIC SOCIETY

WASHINGTON, D. C., U. S. A.

1935

FOREWORD

IN this volume the National Geographic Society presents collected articles and color pages on insects and spiders that have appeared in the NATIONAL GEOGRAPHIC MAGAZINE during the past decade. Taken together these articles and their accompanying color illustrations represent a combined description of insect and spider life without counterpart in our literature.

The chapter "Exploring the Wonders of the Insect World" and its companion chapter "Insect Rivals of the Rainbow," by Dr. William Joseph Showalter of the NATIONAL GEOGRAPHIC MAGAZINE staff form a fitting introduction to insect life and the many strange quirks of nature it exhibits, and the 24 pages of natural color reproductions of insects from the camera of Edwin L. Wisherd and the brush of Hashime Murayama constitute magnificent studies.

When James I. Hambleton undertook to write about and Hashime Murayama to paint the habits of the honeybee, they caught man's sweet-making friend in its most delightful moods. The bee becomes a fascinating creature as writer and artist reveal the magic of its life.

Dr. William M. Mann, Director of the National Zoological Park in Washington, is the author of the chapter on "Stalking Ants, Savage and Civilized." Dr. Mann's activities have ranged from trapping giraffes in Tanganyika to searching for a "long lost" species of ant in Haiti. Every continent has felt the tread of his footsteps as he has added to zoological lore.

Jennie E. Harris, in Chapter V, has written charmingly of "Living Casks of Honey," those ants in Colorado, which, lacking the instinct of building container comb, deliberately elect a life of self-sacrifice and allow their fellows to gorge them with honey until they get so big all they can do is to hang up on the wall until their neighbors want a meal of honey or wish to store some additional nectar.

"Strange Habits of Familiar Moths and Butterflies" and "Where Our Moths and Butterflies Roam," by Dr. Showalter, constitute delightful studies of the ways of these colorful winged insects. The late Dr. Harrison G. Dyar, a devoted butterfly collector and member of the staff of the United States National Museum, made possible the 16 pages of color with these chapters.

In "Afield with the Spiders," which constitutes Chapter VIII, Dr. Henry E. Ewing, Entomologist of the United States Department of Agriculture, spins a most pleasing story about the various members of the spider clan. Indeed he matches in the artistry of his words and the facts spun together the gossamer webs the spiders weave. Set off by the art of Hashime Murayama in a series of color paintings, Dr. Ewing succeeds in making our introduction to the spiders an adventure in wonderland.

Lee Passmore, in Chapter IX, introduces us to the trapdoor spider and the engineering marvels wrought by the California branch of that family.

GILBERT GROSVENOR,
President and Editor.

Contents

A DAINTY MONARCH FINDS A DOWNY COUCH

This beautiful butterfly of the genus *Anosia* (see text, page 186) is posed from life and shown taking a brief siesta on a thistle.

CHAPTER I

Exploring the Wonders of the Insect World

By WILLIAM JOSEPH SHOWALTER, Sc.D., LL.D.

Author of "Exploring the Glories of the Firmament," "Exploring the Mysteries of Plant Life," etc., etc.,
in the NATIONAL GEOGRAPHIC MAGAZINE, and Co-author of "The Book of Wild Flowers"

THOUGH intrepid explorers have conquered the earth's opposite poles, climbed its highest mountains, crossed its most dangerous deserts, penetrated its deepest jungles, and sounded its most profound seas, fortunately they have left many realms closer home and less challenging to human endurance where the humblest of us can lead expeditions and from which the poorest of us may bring back rich trophies of new knowledge.

Insectdom is one of these near-by realms that offers rare rewards to those whose eyes are alert, whose minds are keen, and whose patience is unrelenting. It begins in our own dooryards and stretches as far afield as we choose to wander. The man, or woman, or child who turns explorer there will find among its tiny folk more occasions to marvel than Gulliver in all his travels, more reasons to wonder than the fabled adventurer into the topsy-turvy territories of the Kosekins.

For among the insects one finds habits of life that run the gamut of interest, from the amazing to the bizarre; discovers traits that in some ways seem to transcend human intelligence; beholds untaught powers of foresight that appear to outshine man's most highly trained faculty of taking thought of the future; sees intricate chemical and physical problems solved in a manner worthy of our finest laboratories; gets glimpses of natural powers of perception that go far beyond our unaided senses and rival the detecting powers of the finest instruments that science has brought to the student's aid. One even runs upon solutions of involved social problems that civilization has tried vainly to master.

INSECT FORERUNNERS OF MODERN INVENTORS

Into this wonder world many explorers have gone who could match the intrepid courage of a pole-seeker with the unconquerable patience of a life-history hunter. Whoever reads Fabre and Forel, Comstock and Kellogg, Lutz and Wheeler, the Peckhams and the Raus, and scores of others knows alike what infinite treasures of truth already have been gathered and what bonanzas of interest still lie untouched.

Through such workers as these we have learned that long before our ancestors had emerged from their primeval caves, or had dreamed of a better anesthetic than a club, the glowworm had evolved a sleeping potion so subtle that its victim could not perceive its administration, yet so powerful that nothing could disturb the profound sleep it induced.

When our forebears were dressing in skins and before they had domesticated even the dog, the bagworms, larvae of the Psyche moths, were tailoring themselves snug coats and close-fitting nightcaps, while the ants were keeping "cows" and growing "mushrooms" (pages 16, 17).

Before primeval man had learned to kindle his first fire or dreamed of the use of coal, the social bees were employing in hive ventilation the identical principles that industry now uses in keeping pure air in modern coal mines.

While our race was still without the

© Lynwood M. Chace

A DRAGON-FLY THAT HAS JUST EMERGED FROM ITS NYMPHAL STAGE

This gauzy-winged creature has just transformed itself from a nymph, such as is shown in the lower left corner of the picture. It will cling to the grass stem until the chitin of its body hardens and until the fluid that flows through the hollows of the struts forming the framework of its wings crystallizes. Then it will be ready to fly away, one of the swiftest of all the insect clan.

slightest understanding of the functions of the nervous system, some of the wasps had learned to paralyze their prey and to classify insects according to the unity or multiplicity of their ganglia.

Far antedating man's earliest employment of the principles of cold storage and sterile preserving, the wasp was keeping meat fresh for weeks and the bee was storing honey that remained sweet indefinitely.

Long before modern civilization had appeared upon the face of the earth, the caddis-fly's children were building themselves submarines and some species were attacking their victims without warning.

The Eumenes wasp was a finished potter, employing fine natural cements and excellent hydraulic mortars, ten thousand generations before the human artisan knew how to fashion a flint.

The bombardier beetle employed gas against his enemy unnumbered centuries before the oriental invented the stinkpot or man resorted to gas warfare.

AMAZING ADAPTATIONS TO ENVIRONMENT

While man has progressed mainly through the development of the intellect, meeting his problems of existence through the powers of his mind, Nature has helped the insect hosts climb their ladder of achievement by developing their physical adaptations to the requirements of their environment.

For vast ages and countless generations it has been the great Master Breeder sternly, even if so slowly as to make it an almost imperceptible process, weeding out the weaklings and protecting the fit. In this way every physical and instinctual quality that has made an insect more suited to its environment has been further improved.

These processes, employed with such profit by man in the development of qualities that the better meet his needs in flowers, fruits, grains, horses, cattle, dogs, and poultry, have wrought marvelous transformations in the insect, both in body structure and life habit.

Through them the wasp has achieved the poisoned dagger with which to paralyze its prey; the bee has mastered the secret of sex control; the wingless springtail has produced a triggerlike, stiff hair that provides it with powers of locomotion; the adult May-flies of some species have done away with mouths and stomachs because their mature lives are too short to need them; the dragon-flies have come to possess eyes with as many as thirty thousand facets, to furnish the intense vision required in capturing darting, fast-flying prey.

Through these processes, also, the walking sticks have come to look like twigs; butterflies relished by the birds have developed a close resemblance to those the bird's palate detests; certain flies that prefer the precincts of the bumblebee's nest have copied the bumblebee's clothes and stature in order to be rated as members of the family rather than as interlopers.

The plant-lice have eliminated males from all but one of their many annual generations, and under laboratory tests have produced 94 generations without the interposition or birth of a single male. The ants bring up heirs apparent to the thrones of their kings and queens, and wood-boring grubs have been known to live forty years in seasoned wood. Carpet-beetles have lived two years in a corked bottle with nothing whatever to eat save the cast-off skins of their own transformations.

THE AGE OF INSECTS

From these fragmentary recitals of some of the ways in which the denizens of the insect world meet their problems of life and solve their enigmas of existence, it is plain that nowhere, either in the fields of fact or fancy, can there be found more surpassing marvels than are to be discovered among the humble folk whom most people dismiss from their minds as mere "bugs."

Man proudly refers to the various epochs of his own history as the Stone Age, the Iron Age, the Age of Electricity, etc.; but, after all, and in terms of epochs immeasurably longer, this is preeminently the age of

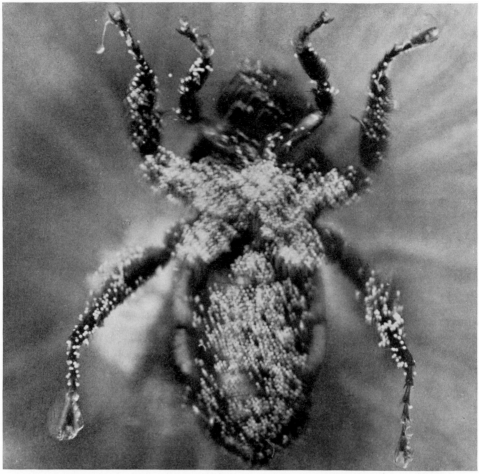

Photograph by Paul Griswold Howes

AN ENLARGED VIEW OF THE UNDER SIDE OF A BUMBLEBEE, SHOWING HOW
POLLEN GRAINS ADHERE TO ITS HAIRS

In visiting the flowers for nectar and pollen out of which to make the paste which it feeds
to the larvae in its nest, the bumblebee gets a liberal coating of pollen grains. As it passes
from flower to flower many of these grains are left on the stigmas, thus fertilizing them.
In this way the bumblebee serves equally well the flowers and the babies of its own household.

Insects. Both in the number of species and of individuals, the insect hosts are the dominant life of the faunal world. As far back as 1907, according to Dr. Frank E. Lutz, more than 384,000 species of them had been described, and the average annual number of new forms found ranges around 6,000. As entomologists penetrate the tropical world more deeply, the annual accretion of new species tends to increase with the passing years.

Estimates of the total number of described and undescribed species range from two to ten millions. Even at the more con-servative figure, this would be six times as many as there are of all other animal species combined.

Within a radius represented by a single hour's motor ride, one may find more kinds of insects than there are species of birds in the whole world, and within an hour's walk, more kinds than there are species of mammals in all creation.

When the first ambitious creatures of the "bug" world, which bore a rather close resemblance to our present-day spring-tails, fish-moths, and silver-fish, began to climb the ladder of winged evolution, re-

Photograph by Paul Griswold Howes

A SMALL BEE SCRAPES POLLEN FROM ITS FURRY COAT

The coming of such pests as the recently arrived Mediterranean fruit-fly (see pages 10, 11), the European corn-borer, and the Japanese beetle sends shivers of well-founded dread through the American people; but if our bee friends were to leave us *en masse* we would be even more alarmed. Without their pollen-carrying activities most of our flowers and many of our fruits would disappear.

leasing themselves from the bondage of feet, they found opportunities for colonization, for multiplication, and for promoting their freedom from enemy attack denied to all creatures limited to legs for locomotion.

AN EONS-LONG STRUGGLE

Chetverikov, the Russian naturalist, describing the trends of early vertebrate and insect life, says that in geological times the vertebrates seemed bent on growing larger, defending themselves in the struggle for survival by accumulating strength. The grass eaters grew larger and stronger, to save themselves from the flesh eaters, and the flesh eaters, in their turn, had to grow stronger and fleeter in order to hold their own in the contest. Finally, both got too big for their environment and both disappeared, leaving no living species to trace descent from them, and with only their fossil remains persisting to proclaim their one-time existence.

The insects chose another route to survival. With the brevity of life cycle that characterized them, a contest with the vertebrates in size would have been futile; but in smallness they could find a vast number of nooks where they could live in safety, thus filling the chinks and crannies of creation. Just as gravel, then sand and dust, more and more firmly fill the free spaces between the stones in a pile, so the hordes of insects, innumerable as gravel and small as sand, fill the crevices in creation left by the vertebrates.

But even with their smallness the insects of bygone geological ages needed protection. They achieved it by wearing their skeletons on the outside of their bodies and in their wings, and ever since have been growing smaller, although retaining their other major characteristics.

Back in those remote eras when the earth's vast deposits of coal were still living vegetation, the forest swamps were inhabited by cockroaches longer than a man's

Photograph by Wide World Photos

A HELMET AND CHIN STRAP OF HONEYBEES

Some strains of honeybees are mild, sweet-tempered, and gentle; others are nervous, excitable, and cross. Most of them seem instinctively to know who is afraid of them and who is not, and to react to the confidence or fear of those who approach their hives. The Ohio beekeeper here shown fashioned his dramatic headgear through a gentle and fearless handling of his swarm.

finger; dragon-flylike creatures with wing spreads of thirty inches pursued the sluggish prey, and ancestors of our May-flies that were as large as a laborer's hand swarmed around at sunset.

Living on the earth long before man came to take his place in the rôle of one having dominion, the insects will, it is freely predicted by many scientists, still remain long after man has ceased to be a mundane tenant. Dr. W. J. Holland, in his classic work on moths, says:

"When the moon shall have faded out from the sky, and the sun shall shine at noonday a dull cherry-red, and the seas shall be frozen over, and the ice-cap shall have crept downward to the Equator from either Pole, and no keels shall cut the waters, nor wheels turn in mills; when all cities shall have long been dead and crumbled into dust, and all life shall be on the very last verge of extinction on this globe; then, on a bit of lichen, growing on the bald rocks beside the eternal snows of Panama, shall be seated a tiny insect, preening its antennae in the glow of the worn-out sun, representing the sole survival of animal life on this our earth, a melancholy 'bug'."

Photograph by Dorothy Smith

A GOOD-SIZED SWARM OF BEES

By the quality of the food given the female larvae, worker bees determine whether these shall develop into full-sexed queens or whether their reproductive organs shall be so stunted as to make them practically sexless—fellow-worker bees. So well is the royal bee jelly compounded in the hive that even the beekeeper, feeding it to the larva in the cell, can produce a queen at will (see text, page 11).

FRIENDS AND FOES OF THE WINGED WORLD

Literally true? Certainly not, but a powerful picture of the tenacity of insect life, which was here eons before the first mammal appeared and which probably will be here eons after man's last city shall have been buried beneath the débris of thousands of centuries!

In the furious struggle for survival which is ever raging among the various species of insects, man gains some wonderful allies in his own fight for a place in the sun. They prey upon our insect foes as these latter prey upon our food supplies, whether in field or garner, and prevent them from eating us out of house and home.

The Hessian fly, the codling moth, the

Photograph by Paul Griswold Howes

A LADY-BIRD BEETLE EATING A PLANT-LOUSE

The plant-lice have eliminated males from all but one of their many annual generations, and under laboratory tests have produced 94 generations without the interposition or birth of a single male (see text, page 3). On the leaf, supported by a hair to keep it out of harm's way, is an egg of a golden-eyed lace-wing fly. The larvae which emerge from such eggs resemble tiny dragons, and, like the lady-bird beetles and their larvae, feed upon plant-lice.

but these are so greedy and so prolific that the damage they do in the United States alone amounts to more than a billion dollars a year (see illustrations, pages 10 and 11).

The insectean warfare does not end on the battle ground between our enemies and our friends. It is estimated, indeed, that about 50 per cent of all the species are engaged in preying on other insects, including those whose tremendous board bill we have to pay. Watch the wasps provisioning their nests with grasshoppers and caterpillars, or the parasitic flies laying their eggs on cut-worms and in the egg clusters of other enemies; watch the dragon-flies devouring mosquitoes, or the lady-bird beetles combating San José scale, and you will see our faithful friends rendering a vast, even if unconscious, service to humanity.

But the service of our insect friends only begins when they hold our foes in check. Where would be our fruits and our flowers, where our clovers and our vegetables, were it not for the insects that enable them to set seed for our welfare!

San José scale, the army cut-worm, the peach-tree borer, the cabbage-caterpillar, the Colorado potato beetle, the Japanese beetle, the Mexican bean beetle, and the apple aphid are only a few examples of the tremendously prolific species that are uninvited and unwelcome "spongers," which insist on being fed before we ourselves can eat.

It is estimated by careful entomologists that only about one per cent of the insect species is directly injurious to man's crops;

CURIOUS QUIRKS OF THE HUMAN APPETITE

Our fruit crops alone are now worth some $600,000,000 annually. They would be negligible in quantity and value without the winged messengers that carry pollen from blossom to blossom.

Strange as it may seem, insects and their eggs form favorite articles of diet in many parts of the world.

The Moors fry locusts in butter made from camel's milk, the pupae of silk-worms are eaten in China, and some species of moths are relished in parts of Africa. Several species of beetles are prized articles of food in Turkey, Moldavia, Walachia, and elsewhere, while in Nyasaland a paste of May-flies and mosquitoes is eaten with gusto. Some tribes of Mexican Indians, by infusing tiger-beetles in alcohol, make a "hooch" that in the amount of "lightning" it possesses excels any U. S. A. brand of bootleg.

The insects make important contributions to the world's commerce as well as to regional food supplies. Shellac, which has so many uses, from wax for our floors to stiffening for our derby hats and disk

Photograph by International

PACKING LADY-BIRD BEETLES IN BAGS FOR SHIPMENT

It would be difficult for man to find a better friend among the insects than the lady-bird beetles. They are raised in large quantities and shipped to fruit- and vegetable-growing districts to become allies of man in holding in check scale-insects and plant-lice, which they devour both in larval and adult forms. This shipment is from California.

material for our phonographs, is made from lac, the secretion of an Asiatic scale. A beetle known as the Spanish fly is transformed into one of the medical world's principal blistering agents and forms an ingredient of many hair washes.

Tannin and ink are derived from various galls; the cochineal, a scale-insect, is used to make a dye found superior to synthetic dyestuffs for coloring soldiers' uniforms, while the silk-worm is the manufacturer of the world's most prized textile threads, and the bee a maker of a delectable sweet.

Some one has remarked that the insects crawl on their backs instead of on their bellies—a statement that is anatomically much more than a half truth. What corresponds in them to our spinal cord lies along the under side of the creatures' bodies; their hearts and stomachs, on the other hand, are near the top surface. The skeletons of insects are made up of a series of segments or rings; and, whether in a grasshopper, a dragon-fly, or a moth, in an ant, a house-fly, or a bee, most of these segments are apparent, if examined closely.

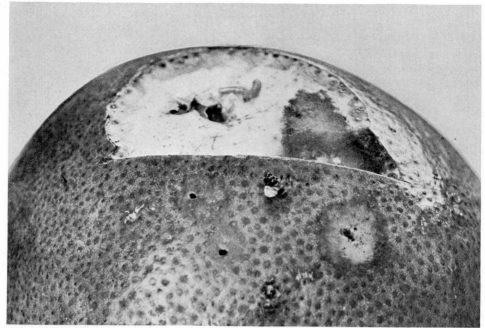

A GRAPEFRUIT FILLED WITH FRUIT-FLY PUNCTURES AND SHOWING THE MAGGOTS

A single fruit often carries as many as a score of punctures and sometimes as many as a hundred. The maggots are shown in the section from which the rind has been cut away.

There are other classes of creatures that have these ringlike segmental skeletons, but to qualify as insects they must have no more than six jointed legs when in their adult form. The "thousand-leggers," the scorpions, the spiders, and the ticks are all cousins, but they are all technically ineligible for membership in the insect "lodge" because they have too many legs.

The circulatory system is amazingly different from our own. In most species the hearts are not complex organs like ours, with divers chambers and sundry valves, but are simple, hollow tubes that contract in waves from end to end. Their blood is not red like ours, but yellowish or greenish. They have no veins or arteries through which the blood moves; rather, it is sent directly through the body cavity, which is filled entirely therewith.

With us, the heart sends the blood to the lungs to be purified and given a new supply of oxygen for its return trip through the capillaries. The insects, having no lungs, get their oxygen, not through the blood, but through little breathing tubes known as tracheae, which penetrate every part of the body.

FEEDING HABITS OF WIDE RANGE

The feeding habits of this class of creatures are of astounding range. The plant-lice, sucking the sap of rosebush, apple twig, or cucumber vine, love plant juices, just as the mosquito and the flea love animal blood. The honeybee and the butterfly, drinking the nectar of the flower, are in strange contrast to the sexton beetle and the flesh fly in the quality of their respective appetites.

The wood-borers, satisfied to spend their larval lives eating naught but insipid wood, as they digest their paths through the heart of oak and hickory and elm, have tastes infinitely less spicy than those of the "weevils" that are never so happy as when feasting on Cayenne pepper, or of the beetles that know no gustatory joy so satisfying as eating cigarettes.

In the reproductive organs one finds the most startling departures from the orthodox. In evolving their social system, the

Photograph courtesy U. S. Department of Agriculture

AN ORANGE GROVE DEVASTATED BY THE MEDITERRANEAN FRUIT-FLY, WHICH
WAS REPELLED ON ITS FIRST APPEARANCE IN AMERICA

In a bulletin published in 1918 the United States Bureau of Entomology said that there was little danger of the fruit-fly gaining entry through the medium of commercial shipments of fresh fruits. "But quarantine officials have found the pest in fruit concealed by tourists and in mail and express packages sent from infested countries by uninformed persons, and it is by such avenues that the pest is most likely to be introduced." The location of the infested area apparently justifies this prophecy.

community-building bees, ants, and wasps have developed highly organized females, which we know as queens, that are marvels of efficiency as egg-laying machines. They mate but once in a lifetime, and therefore have developed a tiny internal pouch in which the male life germs are held.

As they lay their eggs, the honeybee queens (see page 58, figure 2) are able, at will, to open or close the orifice of this pouch that leads to the oviduct, and thus to determine whether each egg shall or shall not be impregnated. The ones that are, produce females, and those that are not produce males. The queens, it will be seen from this, have come to be masters of the art of sex control.

Then the workers (see page 58, figure 4) come along with their own development of this art. By the quality of the food they give the female larvae they determine whether these shall develop into full-sexed queens or whether their reproductive organs shall be so stunted as to make them practically sexless—worker bees. So well is the royal bee jelly compounded in the hive that even the beekeeper, feeding it to the larva in the cell, can produce a queen at will. Yet science never has been able to solve the secret hidden in this queen-making royal jelly.

The sense of smell in some of the insects is almost unbelievably acute. The smelling organs are minute pits or projections on the antennae and possibly in some of the mouth parts, so arranged as to leave the nerve ends exposed to every odor and at the same time protected from harm. For instance, on a single antenna of an ordinary June beetle there are as many as forty thousand of these olfactory pits.

Some species, with their antennae re-

Photograph by Paul Griswold Howes

A COMMON HORNET STANDS GUARD AT THE ENTRANCE
TO ITS NEST

The photographer obtained this picture by building a special scaffold for his camera and using sunlight reflected from a mirror. The hornets and other wasps were the world's first manufacturers of paper. The manner in which they enlarge a little nest smaller than a hen egg into one as large as a half-bushel measure, without disturbing its symmetry or opening up its interior, is a masterpiece in building (see text, page 51).

necktie of white fur. Its wings, sprinkled with gray and brown, are crossed by a faint zigzag, edged with smoky white, and studded by a great eye with a black pupil and a variegated iris containing successive arcs of black, white, chestnut, and purple.

A female moth of this species emerged from her cocoon in Fabre's laboratory one May day. That night there came such a swarm of male moths that everybody was astounded. In the laboratory, in the kitchen, in the dining room they gathered. At least forty lovers had come to pay their respects to the marriageable bride born that morning. In eight days at least 150 wooers came to pay court to the moth virgin. Whence came they? Extraordinarily rare in Fabre's region, he thought that some of them must have traveled at least a mile and a half.

Surrounded with naphthalene, the young virgin's call still went forth and the lovers still came hence; but shut up in an air-tight jar, not a single visitor arrived to pay court. When the antennae of a visitor were cut off, an operation through which he evinced no pain, he became powerless to locate his affinity, though she was only a few feet away.

So it was with the banded-monk, a day flyer. A chance cocoon fell into the entomologist's hands. The oaks, where the banded-monks made their home, were miles

moved or covered with shellac, are unable to find either food or each other. If their eyes are blindfolded with pitch and their antennae left in normal condition they seem to suffer no inconvenience.

Fabre's classic experiments with the great peacock and banded-monk moths and with the truffle beetle show to what inconceivable lengths the sense of smell sometimes is developed.

The great peacock moth, the largest in Europe, is clad in chestnut velvet, with a away. Three years of diligent searching upon his own part and that of his family had failed to reveal a single member of this species in any of its stages from egg to adult.

But as soon as the newly hatched insect had reached the mating age swarms of banded-monk wooers came from somewhere out of the distance to pay court to her. This time the naturalist exhausted the whole list of powerful scents and stenches in an effort to overpower her "call." With what he called the concentrated odors of a gas works, a smoker's divan, a scent shop, an oil well, and a chemical factory, he still was unable to conquer the emanation that called the swains from over the hills.

We admire the amazing delicacy of the bird dog's nose. Going at a gallop, on his zigzag way across a field, he recognizes the scent of the quail from that of any of the thousand and one other odors issuing from grass and flower and shrub, from insect and bird and beast. Not only so; he discriminates between several kinds of quail scents, whether they be of the body, foot, or nest; whether fresh or old, or from birds approaching, standing still, or fleeing.

But even the setter's nose is a dull organ of perception beside the antennae of moths, beetles, bees, and butterflies.

We are so accustomed to seeing animals with their organs of hearing located in their heads that we are astonished to find that insects have other locations for their ears, and that they employ several principles be-

Photograph by Lynwood M. Chace

LOOKING A HORNET IN THE EYE

With its large kidney-shaped eyes, its jointed antennae, and its pincer-like mandibles, a hornet presents a fearsome aspect when magnified. The members of this family feed their young chewed-up bits of other insects (see text, page 53).

side the tympanum in translating air vibrations into sound.

PECULIAR POSITIONS FOR EARS

Among the short-horned grasshoppers (see page 30) the ears are in their abdomens, immediately back of and above the point where the hind legs emerge from their bodies. These appear as small, clear, round spots on the surface of the abdomen.

Katydids and crickets hear with their front legs, in which are located the ears that catch the music of their sweethearts' songs. Among the mosquitoes and midges the ears are in the antennae—very delicate

Photograph by Paul Griswold Howes

ANT GALLERIES IN THE CENTER OF A DEAD CEDAR TREE

At the base of the tree which furnished this picture were found fully two bushels of sawdust and chips which have been removed, bit by bit, by industrious carpenter ants (see, also, illustration, page 16). The termites join the carpenter ants in mining wood. Between them the beams of thousands of houses and other structures are weakened and in many communities the problem of termite-proofing structures becomes a serious one.

hairs that communicate the sense of vibration to certain nerves, which, in their turn, transmit it to the brain.

The throat is no more the source of the insects' song than is the head the seat of their ears. Some employ the principle of the violin; others a variation of the drum; still others the idea of the reed. Some make secondary music with organs built after the fashion of the flute, while many employ sign language as effective means of communication.

DRUMMERS AND FIDDLERS

When one hears the sonorous accusation that Katydid (see page 32, figure 3), it can be written down that another Adam is laying the charge at the door of another Eve, for the females of the Katydid family are voiceless. Mr. Katydid has his say with his wings. He rubs his nervure-roughened front wings together. On the one there is a filelike roughness, and on the other a resonant edge—an application of the fiddle-and-bow method of sound production. The crickets also are Fritz Kreislers instead of Carusos.

The hum of many orders of insects is a sound produced by the reed method—the rapid vibration of a tongue of some material. In the case of the bee and the fly, one wing is the tongue. The droning among the flowers, the quivering notes when enmeshed in a spider's web, the high-pitched buzz when making a getaway from such a trap—all these speak so plainly, even to human ears, of amiability, anxiety, or anger that one cannot avoid the conclusion that the bee knows how to express her moods as well as we.

There is still another kind of sound production. When a fly gets fast in fly paper we hear its shrill, high-pitched, nervous cry, although its wings are pinioned by the glue. That sound comes from tiny tracheae, or tubes, with which the body is shot through.

Photograph by Paul Griswold Howes

A PAIR OF ANTS MAKE THEIR TOILET

Living in dark burrows where the sun never enters, cleanliness is a rule of the ant community. They patiently scrub their bodies with their mandibles, so as to remove all adhering particles of dust. The positions into which they have to get to complete their tasks are often startling. Often one may be seen balancing itself on two legs and swinging its abdomen up to its mouth to brush and stroke it with meticulous care. The photograph is very much enlarged.

The bees have a voice produced in the same way, and any beekeeper will describe the piping of his bees.

It is by piping that the lady mosquito, intent on a meal of warm blood, gives the intended victim warning, thus proving that she is a bold highwaywoman rather than a cowardly thief.

FEATS OF STRENGTH AND ACHIEVEMENTS IN ENGINEERING

When man's strength and achievements in engineering are measured by the standards set by the insects, there are some phases of our success that are overshadowed entirely. The last Olympic record for a standing high jump was 6 feet 4⅜ inches. Yet the common flea—*Pulex irritans,* if you want his more exact name—is capable of jumping a hundred times as high as his own head. Were the Olympic champion high jumper able to do as well proportionately, he could clear the Washington Monument at a single bound, with some eighty feet to spare.

Likewise, if man's biggest structure were as large in proportion to the size of the adult human frame as the Pennsylvania ant hill is to the size of the ants that built it, we could boast of a pile five hundred times as big as that wonder of the ages, the Pyramid of Cheops; and the Eiffel Tower, built with the aid of all sorts of machinery, is no higher, proportionately, than the ant hill reared with claws and mandibles alone. If the modern baggageman could carry loads as heavy, in proportion to size, as the ants, he could lift a half-ton trunk to the top of the Washington Monument without apparent fatigue.

Kirby and Spence have pictured the strength of insects: "A wild bee or a Sphex (see page 54, figure 1), for instance, will dig a hole in a hard bank of earth some inches deep and five or six times its own size, and labor unremittingly at this arduous under-

Photograph by Paul Griswold Howes

CARPENTER ANTS AND THEIR APHID CATTLE

Many ants are stock raisers. They herd their colonies of aphids with as much care as a western plainsman tends his cattle. In utilizing the corn-root aphid a remarkable degree of intelligence is shown. In the fall the little insects are taken, in one or another of their stages of life, into the nests of the ants and carefully protected during the season of cold. In the early spring they are carried to the roots of the smartweed and other related plants, where they are "pastured" until the farmers' corn takes root. Then they are carried to the corn roots, which serve as grazing ground for the summer. Each aphid has a tiny tube on the upper rear part of its body, through which it secretes droplets of a sweetish substance which the ants drink with gusto.

kind of exertion it would require in a man to dig in a few days, out of hard clay or sand, with no other tools than his nails and teeth, five or six caverns twenty feet deep and four or five square, for such an undertaking would not b e comparatively greater than that of the insects in question."

THE COLORS OF INSECTS

Matching the fairest flowers that blow in the richness and iridescence of their coloring, some of the beetles, bugs, and bees rival the butterflies and moths, and even seem to challenge the rainbow itself, in their harmonies of hues (see color pages between 28 and 213).

The dung beetles of the South American pampa, we are told, combine the fire of gems with metallic luster, and, according to the incidence of light, emit the green reflections of the emerald or the gleam of ruddy copper — r a k e r s of muck that would do honor to the jeweler's showcase.

taking for several days, scarcely allowing itself a moment for eating or repose. It will then occupy as much time in searching for a store of food, and no sooner is this task finished than it will set about repeating the process, and before it dies will have completed five or six similar cells or even more.

"If you would estimate this industry at its proper value, you should reflect what

What Golconda do the scarab (see pages 79 and 81), the azure hoplia cockchafer, the golden apple beetle, and other species visit to gather their gems, and in what diggings do they find their golden nuggets?

THE REASON FOR INSECT COLORS

The general harmonizing of insect color and pattern with the color scheme of usual environment is recognized generally. It is the art of camouflage developed by ages of necessity for low visibility. Those insects hardest to see have the best chance to escape the birds, the lizards, the toads, and the predaceous insects of other species. Even in a single species, varieties of coloring are found in different localities. In each case the harmony between the insect and its environment is maintained.

Some insects mimic the colors of other species as a protection. The mimicking species are edible to their natural enemies, while the mimicked ones are noted for their repellent taste and therefore are given a wide berth by insectivorous creatures. The nearer the edible folk can imitate the non-edible, the better chance they have to escape a hungry mouth.

On the other hand, there are some insects noted for their high visibility rather than

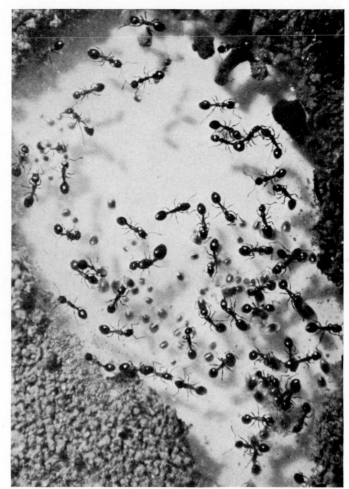

Photograph by Paul Griswold Howes

THE BUSY ROUTINE OF AN ANT HILL

The queen is the largest individual, in the center of the picture. In the group of five ants in the upper right corner two may be seen combing each other, a third is carrying an egg, while the other two rest. At the top is a worker carrying a ball of earth. Whether herding aphid "cows" (see opposite page), making slave raids, growing "mushrooms," or looking after guests of the colony, the ants disclose a remarkable social organization.

for their success at camouflaging. They are nearly all distasteful to the insectivorous folk, and they advertise themselves in bold-face type, so that the foe may "read as he runs" that they do not belong to the edible species. Some moths and flies (see page 52) that are perfectly harmless duplicate in coloration, as well as in outline, bees and wasps that have frightful stings.

THE SEVERAL STAGES OF EXISTENCE

The transformations that take place in the insect world are marvelous adaptations to environment. From the tiny egg to the repulsive caterpillar, and thence to the beautiful butterfly; from the slim egg to the fat grub, and thence to the iridescent June beetle; from submarine-building caddis-worm to the lace-winged fly; from the microscopic bee-louse to the blister-beetle—these are a few of the changes that take place in many species.

Some species undergo no striking changes on their journey from the egg to the grave except to grow wings. Other species, more numerous, such as the locusts, katydids,

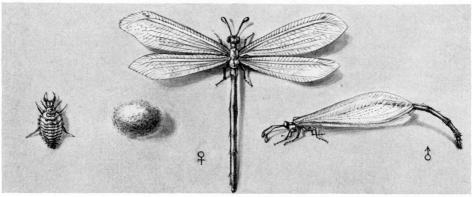

Painting by Hashime Murayama

TRAPS MADE BY WINGED LIONS TO CATCH ANTS

Often one sees symmetrical little craters in dry, sandy spots. These are pitfalls for ants. The winged lion shown below (female left, male right) lays her eggs in sand, and out of these emerge larvae in the form shown at the lower left of the picture and at the bottom of the cutaway crater. The ant that slips over the edge of one of these traps finds the sand exactly at the angle of repose and can get no foothold to crawl out again. The larva, sensing his struggles, comes out of the sand and captures him. One may induce the little creature to come out simply by tickling the sand in the crater with a straw.

crickets, and dragon-flies, undergo striking changes of environment and partial changes in their make-up. In their larvaehood they live in the ground or the water. As adults they could not survive such surroundings. They have many molts. As they outgrow one suit of clothes, it splits open on the back, and they creep out, all "dolled up in a new bib and tucker" of more liberal dimensions. This hardens because of the chitin in it, and splendidly serves its purpose until again the body is too big for its garb, when another splitting on the back marks the acquisition of a more commodious garment.

Various species have their own definite

A GROUP OF SPRING-TAILS BEFORE A BUFFALO NICKEL

These are among the most primitive of the insects. They possess a triggerlike apparatus on the under side of their bodies. When the trigger is released the insect is able to spring great distances. The spring-tails occur all over the world—on land, water, and ice.

number of molts. The Seventeen-year Locust is thought to get twenty-five new costumes during its heyday of life.

But the beetles, the butterflies, the moths, the bees, the ants, the wasps, the fleas, and such undergo utter transformations—from the egg to the maggot, from the maggot to the pupa, and from the pupa to the fly; from the egg to the caterpillar, from the caterpillar to the pupa, and from the pupa to the moth. The muscles change, the digestive tract is transformed, the creature's whole being is so made over that the environment of its one form would be fatal to its other.

Imagine a butterfly eating solid food, a June beetle (see page 79, figure 9) forced to live under ground, or a caddis-fly trying to dwell at the river bottom!

But the caterpillar does not eat for today alone. It foresees a morrow when, undergoing its transformation, it will have to spend days on end without a single bite of food, the while its entire interior, except possibly its nervous system and reproductive glands, turns into a thick fluid in which float bits of degenerating tissue. While the debris of the disintegrating larval body is being melted into liquid in this strange alembic of Nature, the fluid, in its turn, is being transformed into new tissues and new organs.

MARVELOUS MANIFESTATIONS OF INSTINCT

"One marvels," observes an English naturalist, "at the skill displayed by the bird in constructing its first nest; but it may be said that the newly mature bird has at least had a chance of watching a second-year matron of its kind building and getting some hints that way. In the case of the insects there is, as a rule, no possibility of such help. In the majority of species the mother is dead long before the daughter comes to that stage of existence when the necessity of providing for her progeny arises; so the knowledge has to pass by way of transmitted memory.

"Somewhere in the minute speck of protoplasm constituting the egg of one of the

Photograph by Paul Henri Fabre

A PRAYING MANTIS (ACTUAL SIZE) LAYS HER EGGS

The mantids deposit their eggs in curious masses, covered with a quick-drying mucus, on branches and plant stems, in the late summer and fall. From these the young emerge during the following summer and soon grow to maturity, molting several times and developing wings in the interim (see text, page 29).

flowers a n d n e v e r touches green leaves. Its caterpillar, however, would starve on rations of nectar. The butterfly knows, or— to be literally accurate, instead of figuratively correct—acts as if it knows, that the caterpillars which are destined to hatch from the eggs it lays must have green food, so it always lays them on leaves.

Likewise, one of the Meloe blister-beetles, cousin of the Spanish fly, lays its eggs by the thousand—perhaps four thousand the first day, three thousand the second, two thousand the third—near the burrows of certain mining-bees. Then, exhausted by the Herculean task of insuring the perpetuation of the species, the mother beetle crawls away and dies. Presently an innumerable host of small creatures come out of the ground, seek out the flowers frequented by the bees, such as the composites, and then hop onto the bees' backs as they come for nectar and pollen.

solitary bees, for instance, there is an infinitesimal particle of nerve matter which contains the secret of how to cut accurate circles and ovals of roseleaf so that a given number of them will overlap and curve into a perfect cylinder. During the greater part of its life the creature which hatches from that egg will have no need of the secret, but the germ of it will go on developing, and when the bee has reached its adult form there is the idea in the memory cells ready to instruct the nerves that govern the action of wings and legs and cutting jaws."

The milkweed butterfly sips the nectar of

A MURDERER UNMASKED

For a long time these tiny creatures were believed to be a species of louse infesting the bees, until Newport, the English entomologist, found them to be the babies of a Meloe beetle. Then Fabre studied them and found further that after one is safely ensconced in Mrs. Bee's fur it rides around on its animated airplane until she has provisioned her cell with pollen and honey. Then, at the moment the bee lays her egg on the pollen and honey, the little scamp makes a flying leap from the back of its hostess and lands on the newly laid egg, which it proceeds to use both as a life raft and a larder.

The poor bee, aiming to plant a germ of life, unwittingly permits this germ of death to fasten its tentacles to her hopes. She seals up the cell, but not for her own. The baby Meloe promptly tears open the shell and proceeds to feast upon the contents of the egg. Then it goes to sleep. For several years it stays in the cell it stole from the bee, taking divers naps therein, each time waking up transformed, and finally emerges a full-fledged Meloe beetle, ready to start the cycle all over again.

Only once in its life did the tiny creature have occasion to seek out a plant in which to hide; only once, occasion to steal a ride;

Photograph by Paul Henri Fabre

THE DEATH'S-HEAD SPHINX MOTH

Somehow this strangely marked insect has learned the secret of the queen bee's piping and has mastered the art of imitating the call of the mistress of the hive. The bees could without difficulty sting it to death. But they allow it to enter without protest and to lay its eggs. The larvae spin webs that do great damage to the bees' household.

only once, occasion to select a laying place contiguous to the harvest bee's home. Yet, with all the order of the succession of notes in a run on the piano, each act was performed with a sureness and a deftness as only man can show in his doings after years of training.

THREE YEARS IN THE SILENT HEART OF THE OAK

So, too, it is with the oak-boring grub and the long-horned Capricorn beetle (see pages 74 and 75) into which it is transformed. From an egg in a crevice in the bark of a tree does this grub come into existence. The mother is dead long before the grub begins to live. A tiny creature it is when emerging from the egg, but with a powerful set of woodworking tools in its head.

Three years it will spend eating its way through the wood of the tree. In the silent, somber solitude of the oak's inmost heart it eats its ever-broadening, ever-lengthening path. It has no eyes, for of what use could eyes be to a creature living in the utter absence of light? It lacks ears, for what could there be of interest for it to hear when utter

Photograph by Paul Griswold Howes

MASSES OF FROTH MADE BY FROG-HOPPERS

The frog-hoppers are a group of small, flat, brown or gray insects, which occasionally occur in sufficient numbers to injure grapes, cranberries, or pasture grasses. They get their popular name from the belief that these masses are the spittle of tree frogs. Their young, which in the earliest stages have no wings, a little later developing wing pads and finally wings, often are found imbedded in these masses, which apparently are used for a shelter.

stillness reigns perennially? And nose—what warning could a nose give, what gustatory delight, what olfactory happiness, where there is nothing but oak wood to meet, nothing but oak wood to eat, nothing but oak wood to smell?

And yet "this-nothing-at-all is capable of marvelous acts of foresight; this belly, which hardly knows aught of the present, sees very clearly into the future." After three years of eating, it finds itself called into the deep sleep from which it is destined to awaken as a full-fledged, stiff-armored, long-horned Capricorn beetle.

Urged on by an unfathomable presentiment to prepare for what never has happened before in its experience, at this juncture the grub bores to the surface, even braving the keen ears of that ancient foe of its race, the woodpecker, in order to provide an exit way for the beetle-to-be. Then it retreats a bit, excavates a transformation chamber, which is lined with a swan's down fabricated from sawdust. This is barri-caded with triple doors made from uric-acid secretions and bits of wood fiber. After these elaborate preparations, the grub lies down to the deep sleep of the transforming period.

But does this sleep-overtaken grub ever turn its head away from the exit? Not it, for by some strange plan of Nature this animated sausage has inherited the guidance that makes it act as if it had full foreknowledge that it is destined to wake up a full-fledged beetle, too stiffly armored and too well provided with horns to permit it to turn around in its narrow cell.

STRANGE COMBINATIONS OF WISDOM AND IGNORANCE

Perhaps the French larva known as the Pine Processionary, a tent-building caterpillar resembling in some ways our own familiar apple tree tent-caterpillar, affords entomology's classic example of blind ignorance coupled with seemingly surpassing intelligence.

Photograph courtesy American Museum of Natural History

A THOUSAND MIGRATORY MONARCH BUTTERFLIES IN ONE GROUP

In early autumn Monarch butterflies, *Anosia plexippus*, assemble in great swarms in the north-eastern section of the United States. This exhibit is in the halls of the American Museum of Natural History.

Photograph by Paul Griswold Howes

A GROUP OF GALLS MADE BY INSECTS

One often notes galls on plants of many kinds. While some of these peculiar formations are caused by certain kinds of fungi, most of them are produced by insects. The two open and one closed gall are of a type developed by one of the ichneumon flies. The whitish gall was produced by another species, whose young have emerged. In the two opened galls lie small capsules, out of which would have emerged young saw-flies if they had been undisturbed. The gall-making insect lays its egg in the twig, where an irritation results in a swelling which serves as a shelter for the young.

in late summer, the tiny caterpillars set to work to build themselves temporary silken tents; but when the tang of autumn touches the air, they construct a larger habitation of such strong silk that it can weather the winter gales without difficulty. By the end of winter this may be as large as a half-gallon measure—"the interior a combination of a ragshop and a sewage farm."

As they march forth from their tent on a sunny day for a meal of pine needles, the caterpillars travel in single file. There are no natural leaders, whichever happens to go first being, for the moment, the leader. Now it is this one and now that, but each caterpillar leaves a trail of silk behind it that acts as a life line to guide it back from the grazing grounds to the nest.

One day Fabre succeeded in getting a procession to start around the rim of a big palm vase. He cut

Fabre, in his "Souvenirs Entomologiques," gives a dramatic picture of this caterpillar's behavior under varying circumstances. It is the larva of a moth closely related to the silk-worm moth. In laying her eggs, this moth takes down from her own body to make a cover for her eggs, just as the eider duck plucks the downy feathers from her own breast to make a warm nest for her young.

After emerging from the clustered eggs

the line where it reached the rim, and the caterpillars, completing the circuit of the rim of the vase, unwittingly, guided by the life line they had left behind, started around again. All day long they kept marching around and around, for there was a solid ring of caterpillars, each with its head to the tail of the one before it. Far into the night they still journeyed on, slaves to their life line and bound to follow the one ahead. Morning dawned, finding them motionless and in a torpor, but still in formation.

With the warmth of the sun upon them and the urge of their appetites within them, they resumed their patient march. On and on, around and around they went. Night came again, with its weary halt, a n d a n o t h e r morning with its patient resumption of the unending path. A few stragglers sought a way out of the circle, but came back and resumed the gruelling march. T h e t h i r d night came, with its halt, and a n o t h e r m o r n i n g with its m a r c h i n g. So the fourth and the fifth. Footsore and weary, there were stragglers and confusion. The ring of caterpillars became a series of short p r o c e s s i o n s, which again were united before the close of the day. The sixth night, the seventh day, the seventh night, and still the go-round that was far from merry kept up, and with its marchers as footsore and weary as were ever members of Stonewall Jackson's foot cavalry or John J. Pershing's heroes of the Argonne drive. The eighth day dawned, and with it came a desperation that led them singly and in groups to fall out of ranks, and before night had come again the last one had found his nest once more.

Photograph by Paul Henri Fabre

A GLOWWORM EPICURE DINES ON SNAIL

Stealing up on the snail, the assailant administers an anesthetic so subtle that the victim is not aware that it has been attacked. After the anesthetic has become effective the glowworm covers small sectors of the victim's body with a peptonized saliva, which predigests the snail's tissue and turns it into an edible broth.

FORECASTERS OF THE MORROW'S WEATHER

Eighty-four hours on the march and eighty-four in bivouac, with never a mouthful to eat, with never the comforts of the home nest, all because of a slavish devotion to a life line and the instinct to follow the fellow ahead!

Prize "boneheads" of insectdom? Perhaps so. But wait! These same caterpillars, to whom being caught out in a rainstorm would be fatal, have developed, Fabre tells, methods of forecasting the weather that for weeks, during careful observations and comparisons with the records of the French Bureau of Meteorology, showed an amazing foreknowledge of the approach of foul weather.

Fabre, who has been called the "Homer

Photograph by Charles Martin

A FLIGHT OF LOCUSTS OVER AN ISLAND OF THE SULU SEA, PHILIPPINE ISLANDS

of the Insect World" and the "Incomparable Observer," and whose son is following in his footsteps, through his striking photographic researches, as revealed in many of the illustrations accompanying this article, has written at length on the strange intermingling of blank ignorance and surpassing foresight among the winged hosts.

SKILLED INSECT SURGEON HAS A MENTAL "BLIND SPOT"

The Pelopaeus wasp, a splendid potter and an exquisite surgeon, able, with equal facility, to build an ideal cell for her unhatched young and to paralyze, without killing, the spiders with which she provisions it, was unable to detect the removal of the first spider, with its attached egg, when she brought in the second one. Furthermore, she was unable to detect even the removal of the cell itself, and proceeded to plaster the bare spot where it had been, even as if it were there.

Likewise, the familiar Sphex wasp, one of the most highly skilled huntresses of the insect world, knows exactly what species to capture for her future babies, where to sting them so as to produce paralysis instead of death—meat preservation without salt or cold storage—but she seems to display utter stupidity at times. It is her practice to leave her cricket at the entrance while she goes below to see that all is well before she takes it down. Forty times Fabre moved the cricket back from the entrance no more than six inches. Forty times Mrs. Sphex dragged it up to the entrance again, going down each time for another needless inspection.

Some species of Bembex (see page 54) wasps do not provision their burrows, but bring the prey to their young as they need food, after the fashion of the birds. The entrance to their burrows is always in the sand. After getting down a little distance in more substantial soil, the gallery runs approximately parallel to the surface. On the surface there is no mark by which even a Fabre can detect the entrance.

Whether Mother Bembex comes in or goes out, the door of sand always closes behind her. She wanders far in search of prey, but always finds her doorpost as easily and definitely as if it were so plain that even the careless observer might see it. Yet if one excavates the gallery, leaving the entrance intact, she will go through the door, come out of the open gallery, go through the door again, and repeat the performance again and again. At the end of the gallery lies the grub that was the object of her maternal solicitude, the baby for whom she worked day in and day out. She does not recognize it now. She tramples upon it, ignores its presence as if it were only so much clay. It is not recognized for itself; she knows it only when it lies at the end of the gallery to which her doorway leads.

Even when the doorway is obliterated, with the gallery left intact, she recognizes neither the gallery nor the grub at its terminus. Her baby may starve before she will feed it, if either door or hallway is disturbed. She recognizes her offspring only as the grub that lies at the end of an undisturbed gallery leading from a door through which she passes.

COUNTLESS WONDER STORIES

One might wander indefinitely in the realms of insectdom, discovering at every step things that make the most blasé among us pause and ponder.

Parasitism, in which members of one species lay their eggs upon the bodies of other species, or even inject their living young into the bodies of other species; parthenogenesis, in which as many as 94 generations have been produced without the interposition or birth of a single male (page 3); ability to hibernate, in which some individuals have been known to sleep more than forty years and wake up—ten thousand wonder stories might be told of these strange creatures in whose lives is more romance than all the fiction writers in Christendom have been able to conjure up.

Painting by Hashime Murayama, after Paul Měry

SURPRISING EVENTS IN THE LIVES OF CADDIS-FLIES

Airy mannered, filmy winged, and long antennaed, one would hardly suspect the gentle creature perched on the lily as being the mother of the insectean inventor of the first submarine. She drops her eggs on the river bottom. These hatch, and the little wigglers build themselves cases of fiber and pebbles, which they line with silk. In these they can rise or sink at will. The diving beetle preys upon them as shown. The caddis-fly belongs to the family *Limnophilidae* (see text, page 3), and the diving beetle to the family *Hydrophilidae*. The insects illustrated are natural size.

CHAPTER II

Insect Rivals of the Rainbow

IN THIS chapter will be found, in more detail than was possible in the first chapter, some of the outstanding events in the lives of the insect families represented in the 24 accompanying colored pages.

A large number of the species portrayed in color come from the Tropics. But family relationships endure beyond geographic boundaries and are more persistent than either color or cut of clothes. So, every brilliant tropical insect has its drab cousins and common family bonds in temperate lands.

The biographies deal broadly with the families and give details that apply to those members most familiar to man in everyday life.

CRICKETS, COCKROACHES, KATYDIDS, AND THEIR KIN

(Order *Orthoptera*)

Pages 30 and 32

This order embraces six families, represented respectively by the short-horned grasshoppers, the crickets, the katydids, the walking sticks, the mantids, and the cockroaches. The individuals of the first three families sing and jump, while those of the latter three are mute and creep. Almost all of the music of the insect world comes from the three singing families of the *Orthoptera*. Indeed, the cicada is the one famous maestro that does not belong to this order.

Short-horned Grasshopper Family (*Acrididae*). The short-horned grasshopper family, distributed all over the world, has about 500 species in the United States. To it belong the Rocky Mountain locust, which in days gone by caused Kansas to be known as the "hopper" State, the Argentine locust, which frequently descends upon the pampa from the foothills of the Andes and eats everything bare before it, the locust that was among the Plagues of Pharaoh, and that other one which figured in the diet of "locusts and wild honey" mentioned in the Bible.

The life histories of most of the short-horned grasshopper and locust species show little varia-

tion. The females deposit their eggs in small oval, or bean-shaped packets, either in the soil, at the base of the stems of grasses, or in soft wood. The fall-deposited eggs do not hatch until spring.

The species reproduced are: Autumn Yellow Winged Grasshopper (*Arphia xanthoptera* Burm., page 30, figure 1), occurring in the northeastern United States in autumn; African Grasshopper (*Atractomorpha aberrans* Karsch, page 30, figure 2), coming from central Africa; Eastern Lubber Grasshopper (*Romalea microptera* Palis., page 30, figure 6), occurring in the hay fields of southeastern United States; Yellow Winged Grasshopper (*Arphia simplex* Scudd., page 32, figure 2), habitat the Mississippi Valley; European Grasshopper (*Monachidium lunus* Joh., page 32, figure 4), occurring alike in Europe, Asia, and Africa; Desert Grasshopper (*Leprus cyaneus* Cockerell, page 32, figure 6), habitat the arid areas of southwestern United States; Old World Migratory Locust (*Locusta migratoria* Linn., page 32, figure 7), occurring in Europe.

Walking Stick Family (*Phasmidae*). This bizarre group, some of whose members disguise themselves by simulating twigs and leaves, contains about 600 species, mainly tropical. Sixteen species are native American, the most familiar being the walking stick or devil's darning-needle. The eggs, one-eighth of an inch long, of polished black, with a whitish stripe on one side, are scattered on the ground in the fall, where they lie until the warm days of spring. The female, unlike most Orthopters, makes no provision for their safety. If certain species of walking sticks lose a leg another grows in its place.

The species reproduced is: Walking Leaf (*Pulchriphyllium bioculatum* Gray, page 30, figure 3), habitat African coast.

Mantis Family (*Mantidae*). The mantids are a carnivorous tropical tribe, with many species, having wings resembling the leaves of plants, both in coloring and formation. Perhaps a score of species are found in the South, one of them extending its habitat as far north as Maryland and Indiana. The egg cases approximate the size and shape of an almond, and the color of golden grain, the substance of which they are made being akin to silk—a frothy mass whipped until it turns to a foam and hardens.

It has been remarked that although the attitude the mantis assumes may seem to be that of devotion, such sanctimonious airs are a mask of evil habits; "those arms folded in prayer are

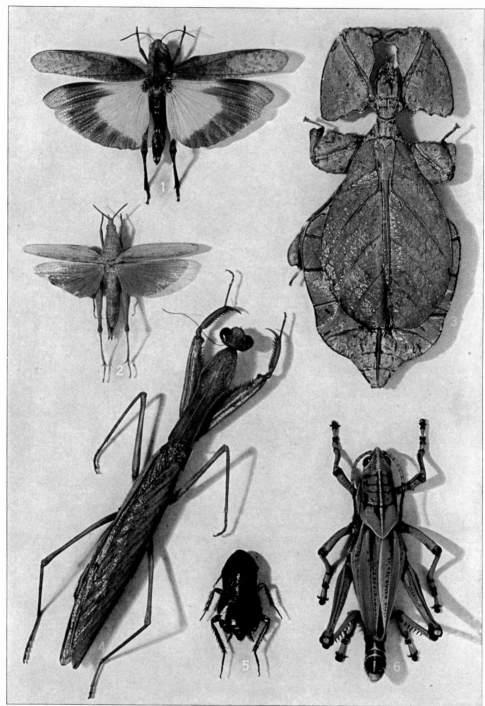

© National Geographic Society   Natural Size

A GROUP OF GRASSHOPPERS AND THEIR CONTRASTING KIN

(1) Autumn Yellow Winged Grasshopper, *Arphia xanthoptera* Burm. [Female]; (2) African Grasshopper, *Atractomorpha aberrans* Karsch [Female]; (3) Walking Leaf, *Pulchriphyllium biocu-latum* Gray [Female]; (4) Chinese Mantis, *Tenodera sinensis* Sauss. [Female]; (5) Oriental Cock-roach, *Blatta orientalis* Linn. [Female]; (6) Eastern Lubber Grasshopper, *Romalea microptera* Palis. [Male]. See text under the following Family headings: Short-horned Grasshopper, Walking Stick, and Mantis, page 29.

cutthroat weapons; they tell no beads, they slay whatever passes within range." At the sight of one of the more formidable kinds of prey the mantis gives a convulsive shiver, strikes a terrifying pose, spreads its wings, curls the tip of its abdomen, and, standing firmly on four hind legs, holds the forward part of its body upright, with forelegs forming a cross. The victim comes within range, the forelegs fall, the claws strike, and the saws clutch the prey. The wretched victim writhes with pain, chews space with its mandibles, and helplessly kicks the air. The mantids are friends of man because they live so largely on insects that are destructive to crops (see, also, page 20).

The species reproduced is: Chinese Mantis (*Tenodera sinensis* Sauss., page 30, figure 4), an immigrant from China.

Cockroach Family (*Blattidae*). Though a thousand species of cockroaches have been described, most of them inhabit tropical countries; only 43 exist north of the Rio Grande River, these usually being found in fields and woods under sticks, stones, and other rubbish. The two major pests are the Oriental Cockroach and the croton bug, both of which come from foreign parts, the former from China and the latter from Europe. Tramp steamers sometimes come into port, after sailing the seven seas, with their sailors wearing gloves when asleep, to save the nails of their hands from being gnawed off by the cockroaches.

Almost any sort of dry organic matter—paste from bookbindings or wall paper, dry bread or leather scrapings, the products of milady's larder or their own egg cases—is "beer and skittles" to the cockroach palate.

The female lays her eggs in a purselike, brown case of horny material, usually about 16 eggs in two rows, arranged so that when the young hatch, each rank will face the other. The mother cockroach, as a rule, carries the egg case with her until the babies are ready to emerge, when she assists them by tearing it open. The young ones are able, as soon as they hatch, to go about without asking odds from anybody, eating the same food as their elders enjoy. They mature in about a year, casting off a number of outgrown suits before becoming adults.

The species reproduced is: Oriental Cockroach (*Blatta orientalis* Linn., page 30, figure 5), found in many countries.

Cricket Family (*Gryllidae*). Most of the true crickets, which belong to the Gryllid family, have developed a fondness for living close to man, and the cheery calls of the Gryllid Romeos to their Juliets are familiar sounds. They are omnivorous eaters, most species spending the day in some dark cranny and going abroad to seek their prey at night. Some species are day hunters, however. The mole-cricket leads a burrowing life, usually in damp earth. The female deposits from 200 to 300 eggs in masses of from 40 to 60. She is one of the few nonsocial insects that look after their eggs until they hatch and then feed their young until the latter are able to shift for themselves. She has to keep a sharp eye on Mr. Mole-cricket, for he does not hesitate to eat his own children when he can get hold of them.

The species reproduced is: European Mole-cricket (*Gryllotalpa gryllotalpa* Linn., page 32, figure 1), introduced into the United States from the Old World.

Long-horned Grasshopper Family (*Tettigoniidae*). Most of the older authorities call this family the *Locustidae*. It embraces the katydids, the meadow grasshoppers, the camel crickets, the sword bearing crickets, the western crickets, and the Jerusalem crickets.

The species reproduced are: True Katydid (*Pterophylla camellifolia* Fab., page 32, figure 3), occurring in eastern United States; Mormon Cricket (*Anabrus simplex* Hald., page 32, figure 5), habitat western United States.

THE BUGS AND CICADAS AND THEIR RELATIVES
(Order *Hemiptera*)
Pages 34, 35, 37, 39, 41.

This order is one of the most versatile in habit and form. While many recent authorities subdivide it into several groups, the more conservative older classification is used by many museums.

The group embraces about 5,000 American species, including plant-lice, scale-insects, and mealy wings; cicadas, lantern-flies, tree- and leafhoppers, and spittle-insects; water-boatmen, striders, and scorpions; ambush-bugs, assassinbugs, stink-bugs, and many others.

Some of the remarkable families not shown because of the minuteness of their members are those which produce plant galls. Typical of these are the sucking bugs of the plant-louse type, which produce the twig gall of the hickory and the root gall of the grape. Another is the family to which belongs the San José scale. The males of some species of this family are mouthless and so have a very brief existence. The females become both footless and blind after settling down.

Statisticians have estimated that leaf-hoppers, by sucking the sap, probably destroy one-fourth of all the grass that grows and that a million of them will kill as much forage as a cow can eat.

Shield-bug Family (*Scutelleridae*). The shield-bugs constitute an attractive clan, of which some 25 American species have been described. None of the latter occurs in sufficient numbers to be of economic importance.

The species reproduced are: Nymph of *Poecilocoris druraei* Linn. (page 34, figure 1), occurring in India and China; *Philia senator* Fab. (page 34, figure 2), occurring in Australia and Malaysia; Nymph of *Poecilocoris nepalensis* H-S. (page 34, figure 4), occurring in India and China; *Chrysocoris bilunulatus* Vollen. (page 34, figure 7), a native of Sumatra; *Calliphara nobilis* Linn.

Natural Size

THE MOLE-CRICKET, THE TRUE KATYDID, AND SOME OF THEIR COUSINS

(1) European Mole-cricket, *Gryllotalpa gryllotalpa* Linn. [Female]; (2) Yellow Winged Grass-hopper, *Arphia simplex* Scudd. [Female]; (3) True Katydid, *Pterophylla camellifolia* Fab. [Male]; (4) European Grasshopper, *Monachidium lunus* Joh. [Female]; (5) Mormon Cricket, *Anabrus simplex* Hald. [Female]; (6) Desert Grasshopper, *Leprus Cyaneus* Cockerell [Female]; (7) Old World Migratory Locust, *Locusta migratoria* Linn. [Male]. See text under the following Family headings: Cockroach, Cricket, and Long-horned Grasshopper, page 31.

Photograph by Leonard Sefing

A HELLGRAMMITE FLY FINDS SAFETY IN MIMICRY

Before man ever dreamed of a World War, insects had come to be masters of the art of camouflage. Some of them employ fearsome aspects, others have acquired a low visibility, and still others imitate creatures that possess qualities distasteful to their natural enemies. The hellgrammite merges itself into its environment so that only sharp eyes detect its presence.

(page 34, figure 9), habitat southeastern Asia; *Calliphara excellens* Burm. (page 34, figure 10), occurring in southeastern Asia; *Chrysocoris grandis* Thumb. (page 34, figure 11), habitat China, Japan, and India; *Chrysocoris sellatus* White (page 34, figure 12), a native of the Philippines; *Tectocoris diopthalmus* var. *schonherri* Esch. (page 34, figure 13), habitat extending from the coast of China to that of Australia; *Tectocoris diopthalmus* var. *cyanipes* Fab. (page 34, figure 14), a native of Java; *Tectocoris peregrina* Kirk. (page 34, figure 15), inhabiting the lands that border the Indian Ocean.

Stink-bug Family (*Pentatomidae*). This family comprises some 4,000 species, about 300 occurring in the United States. Most species are plant feeders, but not a few are omnivorous. Several of the more common American stink-bugs are green, like the large green tree bug and the bound tree bug; other common species are brown.

A few of the American species are as bizarre in their dress as a clown, and it is this character of its coat that gives to one of our worst pests, the Harlequin Cabbage-bug, its everyday name. That insect also might be regarded as the beer bug, for its eggs, neatly arranged in groups of twelve, six in a row, look like a group of miniature beer kegs, even down to the hoops and the bung.

The species reproduced are: Harlequin Cabbage-bug (*Murgantia histrionica* Hahn, page 34, figure 3), habitat United States; *Arocera elongata* Uhler (page 35, figure 1), habitat Brazil; *Dalpada oculata* Fab. (page 35, figure 2), occurring in India, China, and Japan; *Vulsirea violacea* Fab. (page 35, figure 3), ranging from Mexico to Brazil; *Arocera splendens* Blanch. (page 35, figure 4), native ·of Central America and the northern part of South America; *Edessa haedina* Stal. (page 35, figure 5), native of Mexico; *Brachystethus rubromaculatus* Dallas (page 35, figure 6), inhabiting Central America and Mexico; *Nezara hilaris* Say (page 35, figure 7), occurring in the United States; *Chalcocoris rutilans* Stoll (page 35, figure 8), habitat Africa; *Catacanthus incarnatus* Drury (page 35, figure 9), occurring in Japan, China, and Borneo; *Catacanthus carrenoi* LeGuill. (page 35, figure 10), a native of the Philippines; *Edessa rufomarginata* DeGeer. (page 35, figure 11), ranging from Mexico to the Argentine; *Pharypia pulchella* Stoll (page 35, figure 12), ranging from Mexico south to Brazil; *Edessa cervus* Stoll (page 35, figure 13), habitat Brazil to northern South America; *Pygoplatys longiceps* Stal. (page 35, figure 14), occurring in the Philippines; *Loxa variegata* Dist. (page 35, figure 15), occurring in Costa Rica and Panama.

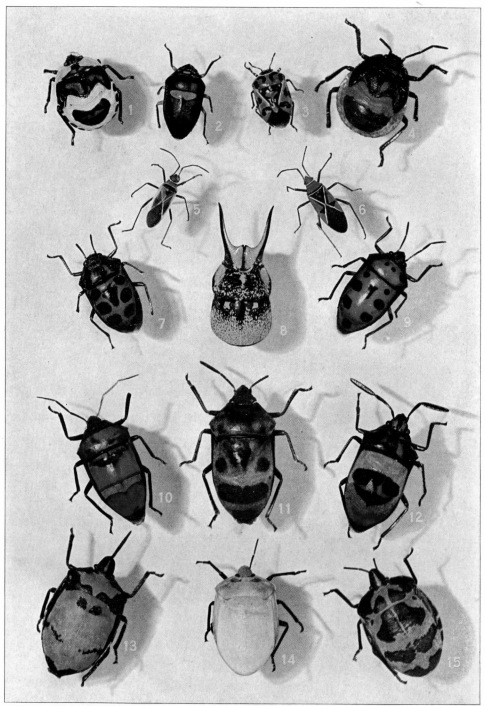

1⅗ times Natural Size

A PLATE OF HEMIPTEROUS JEWELS GATHERED FROM THE ENDS OF THE EARTH

(1) Nymph of *Poecilocoris druraei* Linn.; (2) *Philia senator* Fab. [Female]; (3) Harlequin Cabbage-bug, *Murgantia histrionica* Hahn [Female]; (4) Nymph of *Poecilocoris nepalensis* H-S.; (5) *Dysdercus mimus* Say [Male]; (6) *Dysdercus andreae* Linn. [Male]; (7) *Chrysocoris bilunulatus* Vollen. [Female]; (8) *Ceratocoris bucephalus* White [Male]; (9) *Calliphara nobilis* Linn. [Female]; (10) *Calliphara excellens* Burm. [Female]; (11) *Chrysocoris grandis* Thumb. [Female]; (12) *Chrysocoris sellatus* White [Female]; (13) *Tectocoris diopthalmus* var. *schonherri* Esch. [Female]; (14) *Tectocoris diopthalmus* var. *cyanipes* Fab. [Female]; (15) *Tectocoris peregrina* Kirk. [Female]. See Family headings: Shield-bug, Stink-bug, Cotton-stainer, and Burrowing-bug, pages 31, 33, 36.

Natural Size

SOME BEAUTIFUL MEMBERS OF AN ODOROUS CLAN—THE STINK-BUGS

(1) *Arocera elongata* Uhler [Female]; (2) *Dalpada oculata* Fab. [Female]; (3) *Vulsirea violacea* Fab. [Female]; (4) *Arocera splendens* Blanch. [Male]; (5) *Edessa haedina* Stal. [Male]; (6) *Brachystethus rubromaculatus* Dallas [Female]; (7) *Nezara hilaris* Say [Female]; (8) *Chalcocoris rutilans* Stoll [Male]; (9) *Catacanthus incarnatus* Drury [Female]; (10) *Catacanthus carrenoi* LeGuill. [Female]; (11) *Edessa rufomarginata* DeGeer. [Male]; (12) *Pharypia pulchella* Stoll [Female]; (13) *Edessa cervus* Stoll [Female]; (14) *Pygoplatys longiceps* Stal. [Female]; (15) *Loxa variegata* Dist. [Male]. See text under the heading of Stink-bug Family, page 33.

A BEETLE OF THE BELGIAN CONGO ROLLING A BALL OF DUNG TO ITS NEST

This is a cousin of the famous sacred beetle of the ancient Egyptians, which was placed in the tombs with the dead, whose picture was painted on sarcophagi, and whose image was carved in stones and precious gems. The familiar rose beetle belongs to the same clan.

Cotton-stainer Family (*Pyrrhocoridae*). This family is represented in our fauna by 22 species, which sometimes are known as red-bugs. The cotton-stainers do much damage by piercing cotton stems and bolls with their beaks and sucking the sap. Their principal damage, however, comes from the staining of the cotton in its open boll by the insects' excretions. Some species attack oranges, puncturing the skin and thereby causing the fruit to decay and fall to the ground.

The species reproduced are: *Dysdercus mimus* Say (page 34, figure 5), occurring in the South; *Dysdercus andreae* Linn. (page 34, figure 6), occurring in Florida and the West Indies.

Burrowing-bug Family (*Cydnidae*). Twenty-nine species of this family now are listed in the United States. Their front legs are more or less flattened and fitted for digging, and they are found burrowing in sandy places and under sticks and stones. It is thought that they feed by sucking the sap from plant roots.

The species reproduced is: *Ceratocoris bucephalus* White (page 34, figure 8), habitat southeastern Asia.

Squash-bug Family (*Coreidae*). This family consists of some 1,500 known species, of which 200 are American. The familiar squash-bug is its most widely known representative. To it also belong the box elder bug, which sucks the sap

of the box elder and in adulthood resembles a giant bed-bug, and the cherry bug, which imbibes the juice of the cherry.

Some of the squash-bugs are queer-looking "critters." One has its wing cases higher at the sides than at the middle, thus producing a sort of hopper with a series of spines around the edge. In this the male has to carry the family eggs, but he accepts his task only after his spouse has henpecked him to a point where he sees that opposition is useless.

The species reproduced are: *Anisosceles hymeniphera* Westwood (page 37, figure 1), found in Mexico; *Diactor bilineatus* Fab. (page 37, figure 3), inhabiting northern South America; *Paryphes laetus* Fab. (page 37, figure 4), occurring throughout South America; *Mictis metallica* Sign. (page 37, figure 5), native of Africa; *Mozena lunata* Burm. (page 37, figure 6), ranging from Texas to Central America; *Sephina vinula* Stal. (page 37, figure 8), inhabiting Mexico; *Machtima mexicana* Stal. (page 37, figure 9), habitat Mexico and Central America; *Thasus gigas* Burm. (page 37, figure 10), frequenting the southwestern part of the United States and Mexico; *Sphictyrtus longirostris* Dist. (page 37, figure 11), occurring in Central America.

Assassin-bug Family (*Reduvidae*). This family, embracing some 2,000 species, most of

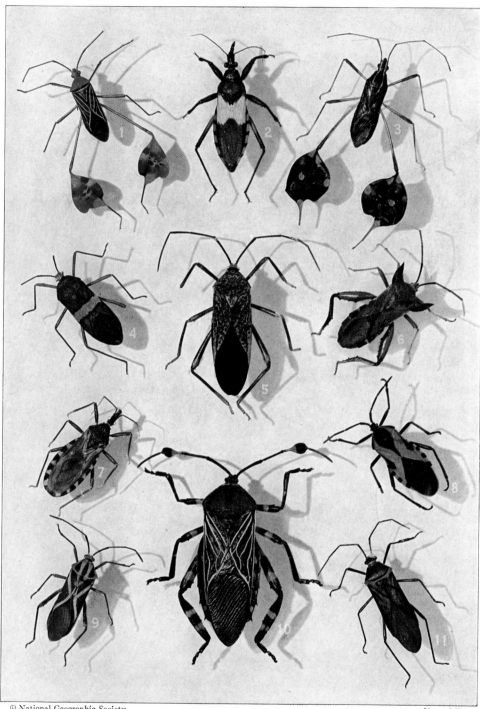

Natural Size

ASSASSIN-BUGS AND SQUASH-BUGS THAT BELIE THEIR NAMES

(1) *Anisosceles hymeniphera* Westwood [Female]; (2) *Microtomus purcis* Drury [Male]; (3) *Diactor bilineatus* Fab. [Male]; (4) *Paryphes laetus* Fab. [Female]; (5) *Mictis metallica* Sign. [Female]; (6) *Mozena lunata* Burm. [Male]; (7) *Triatoma infestans* Klug [Male]; (8) *Sephina vinula* Stal. [Male]; (9) *Machtima mexicana* Stal. [Female]; (10) *Thasus gigas* Burm. [Male]; (11) *Sphictyrtus longirostris* Dist. [Female]. See text under the Family headings: Squash-bug and Assassin-bug, page 36. To the Assassin-bug Family belong two species which figured prominently in the news of several decades ago. They were called the kissing bugs and their reputation spread so far and wide that wherever anyone was bitten by an insect of any kind the inference was that he or she had been the victim of an attack by one of the Assassins.

Photograph by Paul Henri Fabre

A SCARAB OF SPAIN

It is one of the anomalies of Nature that, with few exceptions, the two groups of insects which show maternal solicitude for their young are the bees and the dung beetles. So intense is the affection of the latter for their children that the mother remains for four consecutive months without food, down in her burrow, looking after her brood, attending to their needs as grub, nymph, and finally as insect.

them predaceous, feeds principally on the juices of other insects, draining the prey dry. To it belongs the famous kissing bug of yesteryear, whose young have coats of bristly, sticky hairs to which dust adheres, making a sort of mask from which its other name, masked bed-bug hunter, is derived. It is able to bite hard, inflicting a rather painful wound. Rarely, however, does it bite human beings unless attacked. Usually living out-of-doors, it sometimes invades vermin-haunted houses. In the South lives another member of the family known as the big bed-bug, which is a persistent sucker of human blood, and therefore is frequently rated as a kissing bug. The wheel-bug has a toothed crest resembling a cock's comb on its thorax, and its eggs are shaped like little jugs, laid in masses of about 70.

The species reproduced are: *Microtomus purcis* Drury (page 37, figure 2), inhabiting the southeastern United States; *Triatoma infestans* Klug. (page 37, figure 7), occurring in South America.

Cicada Family (*Cicadidae*). About 74 species of this family are found in our fauna, including the harvest-flies and lyremen. The most famous cicada, however, is the Seventeen-year Locust. Of all known insects it has the longest period of adolescence, spending 17 years under the ground in its larval stage and only a few weeks awing in its adult form.

Emerging from the ground after throwing off its larval clothes, it makes merry for a few days and then dies. In laying her eggs the female pierces the twigs of various trees, and in the slit thus made deposits them. These twigs later break and fall to the ground, and in about six weeks the young hatch and creep down beneath the surface to begin their long subterranean career. They feed on the humus in the soil and, to some extent, on the juices of the roots of trees and other deep-soil plants, and molt from four to six times during their underground life.

The species reproduced are: Malayan Cicada (*Huechys phoenicura* Germ., page 39, figure 1), occurring in the Malay Archipelago; Seventeen-year Locust (*Tibicina septendecim* Linn., page 39, figures 4 and 6), inhabiting the eastern United States; Brazilian Cicada (*Carineta formosa* Germ., page 39, figure 9), habitat Brazil; Mexican Cicada (*Zammara calochroma* Walk., page 39, figure 11), habitat Mexico and South America; Javanese Cicada (*Platypleura fulvigera* Walk., page 39, figure 12), habitat Malay Archipelago; Indian Cicada (*Gaeana sulphurea* Hope, page 39, figure 13), occurring in India.

Lantern-fly Family (*Fulgoridae*). While most of our lantern-flies are small, many of the tropical species are large and bizarre. Someone

Natural Size

THE SEVENTEEN-YEAR LOCUST, WITH OTHER CICADAS AND LANTERN-FLIES

(1) Malayan Cicada, *Huechys phoenicura* Germ. [Female]; (2) Indian Lantern-fly, *Saiva cardinalis* Butl. [Male]; (3) Asiatic Lantern-fly, *Lycorma delicatula* White [Male]; (4) Seventeen-year Locust, *Tibicina septendecim* Linn. [Female]; (5) Mexican Lantern-fly, *Enchophora stillifer* Stal. [Male]; (6) Same as Figure 4; (7) Philippine Lantern-fly, *Aphana astraea* Stal. [Male]; (8) Philippine Frog-hopper, *Gynopygoplax theora* White [Female]; (9) Brazilian Cicada, *Carineta formosa* Germ. [Male]; (10) Brazilian Frog-hopper, *Tomaspis furcata* Germ. [Female]; (11) Mexican Cicada, *Zammara calochroma* Walk. [Male]; (12) Javanese Cicada, *Platypleura fulvigera* Walk. [Female]; (13) Indian Cicada, *Gaeana sulphurea* Hope [Male]. See text under the following Family headings: Cicada, Lantern-fly, and Frog-hopper, pages 38, 40.

Photograph by Paul Griswold Howes

A ROBBER FLY WITH ITS PREY, A SCORPION-FLY

It is estimated that about 50 per cent of all the species of insects are engaged in preying on other species of their own kind. The robber flies are all swift, hairy, ferocious-looking creatures, without exception predatory. Some of them are very large, as much as two inches long. These latter do not hesitate to attack dragon-flies and bumblebees and even the fierce and active tiger-beetles.

has said that their growth has gone to their heads. A Brazilian species looks something like an insectean hippopotamus, there being even the simulation of tusks on its dangerous-looking, but wholly innocent, head. Certain species of lantern-flies in China excrete large quantities of white, flocculent wax, which is used by the Chinese for candles and other purposes.

The species reproduced are: Indian Lantern-fly (*Saiva cardinalis* Butl., page 39, figure 2), living in India; Asiatic Lantern-fly (*Lycorma delicatula* White, page 39, figure 3), occurring in India and China; Mexican Lantern-fly (*Enchophora stillifer* Stal., page 39, figure 5), from Mexico and Central America; Philippine Lantern-fly (*Aphana astraea* Stal., page 39, figure 7), a native of the Philippines; *Fulgora maculata* Olivier (page 41, figure 4), inhabiting Ceylon and India; Chinese Candle Fly (*Fulgora candelaria* Fab., page 41, figure 5), occurring in India and China; Panama Lantern-fly (*Phrictus tripunctata* Dist., page 41, figure 6), habitat Panama; Duck Billed Lantern-fly (*Fulgora samarana* Baker, page 41, figure 8), occurring in the Philippines.

Frog-hopper Family (*Cercopidae*). In rural strolls occasionally one sees small masses of froth adhering to the stems of taller grasses and weeds.

This is a viscid fluid whipped into a heavy froth by an insect which gets its popular name, frog-hopper, from the belief that these masses are the spittle of tree frogs (see illustration, page 22).

One familiar species, the foamy cicadella, uses the froth it creates as a sunshade. With its proboscis sunk deep into a plant stem or leaf, it sucks out the sap, which it passes through a tiny mechanism at the tip of its abdomen. In this process it mixes air and a foam-forming substance with the sap, producing tiny bubbles having a tenacity that causes them to last for many hours.

The species reproduced are: Philippine Frog-hopper (*Gynopygoplax theora* White, page 39, figure 8), inhabiting the Philippines; Brazilian Frog-hopper (*Tomaspis furcata* Germ., page 39, figure 10), occurring in Brazil.

DRAGON- AND DAMSEL-FLIES
(Order *Odonata*)
Page 41

The creatures of this order might be called the hawks of insectdom. There are about 2,000 known species, 300 of which are found in the United States. Though bucolic superstition has it that the dragon-flies are snake doctors, that they sew up the ears of boys who wade in creeks, and that

Four-fifths Natural Size

ANIMATED PURSUIT PLANES AND WINGED CLOWNS OF THE INSECT WORLD

(1) Philippine Damsel-fly, *Pseudophaea refulgens* Selys; (2) Black-wing Damsel-fly, *Agrion maculatum* Beauv.; (3) *Vestalis melania* Selys; (4) *Fulgora maculata* Olivier [Male]; (5) Chinese Candle Fly, *Fulgora candelaria* Fab. [Male]; (6) Panama Lantern-fly, *Phrictus tripunctata* Dist. [Male]; (7) Ruby-spot, *Hetaerina americana* Fab. [Male]; (8) Duck Billed Lantern-fly, *Fulgora samarana* Baker [Female]; (9) Ten Spot Skimmer, *Libellula pulchella* Drury; (10) *Neurobasis chinensis* Linn.; (11) Water-prince, *Epicordulia princeps* Hagen. The pursuit planes belong to the Dragon-fly and True Damsel-fly Families and the clowns to the Lantern-fly Family. See text under these Family headings, pages 38, 40, 45.

Photograph by Ewing Galloway

LOCUSTS HOLD UP A FREIGHT TRAIN ON THE ATHENS-SALONIKI LINE

The locusts that plagued Egypt in Bible times, the ones that figure periodically in the devastation of Palestine, those that made Kansas the "hopper" State some decades ago, and those which from time to time descend on the Argentine pampa and transform luxuriant vegetation into a desert waste, are all of a pattern. They belong to the short-horned grasshopper family. A train cannot get traction on rails that have been "soaped" with the crushed bodies of these insects.

LOCUSTS AND WILD HONEY STILL REMAIN FOOD ITEMS AMONG PRIMITIVE PEOPLE

Ifugao women in Luzon, Philippine Islands, prepare locusts for food by roasting them. Such rich feasts often cause indigestion. According to Mosaic law (Leviticus 11: 22), the Children of Israel were permitted to eat "the locust after his kind, and the beetle after his kind, and the grasshopper after his kind." Flies and fly eggs are made into cakes by some Indian tribes in Mexico, and some species of beetles are used to put more "kick" in certain types of alcoholic beverages drunk by other tribes in the same country (see text, page 9).

43

Photograph by Clifton Adams

AN ILLUSTRATION OF ONE OF THE MEANS BY WHICH INJURI-
OUS INSECTS MAY BE UNWITTINGLY DISTRIBUTED BY MAN

Several insects occurring in south Florida caught in the radiator of
an automobile. Some flew into the path of the car and some were
drawn in by the draft of the motor-cooling fan.

basket in which the victim
is clutched and held until
the two front legs can get
a firm grip on it. In some
species the victim is eaten
on the wing, in others
the captor alights and eats
at leisure. Most species
breathe 118 times a min-
ute as compared with the
average man's 18 times.
Ten pairs of breathing
tubes lead from as many
spiracles into the body.

The young of the dam-
sel- and dragon-flies are
wholly unlike their par-
ents; they are aquatic.
Down on the bed of a
murky stream or muddy
pond they dwell, thick of
body, big of head, and
half concealed in slime.
Through their dirty, gray-
green bodies they possess
low visibility as they lie
in ambush, waiting for
some hapless creature to
come their way.

When a May-fly larva,
or a caddis-worm, or a
water bug passes by on its
unsuspecting way, the biggest mouth one ever saw
on so small a creature
opens wide and the luck-
less forager finds itself
being chewed to pieces.
The large lower lip effec-
tually conceals the big
mouth and sharp jaws
until the prey comes by.
Then the lip is extended
and there shoots from the
head a vicious pincerlike
organ that grasps the victim and draws it in.

they are horse stingers and mule killers, they are,
as a matter of fact, honest-to-goodness friends of
everybody, since their favorite food is the pestifer-
ous mosquito and the bothersome fly.

Compound eyes with as many as 30,000 facets
are possessed by many species. These produce
marvelous mosaics of images and give the pos-
sessor a wide angle of vision. Many species also
have simple eyes to reenforce the powers of their
compound optics. The dragon-fly's head is
mounted on its body with an insectean version of
a ball and socket joint, which enables the insect
to see beneath and above itself—a power denied
all except a few of the other members of the segmented, six-legged order of creatures.

In order to hold its prey, once overtaken, the
dragon-fly groups its six legs together to form a

The nymphs propel themselves by drawing in
and expelling drafts of water through their intes-
tinal tracts. This expulsion is with considerable
force, which, on the principle of the recoil of a
gun, drives them forward a short distance.

Skimmer Family (*Libellulidae*). The dragon-
flies of this family are found all over the country.
The Water-prince is an unusually fine flyer and
a hard creature to capture. The female flies alone
when depositing her eggs, and makes her dips to
the surface of the water some distance apart, so
that her eggs may not be, so to speak, "all in one
basket."

The species reproduced are: Ten Spot Skimmer
(*Libellula pulchella* Drury, page 41, figure 9),
occurring in North America; Water-prince (*Epi-*

cordulia princeps Hagen, page 41, figure 11), also occurring in North America.

True Damsel-fly Family *(Agrionidae)*. This family includes about 75 species in our fauna. The females deposit their eggs in the tissue of aquatic plants by cutting slits in the stems with their sharp ovipositors, or in the rubbish and mud along the border of ditches and the fringes of streams.

The males of some species are famous for the duels they fight. Flying about one another, evidently in a consuming rage, each tries to get into a position to tear the other's wings, and the duel usually ends only when one of the contestants has been vanquished.

The Ruby-spot has been called by Kellogg a perfect masterpiece of insect beauty and grace. Only the males possess the colorful gems in their wings that give the species its name. Sometimes hundreds of them cling to willow branches in graceful festoons, where they look like strings of rubies.

The species reproduced are: Philippine Damsel-fly *(Pseudophaea refulgens* Selys, page 41, figure 1), occurring in the Philippine Islands; Blackwing Damsel-fly *(Agrion maculatum* Beauv., page 41, figure 2), inhabiting the eastern part of the United States; *Vestalis melania* Selys (page 41, figure 3), inhabiting the Philippines; Ruby-spot *(Hetaerina americana* Fab., page 41, figure 7), habitat North America; *Neurobasis chinensis* Linn. (page 41, figure 10), occurring in the Philippines.

Photograph by Charles Martin

AN IFUGAO LOCUST CATCHER WITH HIS NET, IN LUZON

Locusts sometimes swarm in unbelievable numbers. In 1889 a vast army of them spread out over an area of more than 2,000 square miles, while flying over the Red Sea. Cyprus reported an invasion in 1881 during which 1,300 tons of eggs alone were destroyed.

BEES, WASPS, ANTS, AND THEIR KIN

(Order *Hymenoptera*)

Pages 54, 56, 58, 59

More than 30,000 known species are grouped in this order, and there are perhaps ten times as many that never have been described, embracing not only the bees, wasps, and ants, but also the saw-flies, horn-tails, ensign flies, chalcid flies, gall flies, ichneumon flies, cuckoo flies, and many others.

Thread-waisted Wasp Family *(Sphecidae)*. Many species of solitary and hunting wasps, ranging in size and character of prey from the giant Cicada-killer to the little crabros whose quarry consists of harmless flies, are included in this family. They bag their game with rare finesse and preserve it with consummate art.

The familiar mud-daubers that build their several tubular cells side by side beneath porch roofs, on ceilings, and under the eaves of houses are characteristic members of the family. Although they work in mud, the mud-daubers are exquisite in their habits. If we watch one of them gathering a pellet of mud we will see her feet get dirty and the ends of her mandibles soiled; but, figuratively, she has her skirts carefully tucked up and her sleeves as carefully rolled out of

Photograph by James Dorsett

THE ARISTOLOCHIA FLOWER OF CEYLON DETAINS A FLY FOR ITS PURPOSES

The relationships between insects and flowers show many amazing adaptations. The Venus flytrap and the sundew are familiar flowers that capture flies. The aristolochia catches the fly (see on the inner rim at the right) and holds it a prisoner until the pollen carried on the insect's feet has fertilized the stigmas.

Photograph by Lynwood M. Chace

AN INSECTEAN DRILL—(THALESSA) MEGARHYSSA LUNATOR

This ichneumon fly preys on the larvae of the pigeon tremex, one of the horn-tails. The lowest of the three threadlike appendages is a flexible ovipositor. When the female finds the gallery of a pigeon tremex larva she elevates the ovipositor in a loop over her back and brings the tip down to the surface of the wood. She then makes a derrick out of her body and proceeds with great skill and precision to drill a hole into the burrow of the tremex. There she deposits an egg, from which soon emerges a larva to attack the larva of the tremex (see, also, text, page 53).

harm's way. And when her work is over every particle of dirt must be scraped off both mandibles and feet.

When the dog days are with us, and lyremen, harvest-flies, and dog day cicadas begin their yearly din, their big, yellow-banded, rusty-black wasp enemy makes her appearance upon the scene, having come up out of the big burrow in clayey soil where her mother cradled her. Watch carefully and you will see the big huntress flying around in the vicinity of the source of the cicada's song. Suddenly that song ceases, and in its stead there comes a shrill, distressing, discordant note. The big wasp has driven her venomed dagger into the songster's nerve center, and with a shriek of pain the latter tumbles, along with its conqueror, to the ground.

Then comes the huntress's task of carrying her prey to her burrow. It is heavier than she is, so she gets astride it and laboriously drags it up a tree. From that vantage point she volplanes toward her burrow, after the fashion of a flying squirrel, and repeats the process until her home is reached.

Once there, she lays an egg under the middle leg of the victim, seals the cicada in a cell, and starts looking for another quarry. The egg hatches in two or three days, and the grub is assured of juicy meat, for the cicada has been paralyzed and not killed, and keeps fresh as long as the wasp's baby needs fresh meat. The grub attains full growth inside of ten days, and then spends two days spinning a cocoon of mixed silk and earth. In that it spends the winter, emerging from its transformation sleep in time to lend ear to the lyreman's call of a new season.

Another interesting species of this family is the sand wasp, known as the Ammophila. Dr. S. W. Williston, in studying them, discovered that these wasps actually have learned to use tools, but the discovery was so astounding to him that he feared to publish his observations at first, lest all mankind should pronounce him a "Nature faker." But many another entomologist has confirmed his discovery. After a mother Ammophila has finished digging her gallery, she captures a lot of small caterpillars or other insects, according to her species, paralyzes them, stocks the cell with them, and, after laying an egg in proximity to the provender, seals up the nest; then she fills the burrow with dirt. She often has been observed using a small pebble as a "tamping iron"

Photograph by L. G. Saunders

A "BROWNIE" THAT MIMICS A THORN

One needs only to glance at the thorn itself and the tree-hopper
above it to see how difficult it would be for an enemy of this insect
to distinguish it from the thorn, whose protection it seeks through
imitation (see, also, illustration, page 33).

the hunters of flat-headed
wood-borers. Little weevils,
big weevils, highly colored
weevils, and those that are
garbed in drab hues are all
recognized by their wasp exploiters.

Anatomists who are mas-
ters of their art are the members of this family. Whether
they be species that hunt
wood-borers or species that
prey upon weevils, each captive has its nerves centered
in one ganglion. One thrust
from the wasp's poisoned dagger produces complete paralysis, but not death, for death
would mean mortification in
a few days, and the babies
of Cerceris must have fresh
meat.

For weeks the beetle lives
on, under the most powerful
of sense-extinguishers. The
wasp's egg, laid at the ten-
derest spot of the beetle's
abdomen, hatches out, and
the little grub begins to eat
its way into the interior of
the victim's carcass. But
though the beetle's meat is
as fresh as the day it was
stung, there is no movement
and no sense of pain.

Such a skilled surgeon was
the mother of the grub that
with her lance and her drug
she was able to arrest sense
and motion, and yet leave
life. It is as if a man were
to thrust a dagger into a
steer's neck, insert with a
hypodermic syringe a bit of
poison into the wound, and
establish a paralysis that
would enable his child to
carve the victim piecemeal over a period of four
or five weeks, the beef meanwhile retaining its
original freshness.

Another of the thread-waisted wasp family is
Philanthus, a hunter of bees, not for her own
rations but for her babies. For in her adult life
she is a honey drinker and nectar sipper, while
her babies are meat eaters. To present them with
bees whose honey sacs were filled would be like
giving a child a bouquet with a viper hidden in
the flowers. Yet Mrs. Philanthus scarcely would
be able to single out bees with empty crops. She
therefore is under the necessity of emptying the
bees' honey sacs before presenting them to her
grubs. To do this she cannot deal with paralyzed
bees.

Only death itself will produce that muscular

to pack the soil in solidly, so as to remove effec-
tually all trace of the gallery.

The Cerceris wasps, of which there are numerous American species, also belong to this
family. They are exploiters of beetles and weevils.
Some species specialize on the adults of the flat-
headed wood-borers. But though these vary
widely alike in size, color, and aspect, the wasps
that hunt them are able to recognize all of them
with as much accuracy as the entomologist.
Defour found 400 beetles that represented all
the hues of the tar pot and the lapidary's show
case combined, and were of all shapes and sizes,
in Cerceris wasp cells. The wasps that gathered
them never once went out of the wood-borer
clan for their prey. Those Cerceris wasps that
hunt weevils are just as good classificationists as

relaxation necessary to force the last drop out of the bee's crop. Therefore, we find in her a new kind of surgeon. She has discovered that by forcing down the head of the bee, a tiny opening in its armor is found—an opening less than one twenty-fifth of an inch in diameter. With unerring aim Mrs. Philanthus causes her sting to penetrate the vital spot. A little poison is injected into the wound, and almost instantly antennae and mandibles become still. Death supervenes in a minute or so, and then the wasp begins a kneading process that forces out the last drop of honey from the bee's crop. This she drinks with gusto, and then carries the honey-drained victim to her home and gives it to her baby.

The species reproduced are: Sphex Wasp (*Chlorion cyaneum* Dahlb., page 54, figure 1), inhabiting North America; Siamese Wasp (*Chlorion lobatum* Fab., page 54, figure 3), native of Siam; Cicada-killer Wasp, (*Sphecius speciosus* Drury, page 54, figure 10), inhabiting the United States; Solitary Wasp (*Stictia signata* Linn., page 56, figure 2), occurring in Central America; American Mud-dauber (*Sceliphron caementarium* Drury, page 56, figure 7), living in North America; American Hunting Wasp (*Ammobia ichneumonea* Linn., page 56, figure 9), occurring in North and Central America.

Velvet Ant Family (*Mutillidae*). These handsome insects are not ants at all, but rather wingless wasps, which so closely resemble ants as frequently to be confused with them. Only the females are wingless, the males being possessors of the means of flight. Most of the members of this family are guests or parasites in the nests of other wasps and bees. They are strong stingers and swift runners, and number about 200 species in the United States.

The species reproduced is: Velvet Ant (*Dasymutilla occidentalis* Linn., page 54, figures 2 and 6), found in North America.

Photograph by Paul Henri Fabre

STAG-BEETLES READY TO DO BATTLE OVER A FEMALE OF THE SPECIES

The adult beetles are found on trees, where presumably they live, for the most part, on the sap flowing from bruised places, and on honeydew of aphids and scale insects. Their eggs are laid in crevices of the bark near the base of the trunk. The fat-bodied grubs burrow into the tree, where they stay, in some species, for as long as six years.

Spider Wasp Family (*Psammocharidae*). Most species of this family are digger wasps, although a few are masons. The giant tarantula killer, the largest of all our wasps, belongs to this clan, and its sensational combats with the great hairy tarantula often are seen in the Southwest. Occasionally both lose, the tarantula paralyzed by the wasp's sting and the wasp dying from the poisonous wounds made by the great fangs of the spider. Those wasps of the family which burrow in the ground first find their victims and sting them until they are paralyzed. Then they dig a burrow, which is enlarged at the lower end, forming a cell for the reception of the spider; and the quarry then is dragged down into the

A CRICKET'S GOLDEN CASTLE—A PUMPKIN BLOSSOM

"April comes to an end, and the cricket's song begins, at first in rare and shy solos, soon developing into a general symphony, in which every clod of turf boasts its performer." (See, also, text, page 31).

cell and an egg attached to it, after which the passage to the cell is filled with earth.

The species reproduced is: Spider Wasp (*Pepsis cinnabarina* Lucas, page 54, figure 4), which occurs in the southern part of North America and Central America.

Carpenter-bee Family (*Xylocopidae*). The carpenter-bees build their nests in wood. Perhaps the most familiar member of this family is the big, black carpenter-bee, as large as a bumble-bee, which excavates a burrow one-half inch in diameter in dry lumber. This burrow runs across the grain for about half an inch, and then makes a right-angle turn and runs with the grain for from 12 to 20 inches.

The bee works from two to three days on the small section of the tunnel that runs across the grain, and from three to five weeks on the re-mainder. If man did as much in proportion to his size, he could dig a tunnel two feet in diameter from end to end of a log 90 feet long, with no tool but his teeth.

The species reproduced are: Sumatran Carpenter-bee (*Xylocopa caerulea* Fab., page 54, figure 5), inhabiting Sumatra; American Carpenter-bee (*Xylocopa virginica* Linn., page 56, figure 1), occurring in North America; Carpenter-bee (*Xylocopa bombylans* Fab., page 58, figure 8), living in Australia.

Euglossid Bee Family (*Euglossidae*). The several species of this family of bees are solitary in habits. Many of them have not been studied carefully, but those which are known build their nests from bits of boxwood which they fasten together with the resin or gum of trees.

The species reproduced are: Tropical Bee

Photograph by Lynwood M. Chace

A CRICKET CONFERENCE ON AN EAR OF CORN

While the crickets we know best are the black and brown varieties found in houses and fields, there are many others we see less frequently. Some of these live in trees like katydids, others burrow into the ground like moles, and still others dwell as guests in ants' nests. Most of them hear with their legs and sing with their wings (see text, page 14).

(*Eulaema dimidiata* Linn., page 54, figure 7), a native of Central America; South American Bee (*Exaerte frontalis* Guer., page 54, figure 8), found in Central and South America; (*Euglossa variabilis* Friese, page 58, figure 10), found in Central America.

Social Wasp Family (*Vespidae*). This family includes the hornets, the yellow-jackets, and the wasps that build paper nests. Unlike the social bees and ants, the members of the social wasp family found in temperate regions are unable to set up a permanent communal life.

There is a vast lot of work to be done in the making of a hornet's nest as big as a half bushel. In the spring it is smaller than a hen's egg; it has been built by some queen that has survived

the winter. The house must be made roomier as the family grows, not by building additions here and there, but rather by a gradual and symmetrical expansion of the entire structure. Think how often each bit of weatherboarding must be moved to keep the size of the house always expanding uniformly with the increase in the size of the family! (See illustration, page 12.)

But the hornets are equal to the task, though that task is as if we took a six-room house and expanded it into a Windsor Castle without interfering in the slightest with the family routine on the inside, or with the shapeliness of the structure on the outside.

The hornets have the requisite engineering skill to carry the undertaking through to a successful conclusion. They gather from the weathered

Painting by Hashime Murayama

THE BUMBLEBEES GATHERING NECTAR IN THE CLOVER FIELD

The artist here has succeeded in giving a typical picture story of the life of the Bumblebee Family. In the inset the figure on the right is the familiar bumblebee of the East, and that at the left a fly that has copied it in appearance so thoroughly that the bumblebees receive it as a welcome guest in their nests. The species portrayed in the main picture is *Bombus americanorum;* the one in the inset is *Bombus huntii.* The fly belongs to the species *Criorhina kincaidi.* The fly and bumblebee in the inset are 1½ times natural size. (See text, page 53.)

surfaces of boards, rails, and posts the pulp out of which they build the walls of the nest. Bit by bit they take the material from the inside of the nest walls and plaster it on the outside, supplementing it with new material gathered abroad. In this way the inside of the house always is being put on the outside, and the growth of the nest provided for.

Many species of yellow-jackets build their nests in hollow logs and stumps. What most laymen know as the common wasp belongs to the genus *Polistes* of the *Vespidae* family. It builds but a single comb, always in a place protected from the elements, so that there is no need for the outer covering provided by the hornets. Like their cousins, the yellow-jackets and the hornets, they bring food to their babies as it is needed rather than store it up in the cell before the egg is deposited. There are some exceptions to the general rule that the *Vespidae* are social wasps. A few unfamiliar species are solitary in their habits.

The species reproduced are: Asian Wasp (*Vespa mandarina* Smith, page 54, figure 9), found in Asia; European Social Wasp (*Vespa crabro* Linn., page 56, figure 10), a native of Europe and Asia and introduced into North America; Yellow-jacket (*Vespula carolina* Linn., page 58, figure 6), found in North America.

Bumblebee Family (*Bombidae*). The bumblebee family is represented by numerous species in our fauna, most of whose communities are short-lived rather than permanent. The only individuals that live over winter are the fertilized females. They find some cranny or crevice where the frost cannot reach them, and there fall into a winter-long sleep.

When spring arrives they seek a deserted mouse hole, mole burrow, or other cavity in the ground. To these nests they bring pollen and honey which they knead into bread. Then they lay eggs in simple cells, and the larvae that hatch from them grow fat and strong on the bread prepared in advance by the mothers. When the grubs are grown they spin silken cocoons in which they pupate, and out of which they emerge full-fledged bumblebees. Then they immediately set to work looking after the welfare of their newly hatched younger sisters and brothers, serving as nursemaids, housemaids, food gatherers, and what not, and freeing their elder sisters for field work.

When winter approaches the colony dies, leaving behind only a few fertilized females, whose duty it will be to start the work again the next year. There are some species of bumblebees that are parasitic on their more industrious cousins. They closely resemble the working clans and possess no worker caste.

The species reproduced is: Common Bumblebee (*Bombus americanorum* Fab., page 56, figure 3), found in North America.

Ichneumon Fly Family (*Ichneumonidae*). The ichneumon fly family possesses some 6,000 known species. Most of them are parasitic and exploit the caterpillar tribe, thus helping to keep in check some of the worst enemies of the American garden, orchard, truck patch, and field. The adults, as a rule, lay their eggs on the caterpillars, and the larvae hatch out and burrow into the wretched host, literally eating it alive. Anyone who gathers cocoons to see what kinds of insects issue therefrom will have ichneumon flies coming from them almost as frequently as the rightful owners.

An interesting ichneumon is known as (*Pimpla*) *Ichneumon conquisitor*. It preys on the tent-caterpillar. When the latter's cocoon is spun, the ichneumon, with its ovipositor, makes an opening in the silken case and deposits its egg. The parasite has at once a choice cradle and a meal for its needs—at the expense of the sleeping, transforming caterpillar.

Another species, (*Pimpla*) *Ichneumon inquisitor*, preys not only on tent-caterpillars but also on army-worms, tussock moths, caterpillars, and the like.

The most interesting of all the ichneumon flies is probably (*Thalessa*) *Megarhyssa lunator*. The female of this species has an amazing ovipositor, often as long as six inches, which is made up of several hairs and a flexible tube. The hairs form a sheath for the latter, which is the boring-tool proper. Thin and flexible as it seems to be, Mrs. Thalessa, once she has located, deep in the hard wood of a tree, the boring grub of a pigeon tremex, bends her long abdomen down, throws her ovipositor up over her back and brings the end of it down to the wood. She then begins as fine a drilling operation as one would wish to see, often driving the hole down three or four inches into the wood (see illustration, page 47). After the female completes the boring, she converts her drill into an egg-tube, and through it pumps an egg down into the burrow of the pigeon tremex's baby (see, also, Horn-Tail Family, page 55).

This egg promptly hatches, and soon attaches itself to the luckless tremex grub which it gradually devours, and then lies down for a transformation nap.

Sometimes when Mrs. Thalessa starts to drill, the wood is so tough that it grips her drill and she remains a prisoner until starvation ends her career.

The species reproduced are: American Ichneumon Fly (*Amblyteles grandis* Brulle, page 56, figure 4), American Ichneumon Fly (*Trogus elegans* Cress, page 56, figure 5), American Ichneumon Fly (*Trogus rileyi* Cress, page 56, figure 6), *Agathilla bradleyi* Vireck (page 59, figure 1), *Amblyteles jucundus* Brulle (page 59, figure 4), *Platylabus clarus* Cress (page 59, figure 5), *Amblyteles jucundus* Brulle (page 59, figure 6), *Polyaenus spinarius* Brulle (page 59, figure 8),

Natural Size

SOME OF THE FAIREST AMONG THE WASPS, BEES, AND VELVET ANTS

(1) Sphex Wasp, *Chlorion cyaneum* Dahlb. [Female]; (2) Velvet Ant, *Dasymutilla occidentalis* Linn. [Male]; (3) Siamese Wasp, *Chlorion lobatum* Fab. [Female]; (4) Spider Wasp, *Pepsis cinnabarina* Lucas [Female]; (5) Sumatran Carpenter-bee, *Xylocopa caerulea* Fab. [Female]; (6) Velvet Ant, *Dasymutilla occidentalis* Linn. [Female]; (7) Tropical Bee, *Eulaema dimidiata* Linn. [Female]; (8) South American Bee, *Exaerte frontalis* Guer. [Female]; (9) Asian Wasp, *Vespa mandarina* Smith [Female, queen]; (10) Cicada-killer Wasp, *Sphecius speciosus* Drury [Female]. See text under the following Family headings: Thread-waisted Wasp, Velvet Ant, Spider Wasp, Carpenter-bee, Euglossid Bee, and Social Wasp, pages 45, 49, 50, 51. The habits of the several species of these insects show to what a high degree of versatility members of a single Order may attain, whether in social relationships, home-building habits or food-gathering and storing methods.

Amblyteles w-album Cress (page 59, figure 9), *Ichneumon irritator* Fab. (page 59, figure 10), *Amblyteles semicaeruleus* Cress (page 59, figure 11), *Labena grallator* Say (page 59, figure 12), all found in North America; *Macrojoppa blandita* Cress (page 59, figure 2), habitat Central America; *Cyanoxorides caeruleus* Cameron (page 59, figure 3), found in the Philippine Islands; *Callicryptus fasciipennis* Brulle (page 59, figure 7), a species found in Cuba; *Lissopimpla semipunctata* Kirby (page 59, figure 13), native of Australia.

Scoliid Wasp Family (*Scoliidae*). The species of this family neither builds nests nor transports prey to them. Rather it digs into the ground, where the grubs of the family to which the May beetle belongs are to be found. Discovering one of these, the wasp stings and paralyzes it and then builds a crude cell around it, after attaching an egg to the grub. The larva of the wasp, hatching out, consumes the grub and then spins a cocoon in which it develops.

The species reproduced is: South American Burrowing Wasp (*Campsomeris ephippium* Say, page 56, figure 8), found in South and Central America.

Horn-tail Family (*Siricidae*). This family consists of about 100 species, about one-third found in America. Its members are mostly rather large, brightly marked, and well-built. The adult female has an ovipositor consisting of five pieces, the two outside ones forming a sheath, and two of the others being furnished at the tip with a series of fine, hard, transverse ridges arranged like the teeth of a file. With this she is able to match the work of a gimlet or auger in human hands, and can drill innumerable holes in the solid wood of a tree. In each of these she places an egg.

The best-known of the horn-tails is the pigeon tremex, which is about one and one-half inches long, with a rusty head and thorax, and a black abdomen with yellow bands and spots. The female bores a hole half an inch deep into elms, oaks, sycamores, and maple trees. The larvae, hatching from the eggs laid therein, burrow into the heart wood where they grow into cylindrical, blunt-ended, whitish grubs, measuring about an inch and a half in length.

When ready to transform into an adult insect, the grub makes a cocoon of silk and chips, and then goes to sleep. On awakening as a full-fledged pigeon tremex it bores out at right angles to the gallery dug by the grub, instinctively knowing that in such direction lies the shortest way to liberty.

The European grain cephus, whose larvae bore into the stems of wheat and cause the straw to break about harvest time, belongs to the horn-tail tribe. About the time the head of the wheat begins to form, the fly bores a small hole in the straw. When the larva hatches from the inserted egg, it tunnels down the stem, and by wheat-cutting time has passed below the level of the cutter bar. In this way it remains in the stubble, where it makes a silken cocoon and hibernates.

The species reproduced is: Common Horn-tail (*Tremex columba* Linn., page 56, figure 11), found all over North America.

Cimbicid Family (*Cimbicidae*). The most familiar species of the group is the American Saw-fly. Its eggs are laid in June in crescent-shaped slits made in leaves. The food plants are elm, birch, linden, and willow. When disturbed the larva spurts a fluid from glands just above the spiracles. When it is full-grown it burrows in the ground, makes an oval, brownish cocoon, and spends the winter there, not changing to a pupa until spring. It emerges in May or June.

The species reproduced is: American Saw-fly (*Cimbex americana* Leach, page 56, figure 12), habitat North America.

Halictus Bee Family (*Halictidae*). Some of these bees are larger than a fair-sized wasp and some are smaller than a house-fly. Every halictus carries what has been called a clearly written certificate of her guild. It is a smooth, shiny line, or groove, on the last segment of the abdomen that acts as a guide for the sting. Some species build wonderful cells for their babies.

The burrows in which these are located may be rough, but the cradles must be perfect. Leading from the burrow, the cells are excavated so as to resemble water bottles laid on the side. No human plasterer ever did a finer job than these bees. First there is a coating of clay, its surface roughened like the outside of a thimble. On this is laid a smooth coat, mixed with saliva and carefully troweled with the tongue—a glazing that is exquisite in its perfection, and both dampproof and waterproof.

A small fly which the ordinary observer dismisses as nothing but a gnat, makes it her business to lay her eggs in the halictus's cells. Under the microscope she is revealed as a red-eyed, white-faced, gray-corseleted, black-legged marauder.

One species of this family studied by Fabre, the zebra halictus, possesses a quality rarely observed in the insect world—interest in grandchildren. The mother bee, of the spring generation, having passed the winter in some frost-proof retreat, gives the mansion she has built so laboriously to her daughters. Each daughter builds a small addition to the burrow and makes a group of cells of her own, but all use the main burrow in common.

The grandmother of the brood in the cells stands guard at the doorway, to keep out all but the rightful entrants—her daughters. Her velvet dress, so clean and handsome when she was a youthful matron, is now threadbare and dingy. Gone is the nap, all but lost are the beautiful stripes of red and brown.

But she has a grandmother's pride in the newly hatched grubs, and woe betide any creature who

        1⅛ times Natural Size

FROM CARPENTER-BEES TO SAW-FLIES RANGES THE COLLECTION ON THIS PAGE

(1) American Carpenter-bee, *Xylocopa virginica* Linn. [Male]; (2) Solitary Wasp, *Stictia signata* Linn. [Female]; (3) Common Bumblebee, *Bombus americanorum* Fab. [Female, queen]; (4) American Ichneumon Fly, *Amblyteles grandis* Brulle [Female]; (5) American Ichneumon Fly, *Trogus elegans* Cress. [Female]; (6) American Ichneumon Fly, *Trogus rileyi* Cress. [Female]; (7) American Mud-dauber, *Sceliphron caementarium* Drury [Female]; (8) South American Burrowing Wasp, *Campsomeris ephippium* Say [Female]; (9) American Hunting Wasp, *Ammobia ichneumonea* Linn. [Female]; (10) European Social Wasp, *Vespa crabro* Linn. [Female]; (11) Common Horn-tail, *Tremex columba* Linn. [Female]; (12) American Saw-fly, *Cimbex americana* Leach [Male]. See text under the following Family headings: Carpenter-bee, Thread-waisted Wasp, Bumblebee, Ichneumon Fly, Scoliid Wasp, Horn-tail, and Cimbicid, pages 45, 50, 53, 55.

A CHINESE PEDDLER OF BIRD AND CRICKET CAGES

Singing crickets in cages are as familiar in the Orient as singing canaries in the Occident. Even the department stores in the larger cities of Japan cater to the cage-cricket trade. Hundreds of thousands of the insect Kreislers are sold every year.

cannot show the yellow foot of the halictus folk when seeking to reach those grub chambers! A drubbing the marauder never will forget will be his certain portion. At the door, all day long, sits poor, bald-headed grandmother, a ghost of her former self, in a little sentry box at the mouth of the burrow, stepping aside to all those who can give the countersign, but wild as a witch in her anger toward any would-be intruder. Mayhap her remarkable guard over her grandchildren comes from the knowledge that some of them will be males. Denied the privilege of having sons, by that strange quirk of Nature which makes all the children of the spring generation females, she must look to her grandchildren for her male progeny. And each of those grandchildren is hatched into the world without a father.

With no males produced from the eggs of the spring mother, and no males having survived the winter, they perforce are born under that strange departure from the orthodox laws of reproduction known as parthenogenesis.

The species reproduced are: American Burrowing Bee (*Agapostemon splendens* Lep., page 58, figure 1), common in North America; *Nomia nortoni* Cress (page 58, figure 7), occurring in North America.

Honeybee Family (*Apidae*). (See "Man's Winged Ally, the Busy Honeybee," page 91.)

Melecta Bee Family (*Melectidae*). This family is made up of two groups, one of which is parasitic. The members of the parasitic tribe are true cuckoos. They have learned that well-known manner of living recorded in Holy Writ, "Reaping where thou hast not sown, and gathering where thou hast not strawed." Some of them single out some industrious species and take up quarters with them uninvited, eating the viands of their hosts as though they were honored guests instead of lazy spongers. Other cuckoo tribes resort to even a lower form of sponging. These watch around until some busy little mason-bee matron gets her nest well nigh completed and provisioned; then, during her last trip for the final load of provender, they steal into the burrow and lay their eggs in the cell.

Unconscious of what has happened, poor Mrs. Mason-bee lays her egg and closes the cell. But the cuckoo-bee's eggs hatch first, and its larva, eating the ration that never was intended for it, presently grows strong enough to overpower and devour the rightful owner of the cell.

Some species of mason-bees, realizing the purposes of the cuckoos who flourish by nimble wit, never lay an egg in a cell without first having in their mouths the mortar with which to close the cell. If they had to gather the mortar after laying the egg, the plunderer would be the first

Twice Natural Size

A GROUP OF HYMENOPTERS OF STRANGELY CONTRASTING WAYS OF LIFE

(1) American Burrowing Bee, *Agapostemon splendens* Lep. [Female]; (2) Honeybee, *Apis mellifera* Linn. [Female, queen]; (3) *Crocisa crucifera* Ckll. [Female]; (4) Honeybee, *Apis mellifera* Linn. [Female, worker]; (5) *Anthophora zonata* Linn. [Female]; (6) Yellow-jacket, *Vespula carolina* Linn. [Female, worker]; (7) *Nomia nortoni* Cress. [Male]; (8) Carpenter-bee, *Xylocopa bombylans* Fab. [Female]; (9) Honeybee, *Apis mellifera* Linn. [Male, drone]; (10) *Euglossa variabilis* Friese [Female]; (11) *Triepeolus quadrifasciatus* Say [Male]. See text under the following Family headings: Halictus Bee, Honeybee, Melecta Bee, Anthophora Bee, Social Wasp, Carpenter-bee, and Euglossid Bee, pages 50, 51, 55, 57, 60, 91.

1½ times Natural Size

A BAKER'S DOZEN OF ICHNEUMON FLIES THAT ARE MAN'S CONSTANT ALLIES

(1) *Agathilla bradleyi* Vireck [Male]; (2) *Macrojoppa blandita* Cress. [Male]; (3) *Cyanoxorides caeruleus* Cameron [Female]; (4) *Amblyteles jucundus* Brulle [Female]; (5) *Platylabus clarus* Cress. [Female]; (6) *Amblyteles jucundus* Brulle [Male]; (7) *Callicryptus fasciipennis* Brulle [Female]; (8) *Polyaenus spinarius* Brulle [Female]; (9) *Amblyteles w-album* Cress. [Female]; (10) *Ichneumon irritator* Fab. [Female]; (11) *Amblyteles semicaeruleus* Cress. [Female]; (12) *Labena grallator* Say [Female]; (13) *Lissopimpla semipunctata* Kirby [Female]. All of the species represented on this page belong to the single Family of the Ichneumon Flies, page 53. Few among any of the Families of insects render man a greater service than the Ichneumon Flies.

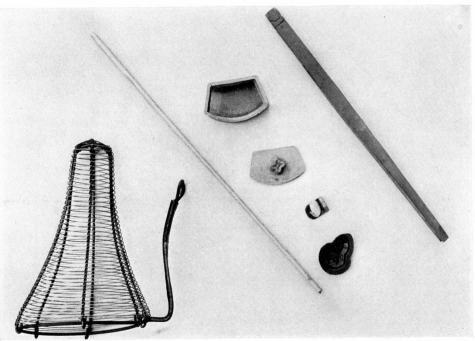

Photograph by James Dorsett

EQUIPMENT USED IN HANDLING FIGHTING CRICKETS IN CHINA

In some parts of the Celestial Republic the sport of cricket fighting is as common as cock-fighting in the countries of the Caribbean. At the left is the wire cage used for transferring the fighters to and from the ring. The light ferrule next to the cage is the tickler, to stir up the fighters to a proper degree of anger. Beyond that are, respectively, from the bottom, the drinking trough, the food rack, the top of the cricket's house, and the house itself. At the right is a set of bamboo tweezers for handling food and equipment (see illustration, page 64).

to improve the opportunity of crossing the un-guarded threshold and laying her own eggs in it.

"With the industrious folk who go quietly about their business—the laborers, masons, foragers, and warehousemen—mingle the parasitic tribe, the prowlers hurrying from one home to another, lying in wait at the doors, watching for an opportunity to settle their families at the expense of the honest toilers."

In those words Fabre sums up the situation in Bee Land. Then, bringing the detached view of the philosopher to man's own attitude toward other creatures, he makes one a little more patient with these home destroyers of the insect world by saying, "Life in general is but a vast brigandage.

"Nature devours herself; matter is kept alive by passing from one stomach to another. At the banquet of life, each is in turn the guest and the dish; the eater of today becomes the eaten of tomorrow. Everything lives on that which lived or has lived; everything is parasitism. Man is the great parasite, the unbridled thief of all that is fit to eat. He steals the milk from the lamb, he steals the honey from the children of the bee, even as the Melecta bee pilfers the pottage of the Anthophora bee's sons."

The species reproduced are: *Crocisa crucifera* Ckll. (page 58, figure 3), occurring in the Philippine Islands; *Triepeolus quadrifasciatus* Say (page 58, figure 11), inhabiting North America.

Anthophora Bee Family (*Anthophoridae*). This family of bees is widely distributed throughout the world. In North America nearly 100 species have been described, but the habits of only a few have been studied. The nests of familiar species usually are built in steeply inclined or perpendicular banks of earth, preferably in those of compact clay. Nearly all of the species are gregarious, hundreds of individuals building nests close together in the same bank of earth. In the construction of their homes the Anthophoras build a cylindrical tube of clay, extending outward and downward from the entrance of the tunnel.

The outside of this tube is rough, but the inside smooth. It is composed of small pellets of earth compacted together, which have been brought out of the tunnel when wet and molded into the desired form. In excavating the tunnel the bees find the clay hard, so they visit a watering place and convert themselves into insectean tanks to carry sufficient supply to the burrow to soften the clay and make it workable like putty.

1½ times Natural Size

TWO-WINGED FLIES—FAMILIAR AND OTHERWISE

(1) Tropical Hover Fly, *Volucella obesa* Fab. [Female]; (2) May Beetle Fly, *Pyrgota undata* Wiedemann [Female]; (3) Florida Ant Fly, *Microdon fulgens* Wiedemann [Female]; (4) Eastern Tachina Fly, *Belvesia bifasciata* Fab. [Female]; (5) Western Tachina Fly, *Paradejeania rutiliodes* Jaennicke [Female]; (6) Central American Bot Fly, *Dermatobia hominis* Linn. [Female]; (7) Scavenger Fly, *Silbomyia fuscipennis* Fab. [Female]; (8) Ox Warble, *Hypoderma lineatum* DeVilliers [Female]; (9) Eastern Hover Fly, *Temnostoma excentricum* Harris [Male]; (10) *Milesia virginiensis* Drury [Male]; (11) California Robber Fly, *Laphria coquilletti* McAtee [Male]; (12) Australian Nimble Fly, *Rutilia splendida* Donovan [Female]; (13) *Achias amplividens* Walker [Female]; (14) Costa Rican Blow-fly, *Mesembrinella umbrosa* Aldrich [Female]. See text under Fly headings, pages 62, 64, 66, 67, 69.

Photograph by Paul Henri Fabre

THE END OF A BATTLE BETWEEN SUITORS IN CRICKET LAND

The conquered suitor scampers away, while the conqueror insults him with a song of triumph.
The lady cricket looks on very demurely from behind.

The Anthophora bees have many foes, before whose attacks they are practically helpless.

The species reproduced is: *Anthophora zonata* Linn. (page 58, figure 5), found in southern Asia, Malay Peninsula, and Philippine Islands.

TRUE FLIES
(Order *Diptera*)
Page 61

This large order of insects embraces all the two-winged flies, which include the horse flies, house-flies, blow-flies, mosquitoes, midges, and gnats, as well as a host of related families. According to Sharp, about 40,000 species have been discovered, but these are only a tithe of those still unknown to science. Aldrich's list of American species now goes far beyond the 8,000 mark.

The *Diptera* are rated by some authorities as physiologically the most advanced of the insects; certainly in them the processes of a complete life cycle are carried on with the greatest rapidity, and the phenomenon of metamorphosis has been most nearly perfected.

A maggot hatching from an egg grows so rapidly that it is mature in a few days; then within an impenetrable skin it dissolves itself almost completely. A little later the liquid content of that skin turns to a sort of jelly, and in a few days this is reconstructed into a being so totally different in appearance, in habits, and in structure, that the resources of science find themselves severely taxed to demonstrate any identity in the organs of the two stages of the insect's existence.

Hover Fly Family (*Syrphidae*). This family is one of the largest and best known among the flies. We see them in our garden, where, when the sun is bright, they hover over flowers or beneath trees where the sun finds its way through the leaves. Many of them mimic bumblebees, others pattern after honeybees, and still others imitate the wasps.

It is said that the old myth about the carcasses of animals generating swarms of honeybees probably arose from the fact that one species of this family so closely resembles the drones that they have been taken for honeybees. That species breeds in carcasses, and its mistaken identity is found in China and Japan, as well as in Russia. Even the Book of Judges in the Old Testament shows this error of identification in the story of Samson. The majority of species, however, are content to play the simple rôle of an ordinary fly.

The family embraces some 3,000 species distributed all over the world, of which about 300 are represented in our American fauna. Some species live as guests in ants' nests and others dwell with bumblebees.

The species reproduced are: Tropical Hover Fly (*Volucella obesa* Fab., page 61, figure 1), common

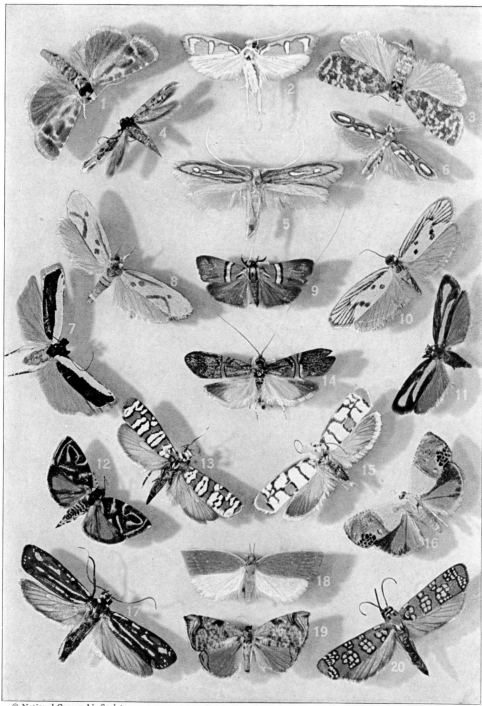

Twice Natural Size

LILIPUTS OF THE SCALY-WINGED WORLD—MICRO-LEPIDOPTERA (SEE PAGE 69)

(1) European Pine Shoot Moth, *Rhyacionia buoliana* Schiffermüller [Female]; (2) *Lupercalia ignita* Busck [Male]; (3) Virginia Pine Moth, *Petrova virginiana* Busck [Female]; (4) *Psacaphora edithella* Barnes and Busck [Male]; (5) Palmetto Leaf-miner, *Homaledra heptathalama* Busck [Female]; (6) *Filinota hermosella* Busck [Male]; (7) *Atasthalistis tricolor* Felder [Female]; (8) *Mieza citrina* Busck [Male]; (9) *Tortyra cuprinella* Busck [Female]; (10) *Mieza laetae* Hubner [Female]; (11) *Mieza spatula* Busck [Male]; (12) *Hemerophila albertiana* Stoll [Male]; (13) *Atteva exquisita* Busck [Female]; (14) *Nematois chrysoprasias* Meyrick [Male]; (15) *Ethmia festiva* Busck [Female]; (16) *Grapholitha egregiana* Felder [Female]; (17) *Atteva hysginiella* Wallengreen [Female]; (18) *Phytomimia chlorophylla* Walsingham [Female]; (19) *Mictopsichia durranti* Walsingham [Male]; (20) *Atteva pustulella* Fab. [Male].

A CHINESE CRICKET ARENA

In the bowl is the cricket house with the lid on, at the upper left a food rack with a bean lying beside it, and at the upper right a water trough (see, also, page 60).

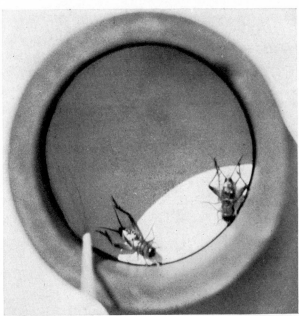

Photographs by James Dorsett

CRICKET GLADIATORS

The fighting ring is made of a portion of a large bamboo culm. Betting in China on the results is as lively as that at a horse race or at a game of *jai alai* in Cuba.

throughout the American Tropics; Florida Ant Fly (*Microdon fulgens* Wiedemann, page 61, figure 3), occurring in Florida; Eastern Hover Fly (*Temnostoma excentricum* Harris, page 61, figure 9), living in the eastern part of the United States; *Milesia virginiensis* Drury (page 61, figure 10), inhabiting the eastern United States.

Pyrgota Fly Family (*Pyrgotidae*). The members of this family, by many authorities, are placed in the family of Ortalids. Some species of the family are parasitic upon various beetles.

The species reproduced is: May Beetle Fly (*Pyrgota undata* Wiedemann, page 61, figure 2), parasitic upon the May beetle and found in the eastern United States.

Tachina Fly Family (*Tachinidae*). There is no family of the fly order to which man is more deeply indebted than to the Tachina. Its species are practically all parasitic in their habits. Frequenting the flowers and vegetation where other insects gather, they watch their chance to attach their eggs to the skins of young caterpillars and grubs.

When these eggs hatch, the larvae bore into their victims and live on the tissues. Sometimes the victim is killed before pupation, but usually the parasite's attacks are not fatal so soon, and pupation takes place. Later the parasite grub itself pupates within the carcass of its victim and then emerges a full-fledged fly. Many species of this family help to hold in check the great hosts of army-worms, locusts, and other of our worst insect foes, which otherwise would overwhelm a community. A single species is almost the only check on the destructive flower-eating Diabrotica of California, which, Kellogg tells us, if allowed to increase unhindered, soon would destroy every blossom in that land of flowers.

More than 1,400 American species have been reported in our fauna. Some species give birth to live larvae instead of laying

1⅓ times Natural Size

A CHARMING GROUP OF MICRO-LEPIDOPTERA ARRAYED IN RESPLENDENT ROBES

(1) *Coryptilum klugii* Zeller [Male]; (2) *Lactura conflagrans* Walker [Male]; (3) *Atasthalistis concinnalis* Feisthamel [Male]; (4) *Hypercallia miniata* Dognin [Female]; (5) *Pseudotalara regia* Schaus [Female]; (6) *Cerace onustana* Walker [Male]; (7) *Pseudatteria leopardina* Butler [Female]; (8) *Paranthrene palmi* Harry Edwards [Female]; (9) *Pseudatteria mimica* Felder [Female]; (10) *Imma grammozona* Meyrick [Male]; (11) Western Clear Winged Moth, *Melittia gloriosa* Harry Edwards [Male]; (12) *Megalodoris electrina* Meyrick [Male]; (13) *Stenoma elegans* Zeller [Female]; (14) *Tortrix animosana* Busck [Female]; (15) *Stenoma armata* Zeller [Male]. The Micro-lepidoptera Families lack common names. The species represented on this page will be found in the text under the Order heading The Little Moths, page 69.

western part of the United States.

Bot Fly Family (*Oestridae*). Although this family consists of fewer than 100 species in the whole world, it is one of much interest on account of the habits of its members, which, though large in size, live entirely at the expense of living vertebrates. Some dwell in the alimentary canals of their hosts, others occupy the respiratory passages, and still others live beneath the skin of the animals they attack. Some species of the bot fly family in the Tropics are parasitic on monkeys and even have been reared from human beings.

The Ox Warbles are aliens from Europe. They attach their eggs to cattle, usually on the hind legs and occasionally on the flanks. When the larvae hatch they crawl down the hair follicle and penetrate the skin. In their second stage they are found in the wall of the esophagus. The exact course from the hind legs to the esophagus has not been determined, but it is believed that the larvae probably travel in the loose connective tissues under the skin to the region of the throat and into the esophagus. Here they remain for three months and then migrate to the

Photograph by International

A CHINESE MERRY-GO-ROUND DRAWN BY A FLEA

The tiny bit of motive power is seen in the foreground, under the rim of the wheel. Harnessed to the little toy, the insect is able to move eleven hundred times its own weight. In the United States men have trained fleas to draw tiny wagons and to do acrobatic stunts that make the flea circus a fascinating vaudeville performance.

eggs. The skin of the prospective host is punctured by the viviparous female with her ovipositor and her larvae deposited within the body of the host. In the case of *Eupeleteria magnicornis,* which infests the larvae of the brown-tail moth, the female attaches its larva to the surface of a leaf by a thin membranous case which is cup-shaped and surrounds the anal end of the larva. The little maggot reposes on the silken thread which the caterpillar uses as a guide back to its nest, lying in wait until the victim returns from the feeding ground.

The species reproduced are: Eastern Tachina Fly (*Belvesia bifasciata* Fab., page 61, figure 4), occurring in eastern and southern United States; Western Tachina Fly (*Paradejeania rutiloides* Jaennicke, page 61, figure 5), inhabiting the

back, where they finally emerge through holes in the skin.

The horse bot fly is well known to every lover of horseflesh. During the summer time it flies about the forelegs of horses, laying its eggs on the long hairs above and below the knee joints.

These eggs rarely hatch when left untouched, but the horse, by scratching the legs with its teeth, removes the small cap of the eggshell and inadvertently takes the larvae into its mouth. The latter then are carried with food or water into the stomach, where they fasten themselves to the inner coating and remain until full grown. Horses have an instinctive fear of the gad fly, as the adult more properly is called.

The species reproduced are: Central American Bot Fly (*Dermatobia hominis* Linn., page 61, figure 6), habitat Central America; Ox Warble (*Hypoderma lineatum* DeVilliers, page 61, figure 8), occurring in eastern and southern United States.

Blow-fly Family (*Calliphoridae*). The most familiar members of this group are the blue-bottle and green-bottle flies. The blow-flies live normally out of doors, but often enter houses in search of material on which to deposit their eggs. Their larger size and loud buzzing, as well as their striking hues, make them conspicuous in any fly company. They lay their eggs on meat, cheese, and other provisions. These soon hatch and their larvae rapidly develop.

It seems rather strange that until only a few centuries ago maggots were supposed to be the product of spontaneous generation. Then some early scientist decided to spread a piece of fly netting above a block of cheese so that the flies could hover about the cheese but not reach it. They thereupon laid their eggs upon the netting and these in due time produced the usual larvae of maggots, and the ghost of spontaneous generation was banished for a long time. But when bacteria were discovered it came back, and so strenuously asserted itself that faith in it was held firmly in many quarters until Pasteur, through a long series of experiments, thoroughly put it to rout as an explanation even of the minutest form of life.

The species reproduced are: Scavenger Fly (*Silbomyia fuscipennis* Fab., page 61, figure 7), from Java; Costa Rican Blow-fly (*Mesembrinella umbrosa* Aldrich, page 61, figure 14), from Costa Rica.

Robber Fly Family (*Asilidae*). More than 3,000 robber fly species have been described, of which 500 are found in our fauna. Some are short, thick, and extremely hairy, superficially resembling bees and bumblebees, but the majority of them are long and slender. As is the case with

Photograph by Paul Henri Fabre

THE LARVA OF A CICADA IN ITS BURROW

The females of innumerable species of insects lay their eggs in the ground. When these hatch the larvae dig themselves burrows in which they remain, usually until a short time before they are ready to develop wings and fly away in the adult stage of their life cycle. Many other species lay their eggs in fruits, nuts, and branches. When these fall to the ground the larvae emerge and dig into the soil, where they make cells in which they sleep until the metamorphosis is complete.

most insects which feed upon other insects, the robber flies are a ravenous host. A single individual has been observed to kill eight moths in 20 minutes.

They are fierce foes and seem to fear nothing. The stronger species will attack wasps and other stinging insects, and have been observed to capture dragon-flies and tiger-beetles. The larvae of most species are like the adult flies in their predaceous habits. They feed upon other larvae in rotting wood, under bark or fallen leaves, or in loose soil.

The species reproduced is: California Robber Fly (*Laphria coquilletti* McAtee, page 61, figure 11), found in California.

Painting by Hashime Murayama

THE JAPANESE BEETLE AND THE HIGH SPOTS OF ITS CAREER

The story of the career of this newest of our American pests is broadly typical of the whole Beetle Order. Not all of them spend their larval stages in the ground, however. The parasitic fly shown on the magnified female beetle was imported by the United States Bureau of Entomology. In Japan it and other parasites have been able to prevent the beetle from becoming a menacing pest. The entomological name of the Japanese beetle is *Popillia japonica* and of the fly parasitizing it *Centeter cinerea*. The beetles at the top are natural size; those under the magnifying glass are 4½ times natural size; those at the bottom are 1½ times natural size. (See page 87.)

Photograph by Lynwood M. Chace

BLACK-AND-WHITE PAPER WASPS IN THE DARK CORRIDORS BETWEEN TIERS OF CELLS

The wasps never have been able to solve the problem of a year-to-year existence of their colonies, as have some of the bees and ants. Each fall the community dies out, and only a few fertilized females, which have hibernated as adults in sheltered places, such as crevices in stone walls and protected spots under logs, are able to survive the winter. When spring comes these reawaken into an active life and make themselves small nests containing a few brood cells. From these humble beginnings the summer colonies grow.

Nimble Fly Family (*Dexiidae*). This family possesses about 50 species in this country. The legs of the American species are usually long, and in their early stages our nimble flies are parasitic on various insects, especially beetles. Snails also are known to be forced to act as hosts for their larvae.

Members of the Nimble Fly Family so closely resemble the Tachina Fly Family (see text, page 64) that they are easily confused. The nimble flies are sometimes quite handsome, with brilliantly striped thoraxes.

The species reproduced is: Australian Nimble Fly (*Rutilia splendida* Donovan, page 61, figure 12), found in Queensland, Australia.

Ortalid Family (*Ortalidae*). This is a small family which possesses a number of American species. In the larval state they usually occur under the bark of pine and poplar trees, in the burrow of wood-boring insects, and in onions, cotton bolls, and apples. Most species are regarded merely as scavengers, but some are parasitic on caterpillars.

On the whole, the American Ortalids are a group of insects that have few foes and many friends.

The species reproduced is: *Achias amplividens* Walker (page 61, figure 13), occurring in Australia.

THE LITTLE MOTHS

(Order *Micro-lepidoptera*)

Pages 63 and 65

Among the *Micro-lepidoptera* are some of the worst pests of the whole insect world. The Psyche moth, which in its larval stage is known as the bagworm, belongs to this order. So do the green slug-moth, with its bright scarlet caterpillar; the hag-moth, which gets its name from the disheveled appearance of its larva; the raspberry root-borer and the peach-tree borer, which are such foes of the berry patch and the peach orchard; the bee-moth, the flour- and meal-moths, the clothes-moth, the codling moth, and many others of their ilk.

Olethreutidae Family. More than 400 North American species of this family have been described. Perhaps its most disliked member is the codling moth, whose larvae are the nasty little worms too frequently found feeding near the core of apples. The grape berry moth, which is the most common cause of "wormy" grapes, also belongs to this group, as do the apple bud moth and the clover seed moth.

The species reproduced are: European Pine

Twice Natural Size

LIVING JEWELS THAT MOCK THE LAPIDARY WITH THEIR BEAUTY

(1) *Desmonota variolosa* Web.; (2) *Leptinotarsa 10-lineata* Say; (3) *Leptinotarsa flavitarsis* Guer.; (4) *Tauroma casta* Boh.; (5) *Chrysobothris femorata* Oliv.; (6) *Epicauta vittata* Fab.; (7) *Saperda candida* Fab.; (8) *Cicindela scutellaris* Say; (9) *Lema trilineata* Oliv.; (10) *Epilachna borealis* Fab.; (11) *Macrodactylus angustatus* Beauv.; (12) *Cyphus 16-punctata* Linn.; (13) *Popillia japonica* Newman; (14) *Hypomeces squamosus* Fab.; (15) *Omaspides bistriata* Boh.; (16) *Dolicho-toma bisbiplagiata* Boh.; (17) *Aspidomorpha miliaris* Fab.; (18) *Doryphora flavozonata* Blanch.; (19) *Doryphora kollari* Stal.; (20) *Doryphora mirabilis* Stal.; (21) *Mesomphalia beatula* Boh. See headings: Tortoise Beetle, Leaf Beetle, Metallic Wood-borer, Meloid Beetle, Long-horned Beetle, Tiger-beetle, Lady-bird Beetle Scavenger Beetle and Leaf Chafer, and Snout Beetle, pp. 80, 82, 84, 87.

Photograph by Lynwood M. Chace

CELLS OF A BLACK-AND-WHITE PAPER WASP

From some of the cells the young wasps have emerged, in others they are getting their first view of the world round about, and in still others the occupants remain undisturbed by the events of their community. The seals of their living tombs have not yet been broken, but presently the day of emergence will arrive, and, biting away the coverings, they will come forth full-panoplied for a short and merry life of a few weeks.

Shoot moth (*Rhyacionia buoliana* Schiffermuller, page 63, figure 1), a native of Europe, also found in New York; Virginia Pine moth (*Petrova virginiana* Busck, page 63, figure 3), found in Virginia and eastern United States; *Grapholitha egregiana* Felder (page 63, figure 16), found in the Solomon Islands.

Oecophoridae Family. The *Oecophoridae* moths embrace about 100 American species of rather diverse habits, most of which, in their larval stages, live in webs or feed in decayed wood. Perhaps the most familiar species is the parsnip web moth, whose larvae web together and devour the unfolding flower heads of celery, parsnip, and wild carrot. After having consumed the flowers and unripe seeds and become nearly full-grown, they burrow into the hollow stems of the plants, feed upon the pith and then pupate.

The species reproduced are: *Lupercalia ignita* Busck (page 63, figure 2), occurring in Panama; *Filinota hermosella* Busck (page 63, figure 6), habitat French Guiana; *Phytomimia chlorophylla* Walsingham (page 63, figure 18), inhabiting Guatemala; *Hypercallia miniata* Dognin (page 65, figure 4), habitat Ecuador.

Cosmopterygidae Family. In spite of the fact that this family has no common name, some of its members are well known. One of these is the Palmetto Leaf-miner, which lives on the saw palmetto. Its larvae are social, working together in small companies. They make nests consisting of a delicate sheet of silk covering that part of

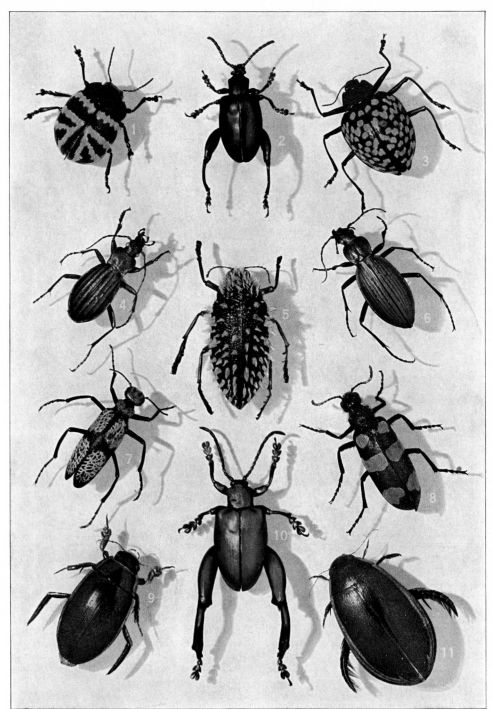

1¼ times Natural Size

BEETLES FROM MANY LANDS DISPLAY THE VERSATILITY OF THEIR ORDER

(1) *Doryphora flavozonata* Blanch.; (2) *Sagra borneoensis* Lac.; (3) *Erotylus giganteus* Linn.; (4) *Carabus auronitens* Fab.; (5) *Julodis viridipes* Cast.; (6) *Ceroglossus gloriosus* Gerst.; (7) *Tegrodera aloga* Skinn.; (8) *Zonabris oculata* Thunbg.; (9) *Dytiscus fasciventris* Say; (10) *Sagra fabricii* Lac.; (11) *Cybister fimbriolatus* Say. See text under the following Family headings: Leaf Beetle, Erotylidae Beetle, Carabid Beetle, Metallic Wood-borer, Meloid Beetle, and Predaceous Diving Beetle, pages 80, 82, 84, 89. The Predaceous Diving Beetles and their kin are the principal foes of the larvae living at the bottom of ponds, creeks, and rivers. The Diving Beetles are frequently confused with the diving insects of the Order *Hemiptera*.

Photograph by Herbert

GRASSHOPPER GUESTS OF THE U. S. S. "MINDANAO"

When America's new Yangtze River gunboat reached a point a thousand miles from the Yellow Sea, a huge swarm of grasshoppers swooped down, rested a while, and then took wing again. Many species of insects have colonized the whole world by becoming stowaways aboard the ships that sail the seven seas.

the leaf upon which they are feeding. The cattail moth, which infests the heads of cattail plants, is another member.

The species reproduced are: *Psacaphora edithella* Barnes & Busck (page 63, figure 4), occurring in Colorado; Palmetto Leaf-miner (*Homaledra heptathalama* Busck, page 63, figure 5), inhabiting Florida.

Gelechiidae Family. This family includes a number of our worst pests and possesses more than 400 species. Some are leaf-miners, others attack the heads and bolls of plants, and still others prey upon stored grain. The Angoumois grain-moth, whose larvae feed within the seeds of oats, rye, wheat, barley, sorghum, and cow peas, and the pink boll worm, which is one of the worst of our insect pests, are the outstanding members of the family. The peach twig borer, which burrows into the tender shoots of the peach tree in early spring, and the goldenrod gall moth, whose larvae cause the galls in the stems of goldenrod, also belong to this group of *Micro-lepidoptera*.

The species reproduced are: *Atasthalistis tricolor* Felder (page 63, figure 7), living in the Solomon Islands; *Atasthalistis concinnalis* Feisthamel (page 65, figure 3), occurring in New Guinea.

Hyponomeutidae Family. This is another family of *Micro-lepidoptera* which is somewhat

noted for its pest species. One of them is the apple fruit miner, which has developed into a serious menace in orchards in western Canada. It burrows in all directions through the fruit, causing it to decay. The family also embraces the ailanthus web-worm moth and the ermine moth. One species of the latter has been introduced into the United States and is becoming an apple and cherry pest.

The species reproduced are: *Mieza citrina* Busck (page 63, figure 8), living in Costa Rica; *Mieza laetae* Hubner (page 63, figure 10), occurring in Guatemala; *Mieza spatula* Busck (page 63, figure 11), living in Costa Rica; *Atteva exquisita* Busck (page 63, figure 13), a native of Mexico; *Atteva hysginiella* Wallengreen (page 63, figure 17), inhabiting the Galápagos Islands; *Atteva pustulella* Fab. (page 63, figure 20), an inhabitant of San Salvador; *Lactura conflagrans* Walker (page 65, figure 2), occurring in New Guinea; *Pseudotalara regia* Schaus (page 65, figure 5), occurring in Mexico.

Glyphipterygidae Family. This family is of world-wide distribution. There are about 40 species which belong to it in the North American fauna.

The species reproduced are: *Tortyra cuprinella* Busck (page 63, figure 9), occurring in Panama; *Hemerophila albertiana* Stoll (page 63, figure

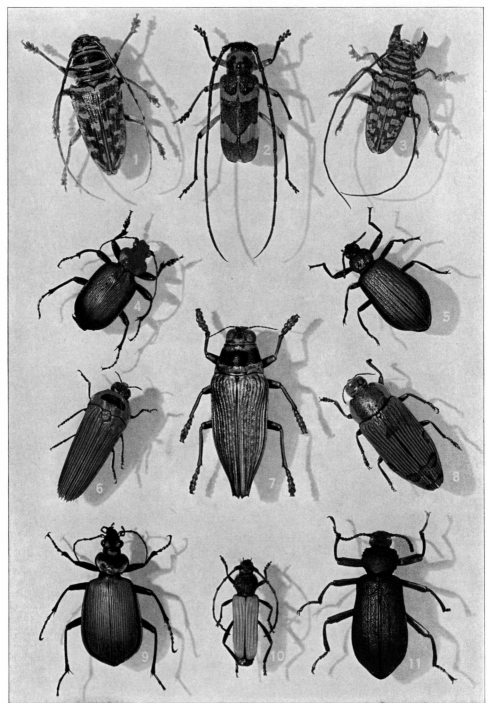

1¼ times Natural Size

A STRIKING GROUP OF WOOD BORING, GROUND-, AND DARKLING BEETLES

(1) *Sternotomis virescens* Westw.; (2) *Crioprosopus magnificus* Le Conte; (3) *Sternotomis mirabilis* Drury; (4) *Calosoma bonariense* Dej.; (5) *Metallonotus metallicus* Fab.; (6) *Hyperantha haemorrhoa* Fairm.; (7) *Psiloptera bicarinata* Thunbg.; (8) *Stigmodera variabilis* Don.; (9) *Calosoma scrutator* Fab.; (10) *Tragidion fulvipenne* Say; (11) *Odontopezus cupreus* Fab. See text under the following Family headings: Long-horned Beetle, Darkling Beetle, and Carabid Beetle, pages 84, 89. Some of the long-horned beetles spend three years in their grub stage and always pupate with their heads toward the exit from their tunnels.

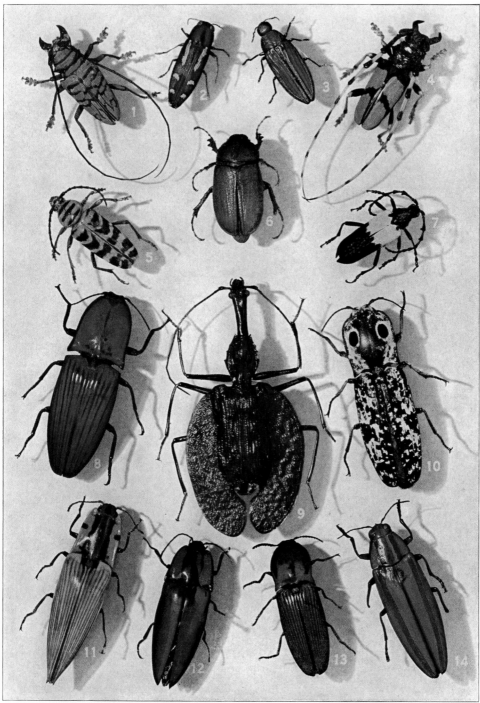

1¼ times Natural Size

SOME OF NATURE'S LITTLE JOKES ATTENDED BY A RESPLENDENT COURT

(1) *Sternotomis bifasciata* Fab.; (2) *Buprestis rufipes* Oliv.; (3) *Buprestis aurulenta* Linn.; (4) *Dendrobias reducta* Casey; (5) *Cyllene decora* Oliv.; (6) *Phyllophaga torta* Lec.; (7) *Desmocerus palliatus* Forst.; (8) *Chalcolepidius lacordairei* Cand.; (9) *Mormolyce hagenbachi* Westw.; (10) *Alaus lusciosus* Hope; (11) *Semiotus imperialis* Guer.; (12) *Campsosternus gemma* Cand.; (13) *Chalcolepidius rubripennis* Lec.; (14) *Chrysochroa fulgidissima* Schoenh. See text under the following Family headings: Long-horned Beetle, Metallic Wood-borer, Scavenger Beetle and Leaf Chafer, Carabid Beetle, and Click Beetle, pages 82, 84, 87, 89.

Photograph by Paul Henri Fabre

LONG-HORNED BEETLES ON A LOG

Some wood-boring beetles spend their larval stage in the heart of oak trees, while others spend this period driving mines between the bark and the wood. The latter species are known as engraver beetles. One tiny member of the order has been a source of much trouble to transcontinental telephone cables. They bore through the lead sheathing, thereby admitting moisture and destroying the insulation.

12), native of British Guiana; *Mictopsichia durranti* Walsingham (page 63, figure 19), native of Guatemala.

Adelidae Family. The tiny moths of this family in their larval stage feed on the leaves of various herbs and shrubs. In their earliest stages the larvae are miners, but later they live in portable cases. The male members of the family are characterized by the unusually long and fine antennae, which may be twice or more than twice the length of the wings.

The species reproduced is: *Nematois chrysoprasias* Meyrick (page 63, figure 14), occurring in Assam.

Ethmiidae Family. The larvae of this family are usually social, living in a light web and feeding chiefly on plants of the borage family. Most of the American species belong to the genus *Ethmia*.

The species reproduced is: *Ethmia festiva* Busck (page 63, figure 15), found in Guatemala and Panama.

Tineidae Family. Some 4,000 species of this family, which includes among others the clothes-moths and many of the leaf-miners, have been described, of which 125 have a North American habitat. Each of the three species of clothes-moths belongs to a different genus, and all of them came with the American people from the Old World. One of them is the parent of the case-bearing larva.

Whenever this larva grows too large for its little case, it expands its home without emerging therefrom. Cutting a triangular slit down one side, in the one end it inserts triangular gores of the woolen material upon which it is feeding, after which it turns around and enlarges the other end in the same way. That process takes care of the diameter, but not the length of the case. To make it longer, each end is opened and an addition is built.

The web clothes-moth makes no case, but hides in a fold or crevice of the material it is eating and spins a little web of silk to cover it. The third species is found in fur robes, horse blankets, upholstering, and the like. Species of the genus *Stigmella* are mostly leaf-miners. The leaves of Juneberry, oak, chestnut, hazel, walnut, sycamore, ironwood, apple, wild cherry, sweetbrier, and blackberry each have their own special species of these miners.

The species reproduced is: *Coryptilum klugii* Zeller (page 63, figure 1), found in New Guinea.

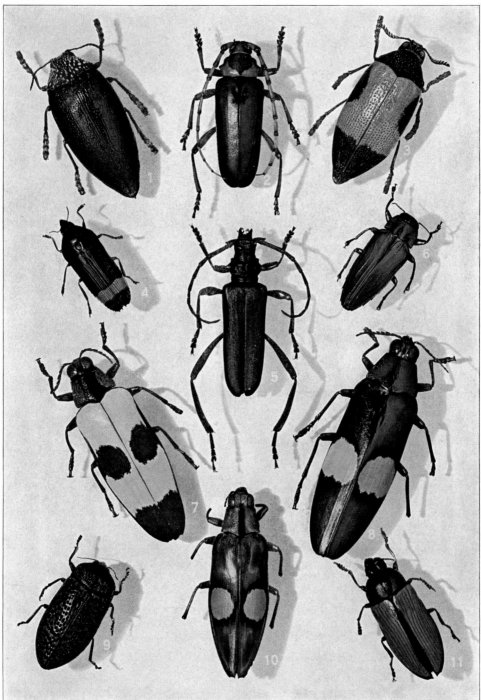

1¼ times Natural Size

FROM WHAT GOLCONDA DO THE BEETLES GET THEIR GEMLIKE GARMENTS?

(1) *Sternocera bennigseni* Kerrem [Male]; (2) *Stenaspis verticalis* Serv. [Female]; (3) *Sternocera hunteri* Waterh. [Male]; (4) *Conognatha amoena* Kirby [Female]; (5) *Callichroma schwarzi* Fisher [Female]; (6) *Belionota sumptuosa* Cast. and Gory [Male]; (7) *Chrysochroa buqueti* Gory [Female]; (8) *Chrysochroa edwardsi* Hope [Male]; (9) *Stigmodera macularia* Donovan [Male]; (10) *Chrysochroa ocellata* Fabricius [Female]; (11) *Stigmodera suturalis* Donovan [Female]. See the following Family headings: Metallic Wood-borer and Long-horned Beetle, pages 82, 84.

Photograph by Paul Henri Fabre

TWO INSECT WEATHER PROPHETS CONFER (SEE TEXT, PAGE 14)

These green grasshoppers are close relatives of the katydids. The males sing both by day and by night. The eggs of most species are laid usually in the stems of root leaves of grasses or the pith of twigs.

Tortricidae Family. This large family, mostly made up of leaf-rollers, possesses about 165 North American species. The *Cacoecia* include the rose ugly nest, the cherry tree ugly nest, the oak ugly nest, and the fruit tree ugly nest, the latter being much of a nuisance in orchards. The eggs are laid on the bark of the twigs in June. The larvae hatch in May of the following year and enter the opening buds.

The species reproduced are: *Cerace onustana* Walker (page 65, figure 6), found in Japan; *Pseudatteria leopardina* Butler (page 65, figure 7), occurring in Costa Rica; *Pseudatteria mimica* Felder (page 65, figure 9), habitat Brazil; *Megalodoris electrina* Meyrick (page 65, figure 12), living in the Philippine Islands; *Tortrix animosana* Busck (page 65, figure 14), occurring in Guatemala.

Clear Winged Moth Family (*Aegeriidae*). This is a small family of unorthodox *Microlepidoptera,* since many of them have no scales on their wings and some of them only a few. Likewise they depart from the moth habit in being day rather than night flyers. The majority of the species of the family mimic bees, wasps, and flies. This mimicry is not a superficial one, since even the motions of the insects captured or disturbed closely resemble those of the ones they imitate. Their attitude while resting, the sounds

they produce, their hyaline wings, the rings on their bodies, even the odors they give off, stamp them as being what they are not. Some of them carry the deception so far that they even pretend to sting, and go through all the motions of doing so, although they are entirely lacking in the necessary organ for that purpose.

The larvae of the family are all borers. One of them, *Sanninoidea exitiosa,* is the worst of all the peach-tree borers, and is estimated to damage the peach crop to the extent of $6,000,000 a year. While it formerly preyed on wild cherries and plums, it later adopted the peach tree.

The species reproduced are: *Paranthrene palmi* Harry Edwards (page 65, figure 8), occurring in New York State; Western Clear Winged Moth, *Melittia gloriosa* Harry Edwards (page 65, figure 11), living in Oregon.

Plutellidae Family. This family is of wide distribution, with about 50 North American species. The most familiar member is the diamond back moth whose larvae infest cabbage and other cruciferous plants, eating holes in the leaves. The moth is sometimes a pest in greenhouses, infesting stocks, wallflowers, sweet alyssum, and candytuft.

The species reproduced is: *Imma grammozona* Meyrick (page 65, figure 10), habitat New Guinea.

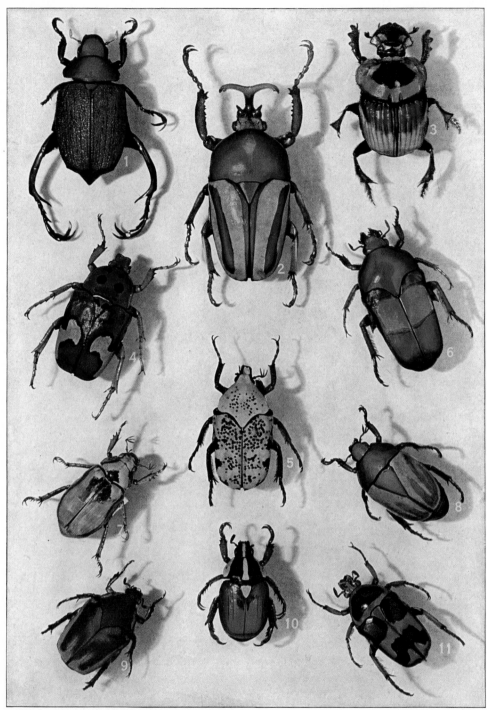

1¼ times Natural Size

DUNG BEETLES IN HABIT, BUT IN ARMOR ROYALLY CLAD

(1) *Chrysophora chrysochlora* Latr. [Male]; (2) *Eudicella morgani* White [Male]; (3) *Phanaeus imperator* Chevr.; (4) *Genyodonta flavomaculata* Fab.; (5) *Argyripa lansbergei* Salle; (6) *Ischiopsopha jamesi* Waterh.; (7) *Plusiotis resplendens* Bouc.; (8) *Macraspis pantochloris* Blanch.; (9) June Bug, *Cotinus nitida* Linn.; (10) *Rutela laeta* Weber; (11) *Heterorrhina macleayi* Kirby. See text under the following Family headings: Scavenger Beetle and Leaf Chafer, page 87.

A BEETLE DRAGS A CICADA INTO ITS BURROW

The most striking hunters of the insect world belong to the wasp clan. However, many of the beetles are also carnivorous.

Stenomidae Family. This family possesses some 20 North American species and has a rather wide distribution. The larvae live in webs, most frequently infesting the oak.

The species reproduced are: *Stenoma elegans* Zeller (page 65, figure 13, occurring in Peru; *Stenoma armata* Zeller (page 65, figure 15), inhabiting Paraguay.

THE BEETLES

(Order *Coleoptera*)

Pages 70, 72, 74, 75, 77, 79, 81

The beetles are the predominant order of the insect world. The transformation of what was once their forward pair of wings into wing cases makes them poor flyers, but it gives them a protection that has brought prosperity to their kind. The order consists of about 150,000 known species, which are grouped in upward of 80 families. Although representatives of nearly all of these families are to be found in our fauna, less than 40 families contain the species that are familiar to most of us. Among the families not illustrated are those to which belong the fireflies, curculios, bark beetles, grain beetles, burying beetles, death-watch and drug-store beetles, rove beetles, water pennies, and whirligigs.

Tortoise Beetle Family (*Cassididae*). These beetles get their name from the striking similarity

of their shape to that of the tortoise. Many of them possess striking colors in life which incline to fade in death. To this family belong the striking argus and the brilliant gold-bug. Beautiful as are the adults, their grubs are ugly and disagreeable. They possess taillike forks at the end of the body, upon which is heaped their excrement and cast skins, used as a sort of shelter.

Each successive molt brings a new cast skin to the shelter, which gradually comes to resemble a pack, so that the grubs become known as peddlers. The gold-bug seems to possess some of the characteristics of the chameleon. Some times it appears in a dull yellow costume and at others in an armor that shines like burnished gold. At still other times it is arrayed so that it presents the variable tints of pearls.

The species reproduced are: *Desmonota varioloso* Web. (page 70, figure 1), from Bahia; *Tauroma casta* Boh. (page 70, figure 4), native of Costa Rica; *Omaspides bistriata* Boh. (page 70, figure 15), occurring in Colombia, Venezuela, and Costa Rica; *Dolichotoma bisbiplagiata* Boh. (page 70, figure 16), habitat Guatemala; *Aspidomorpha miliaris* Fab. (page 70, figure 17), habitat the Philippines, New Guinea, Yünnan, and Tonkin; *Mesomphalia beatula* Boh. (page 70, figure 21), occurring in Brazil.

Leaf Beetle Family (*Chrysomelidae*). There are some 18,000 known species in this family, nearly 1,000 of which occur in our North

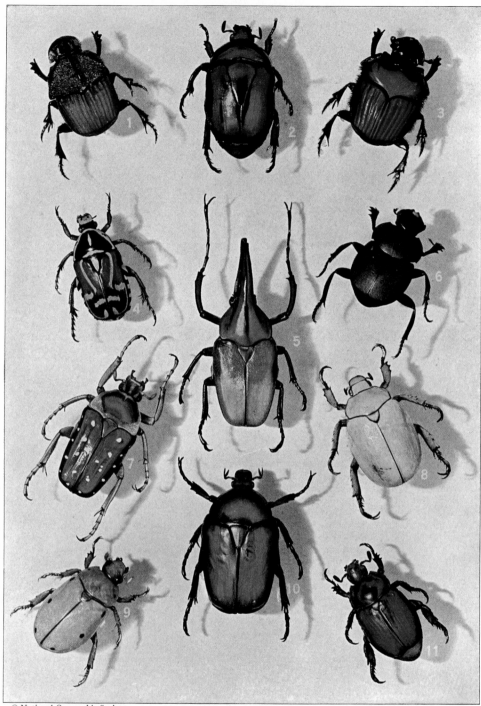

1¼ times Natural Size

SCARABS THAT MIGHT HAVE MADE A PHARAOH ENVIOUS

(1) *Phanaeus vindex* MacLeay; (2) *Macraspis lucida* Olivier; (3) *Oxysternon festivum* Linn.; (4) *Eupoecila australasiae* Donovan; (5) *Theodosia westwoodi* J. Thoms.; (6) Tumble Bug, *Canthon chalcites* Hald.; (7) *Stephanorrhina guttata* Olivier; (8) Goldsmith Beetle, *Cotalpa lanigera* Linn.; (9) *Pelidnota punctata* Linn.; (10) *Potosia speciosa* Adams; (11) *Pelidnota sumptuosa* Vigors. See text under the following Family headings: Scavenger Beetle and Leaf Chafer, page 87.

Photograph by Paul Griswold Howes

AN ASSASSIN-BUG FEEDING ON A CAPTURED INSECT

These hairy-legged creatures feed mainly on other insects, but have been known to bite human beings. The kissing bugs, which occupied so much space in the newspapers several decades ago, belong to this family. The hairs on their bodies are often sticky, and particles of dust, lint, and other material adhere to them, practically concealing them. Its appearance has given to one of the species the common name of masked bed-bug hunter (see text, page 36).

American fauna. It includes the long-horned leaf beetles, the 3-lined potato beetle, the asparagus beetle, the grape root worm, and the familiar Colorado potato beetle. The latter is the largest species of the family, and the damage it does to potato leaves is typical of the ravages of the family on different forms of foliage on which the several species feed.

The story of the spread of the Colorado beetle constitutes one of the most surprising adventures of an insect species in American entomological history. When civilization moved west to Colorado it found there, feeding on sand burs, a yellow- and black-striped beetle with a disgusting odor, but with no hint of its deadly possibilities.

About 1850 it began to cultivate a taste for potato leaves; nine years later it had spread to Nebraska, reached Iowa at the beginning of the Civil War, and crossed the Mississippi the summer that Lee surrendered at Appomattox. It then spread eastward, and by the centennial year had succeeded in forcing the barriers of the Alleghenies and reaching the Atlantic seaboard. Europe was heartily alarmed when a few of them sailed across the Atlantic as stowaways, but prompt preventive measures and rigid quarantine have prevented them from colonizing the world's principal potato-growing continents.

The species reproduced are: *Leptinotarsa 10-lineata* Say (page 70, figure 2), habitat Canada to Costa Rica; *Leptinotarsa flavitarsis* Guer. (page 70, figure 3), occurring in Guatemala; *Lema trilineata* Oliv. (page 70, figure 9), habitat North America and the West Indies; *Doryphora flavozonata* Blanch. (page 70, figure 18), habitat Bolivia; *Doryphora kollari* Stal. (page 70, figure 19), occurring in Brazil; *Doryphora mirabilis* Stal. (page 70, figure 20), habitat Mexico and Guatemala; *Doryphora flavozonata* Blanch. (page 72, figure 1), native of Bolivia; *Sagra Borneoensis* Lac. (page 72, figure 2), native of Borneo, and ranging all through the oriental region; *Sagra fabricii* Lac. (page 72, figure 10), habitat Java.

Metallic Wood-borer Family (*Buprestidae*). There are some 5,000 known species of metallic wood-borers, or Buprestids, in the world, of which about 200 are found in America. Many of them are among our most showy beetles, their metallic wing cases often being rich in brilliant iridescence. The wing cases of some eastern species are a brilliant green, and are used for dress trimmings. South American Indian chieftains often make anklets of the bronze wing cases of a gigantic South American species.

The larvae of the larger species of Buprestids

Photograph by George R. King

TENT-CATERPILLAR NESTS IN WESTCHESTER COUNTY, NEW YORK

The larvae of many species of moths, butterflies, and *Micro-lepidoptera* are gregarious in their habits and build community nests, where they stay together until time to pupate. Then they become individualistic again and each goes its own way.

are nearly all wood-borers. They usually live under bark, and make broad, shallow burrows, galleries, and chambers.

So regular are their habits of burrowing that a trained entomologist can recognize the species that made the traceries long after they are gone, just as a bank teller recognizes the signature of a customer. Their bodies are long, somewhat flattened, the forward segments so joined with the small head as to make them appear to possess large, flat heads—hence their popular name of hammerheads and flat-headed borers.

The most injurious of the Buprestid beetles is the flat-headed apple-tree borer, which prefers apple trees, but makes itself at home in many other kinds. The adults appear about May, and are a dull, metallic brown, except the abdomen, which is a rich, metallic greenish blue. The young larvae build their nests in the soft sapwood, but as they grow older, bore deeper into the heartwood where they hibernate. In the spring, they bore back almost to the surface, where they build their pupal cells in which to undergo the sleep out of which they shall awaken full-fledged beetles.

Another injurious Buprestid is the peach-tree borer. With wing cases that look like hammered copper, it is a beautiful creature. Still another is the red-necked cane-borer which causes the "gouty galls" on blackberries and raspberries.

The adults emerge in May or June, and lay their eggs where the leaf axil joins the stem. Their larvae girdle the stem, and by early August the galls begin to form, if the girdling operation has been successful.

The larvae spend the winter in the gall, or, if none has been formed, burrow into the pith of the brier stem. Many of the larger American Buprestids are particularly fond of pine trees, and prey on conifers exclusively. Some of the smaller species are leaf-miners.

The species reproduced are: *Chrysobothris femorata* Oliv. (page 70, figure 5), a North American species; *Julodis viridipes* Cast. (page 72, figure 5), occurring in Africa; *Hyperantha haemorrhoa* Fairm. (page 74, figure 6), a South American species, living especially in Venezuela; *Psiloptera bicarinata* Thunbg. (page 74, figure 7), occurring in French Guiana; *Stigmodera variabilis* Don. (page 74, figure 8), habitat Australia; *Buprestis rufipes* Oliv. (page 75, figure 2), habitat eastern United States; *Buprestis aurulenta* Linn. (page 75, figure 3), occurring in northwestern United States; *Chrysochroa fulgidissima* Schoenh. (page 75, figure 14), a Japanese species; *Sternocera bennigseni* Kerrem. (page 77, figure 1), habitat Africa; *Sternocera hunteri* Waterh. (page 77, figure 3), habitat Africa; *Conognatha amoena* Kirby (page 77, figure 4), habitat Brazil; *Belionota sumptuosa*

Cast. and Gory (page 77, figure 6), habitat Malaysia; *Chrysochroa buqueti* Gory (page 77, figure 7), habitat Indo-China and Java; *Chrysochroa edwardsi* Hope (page 77, figure 8), occurring in southern Asia; *Stigmodera macularia* Donovan (page 77, figure 9), habitat Australia; *Chrysochroa ocellata* Fabricius (page 77, figure 10), habitat southern Asia; *Stigmodera suturalis* Donovan (page 77, figure 11), an Australian species.

Meloid Beetle Family *(Meloidae)*. The Meloid beetles, of which there are some 1,500 known species, including the 200 that are American, have a fascinating life history. Some species prey on bees, others on locusts, and still others on divers forms of insect life. The one parasitic on locusts lays its eggs in spots frequented by the locusts. In a few days these hatch, and the baby Meloes proceed early and actively with their prime business of finding a host. Crawling around in large numbers, locust egg deposits soon are found, and presently most of the eggs become provender for the wandering host. After a preliminary feast the youngster makes seven different changes before reaching the adult stage. At one point a change results in a retrogression in its climb to adulthood.

The species reproduced are: *Epicauta vittata* Fab. (page 70, figure 6), found in North America; *Tegrodera aloga* Skinn. (page 72, figure 7), habitat California; *Zonabris oculata* Thunbg. (page 72, figure 8), a South African species.

Long-horned Beetle Family *(Cerambycidae)*. There are about 13,000 species of long-horned beetles in the world, of which some 600 belong to North America. They include such pests as the round-headed apple-tree borer, the oak pruner, and the twig girdler.

The round-headed apple-tree borer is perhaps the worst pest among the Cerambycids. In its adult form, it is about three-fourths of an inch long, with two creamy stripes along its brown back from mouth to tail. It deposits its eggs on the bark at the base of the tree it exploits in June and July. These hatch in a few days and the tiny grub works its way into the soft sapwood under the bark.

After its fine chisellike mandibles get the temper of age, it begins to tunnel its way into the heart of the tree, swallowing the borings of the tunnel as it goes. Finally, after three years of eating a path through the wood, it directs its operations toward the surface.

Just before reaching the outer air, and leaving only a tiny membrane ahead of it to be ruptured when it wakes up from its transformation sleep, the grub excavates a nice little chamber, which it carefully lines with smooth, soft materials made from wood fiber, and then lies down for its change-working nap. After two or three weeks of unconsciousness, it awakens no longer a grub, but a fully accoutered long-horn.

The oak pruner has a different method of attack. It lays its egg on a tender twig. When the grub hatches, it enters the twig and feeds on its juicy fiber. As it grows, it relishes a harder diet, so it bores its way into a mature limb, which it finally cuts so thoroughly that when a high wind comes it is blown to the ground. The limb thus acts as a parachute for the grub, allowing it to reach the ground safely. It now uses the severed limb both as a food supply and a habitation. The oak pruner also attacks other trees.

Some species of Cerambycid larvae remain in wood for surprising periods. After timber is cut and dried and used in the building of houses or the manufacture of furniture, it lacks nutritive qualities, and the growth of the wood-boring grub is so arrested that it often requires many years for the attainment of maturity. I have seen them issue from a porch column that had been standing twenty years, and recently a western college professor reported the issuance of one from the wood of a bookcase that had been in his family for nearly fifty years.

The species reproduced are: *Saperda candida* Fab. (page 70, figure 7), found in North America; *Sternotomis virescens* Westw. (page 74, figure 1), an African species; *Crioprosopus magnificus* LeConte (page 74, figure 2), from Arizona; *Sternotomis mirabilis* Drury (page 74, figure 3), found in the African Gold Coast; *Tragidion fulvipenne* Say (page 74, figure 10), found in central and western United States; *Sternotomis bifasciata* Fab. (page 75, figure 1), found in West Africa; *Dendrobias reducta* Casey (page 75, figure 4), habitat southern California; *Cyllene decora* Oliv. (page 75, figure 5), habitat southeastern and central United States; *Desmocerus palliatus* Forst. (page 75, figure 7), a native of eastern United States; *Stenaspis verticalis* Serv. (page 77, figure 2), found in Texas, Arizona, and Mexico; *Callichroma schwarzi* Fisher (page 77, figure 5), found in Texas.

Tiger-beetle Family *(Cicindelidae)*. The tiger-beetles are fast runners and quick flyers, and in the larval stage live up to their name, being carnivorous and voracious eaters. In that stage they are uncouth grubs, with big heads and sturdy jaws. They usually dig burrows in the ground, and lie in wait at the entrance for some unfortunate insect that chances to pass that way. In catching their prey the tiger-beetles' larvae seize the victims with their long, sharp mandibles, and drag them to the bottom of the burrow, where they are eaten at leisure.

The larva is provided with a little hump on the fifth segment of the abdomen, on which are two strong, forward-curving hooks. These it uses to hold itself firmly in position while attacking a victim, lest the latter give a sudden jerk and pull the "bushwhacker" from its hole.

The adult beetles catch their victims and drink the blood after the fashion of a weasel. With

Photograph by Paul Griswold Howes

A LARVAL WATER-TIGER FEEDING ON A YOUNG EEL

The insect fastened its jaws in the flesh of the eel and swam with great effort to a higher perch in the aquarium. Here it sucked the body juices of the victim until it became white. The water-tigers are among the most ferocious of all the insects.

JAPANESE BEETLES DINE ON A PEACH

At the beginning of the season the beetles attack the fruits prematurely ripening because of infestation by other foes, but later they turn their attention to the sound peaches, apples, etc. As many as 278 beetles have been removed from a single fruit.

Photographs courtesy U. S. Department of Agriculture

JAPANESE BEETLES COLLECTED BY BOYS AT RIVERTON, NEW JERSEY

In 1916 only a few beetles could be collected by one person in a single day. By 1919 they had become so thick that one person could collect as many as 20,000 in 12 hours. During a recent season an average of one and one-third gallons of beetles were shaken from each of 156 ten-year-old peach trees, all of which seemed as full as ever 24 hours later. An average of 175 larvae were found in each square yard of a New Jersey pasture.

their big eyes, long legs, sharp mandibles, and fleet movements, the tiger-beetles are identified easily.

The species reproduced is: *Cicindela scutellaris* Say (page 70, figure 8). It ranges between Texas, Arkansas, Nebraska, and Wyoming.

Lady-bird Beetle Family (*Coccinellidae*). Perhaps no beetle clan surpasses the lady-birds as friends of man. Their pretty polka-dot wing cases and their gentle demeanor are in keeping with their beneficent relation to man. But to certain of our insect foes the larvae of this family are veritable roaring lions and stalking tigers going about seeking whom they may devour. Plant-lice, scale insects, and many others of the "wee beasties" of insectdom the lady-birds destroy by the billions.

The larvae are more active than beetle grubs usually are, running about on plants in search of game. They ordinarily "change their clothes" three times before reaching maturity, sometimes changing their color in doing so. They spend four or five weeks in the larval stage; the eggs are laid on the bark, stems, and leaves of the trees or plants they visit, and hatch in a few days.

There are about 2,000 known species of lady-birds in the world, of which about 150 species are natives of America. Some have the curious habit of congregating in great masses on mountain tops, to spend the winter, once they have grown their wings. California fruit growers collect them, and put them in cold storage where they are retained until they are needed for keeping down plant-lice the following summer (see illustration, page 9).

The species reproduced is: *Epilachna borealis* Fab. (page 70, figure 10), which ranges over North America and Mexico.

Scavenger Beetle and Leaf Chafer Family (*Scarabaeidae*). The Scarabaeid family has two branches, well differentiated by their habits— the scavengers, of which the tumble bug or dung beetle is typical; and the leaf chafers, of which the rose bug or rose chafer is a representative species.

There are about 13,000 known species of Scarabaeids, of which about 5,000 belong to the dung beetle branch of the family.

The ancient Egyptians, observing the beetle's habit of rolling around pills of dung and dirt, are supposed to have interpreted this practice as a typification of the planetary and lunar revolutions, and therefore held that its disappearance and return was emblematic of eternal life (see, also, illustration, page 36).

The leaf chafers constitute the more numerous branch of the Scarabaeid family. In size, the species range from the big June bug or May beetle down to the small rose chafer or rose bug. The larvae of the iridescent May beetle are big fat grubs found in lawns, fields, and gardens. They spend three years in their journey from the egg

to the possession of wings. In the fall they dig below the frost line, and in the spring come up again to spend the summer feeding on the tiny roots of vegetation.

The rose chafer larvae seem to thrive best in sandy ground. Observers have noted that in regions where there is a strip of land underlaid with a clay subsoil, bordered by another strip in which there is a sandy subsoil, very few rose chafers appear until the wind blows from the sandy subsoil region. They then come in hosts to the land underlaid with clay.

A newly imported member of the Scarabaeid family is the destructive green Japanese beetle, which a few years ago gained a foothold above Philadelphia on the Jersey side of the Delaware River.

The species reproduced are: *Macrodactylus angustatus* Beauv. (page 70, figure 11), found in North America; *Popillia japonica* Newman (page 70, figure 13), introduced into the United States from Japan; *Phyllophaga torta* Lec. (page 75, figure 6), found in North America; *Chrysophora chrysochlora* Latr. (page 79, figure 1), found in Ecuador and Peru; *Eudicella morgani* White (page 79, figure 2), native of West Africa; *Phanaeus imperator* Chevr. (page 79, figure 3), habitat South America; *Genyodonta flavomaculata* Fab. (page 79, figure 4), found in Africa; *Argyripa lansbergei* Salle (page 79, figure 5), habitat Brazil; *Ischiopsophajamesi* Waterh. (page 79, figure 6), a species from British New Guinea; *Plusiotis resplendens* Bouc. (page 79, figure 7), a native of Costa Rica; *Macraspis pantochloris* Blanch. (page 79, figure 8), found in South America; June Bug (*Cotinus nitida* Linn., page 79, figure 9), a native of eastern and southern United States; *Rutela laeta* Weber (page 79, figure 10), found in northern South America; *Heterorrhina macleayi* Kirby (page 79, figure 11), a native of Central America; *Phanaeus vindex* MacLeay (page 81, figure 1), found in eastern United States; *Macraspis lucida* Olivier (page 81, figure 2), found in Central and South America; *Oxysternon festivum* Linn. (page 81, figure 3), South American species; *Eupoecila australasiae* Donovan (page 81, figure 4), native of Australia; *Theodosia westwoodi* J. Thoms. (page 81, figure 5), habitat Borneo; Tumble Bug (*Canthon chalcites* Hald., page 81, figure 6), a native of North America; *Stephanorrhina guttata* Olivier (page 81, figure 7), found in West Africa; Goldsmith Beetle (*Cotalpa lanigera* Linn., page 81, figure 8), found in eastern United States; *Pelidnota punctata* Linn. (page 81, figure 9), familiar species in eastern United States; *Potosia speciosa* Adams (page 81, figure 10), habitat southwestern Asia; *Pelidnota sumptuosa* Vigors. (page 81, figure 11), found in South America.

Snout Beetle Family (*Otiorhynchidae*). This family is represented in our fauna by more than 200 species. It includes Fuller's rose beetle, the strawberry crown girdler, and the black vine

COLLECTORS OF PARASITIZED JAPANESE BEETLES AT SAPPORO, JAPAN

Scores of women and children of Japan have been enlisted in the work of gathering proved parasites of the Japanese beetle to send to the United States to help us destroy the beetle by this means.

Photographs courtesy U. S. Department of Agriculture

ARMIES OF ALLIES BEING SHIPPED FROM KOIWAI, JAPAN, TO RIVERTON, NEW JERSEY

Nearly 8,000 parasitized grubs of the Japanese beetle are contained in the boxes of this shipment. The parasites belong to the Scoliid wasp family. While man probably will continue to resort to mechanical warfare in holding the Japanese beetle in check, the major offensive is being conducted by insect allies imported from Japan, including three species of the Tachina fly family (see text, page 64), two species of the Dexiid fly family (see text, page 69), four species of the Scoliid wasp family (see text, page 55), and one species of the Carabid beetle family (see text, page 89).

weevil. Many of its members are notorious as greenhouse pests.

The species reproduced are: *Cyphus 16-punctata* Linn. (page 70, figure 12), found in South America; *Hypomeces squamosus* Fab. (page 70, figure 14), found in India.

Erotylidae Family. This is a small family which resembles click beetles in form, and whose larvae bore into the stalks of clover. The larvae of some species feed on fungi.

The species reproduced is: *Erotylus giganteus* Linn. (page 72, figure 3), which occurs in Cayenne, French Guiana.

Carabid Beetle Family *(Carabidae).* The 1,200 species of this group of beetles contain many interesting insects. One of these is the bombardier beetle which, when pursued or attacked by an enemy, fires at the foe a tiny puff of acrid, reddish "smoke," with a popgun report. Comstock has found that the bombardier is able to use four or five rounds of ammunition without exhausting its supply.

One species belonging to the Carabid family is known as *Calosoma scrutator,* the latter part of its name being derived from its habit of scrutinizing everything in its search for caterpillars. It and its close cousins are popularly known as caterpillar hunters. One species has been brought to America from Europe to help wage war on the brown-tail moth. Some of the Calosomas are aggressive foes of the hairy tent-caterpillar that is such an enemy of the orchardist and landscape gardener.

Other Carabids eat the larvae of codling moths and of the plum curculio. Some species here and elsewhere dwell in caves, and are sightless. Other species dwell in moist, damp places where snails may be found, and have their palpi shaped like long-handled spoons suitable for drawing snails out of their shells.

The species illustrated are: *Carabus auronitens* Fab. (page 72, figure 4), a native of Central Europe; *Ceroglossus gloriosus* Gerst. (page 72, figure 6), found in Chile; *Calosoma bonariense* Dej. (page 74, figure 4), found in Brazil and Argentina; *Calosoma scrutator* Fab. (page 74, figure 9), a North American species; *Mormolyce hagenbachi* Westw. (page 75, figure 9), a native of Sumatra.

Predaceous Diving Beetle Family *(Dytiscidae).* There are some 300 species of this family of predaceous carnivorous diving beetles in America. They get their name of water-tigers from the persistent manner in which their larvae search for living food. Research indicates that the adults hibernate in mud, under water. It is believed that the water-tigers were once dry-land dwellers.

Nagel states that the water-tigers secrete a digestive fluid which they inject into the body of their victims, turning the latter's flesh to broth. On this they sup at their pleasure. The mature beetles live for a long time, one entomologist having kept a *Dytiscus* three and a half years in perfect health in a glass vessel filled with water. He fed it bits of raw meat.

The species reproduced are: *Dytiscus fasciventris* Say (page 72, figure 9), and *Cybister fimbriolatus* Say (page 72, figure 11), both found in North America.

Darkling Beetle Family *(Tenebrionidae).* These insects occur chiefly in dry and warm regions. Most of the American species, of which there are more than 400, occur in the southern section of the United States. The family includes the *Tenebrio* meal-worm, the forked fungus beetle, and the pinacate bugs. The latter defend themselves when disturbed by elevating the hind part of the body and discharging an oily fluid. After being attacked they walk off clumsily, presenting an absurd appearance with the end of the body held as high as possible.

The species reproduced are: *Metallonotus metallicus* Fab. (page 74, figure 5), and *Odontopezus cupreus* Fab. (page 74, figure 11), found in Africa.

Click Beetle Family *(Elateridae).* The click beetles form a most interesting and cosmopolitan family. There are about 7,000 known species, of which some 350 are found in North America.

The larvae of the click beetles are the familiar wire-worms which often do so much damage to crops just beginning to grow. Corn, meadow grass, wheat, and other cereals suffer severely from the periodic invasion of the wire-worms. The beetles fly about the fields in the late spring, depositing their eggs in plowed or grassy ground.

In Cuba there are phosphorescent species which emit a strong greenish light. Many women keep them alive in little lace pockets, or fastened to delicate golden chains.

My friend Dr. Frank E. Lutz of the American Museum of Natural History tells the following amusing story about these beetles: "Once in Arizona I made some of the species perform for my guide. He christened them Break-backs and began to count up how much he would win after he got back to Tucson, by betting on 'whether they would or wouldn't land right side up.' I advised him to put his money on 'would' and for nights thereafter he turned Elaterids on their backs to see whether they would or wouldn't. I do not know how he made out."

The species reproduced are: *Chalcolepidius lacordairei* Cand. (page 75, figure 8), found in Mexico and Nicaragua; *Alaus lusciosus* Hope (page 75, figure 10), found in Mexico and southwestern United States; *Semiotus imperialis* Guer. (page 75, figure 11), a native of South America, especially Colombia, Venezuela, and Peru; *Campsosternus gemma* Cand. (page 75, figure 12), a native of China; *Chalcolepidius rubripennis* Lec. (page 75, figure 13), a native of Lower California and Honduras.

Photograph courtesy U. S. Department of Agriculture

PREPARING TO RAISE AN ARMY OF ALLIES TO FIGHT JAPANESE BEETLES

These workers in the Moorestown, New Jersey, laboratory of the United States Bureau of Entomology are unpacking material just received from Japan. The shipment contains eggs of a little Tachina fly (see text, page 64) which preys on Japanese beetles in the Land of the Mikado. It is hoped that the flies from these eggs will slaughter millions of beetles.

The natural-color illustrations of 263 insects in this chapter are the result of more than three years of research, selection, and experimentation by the Illustrations Division of the National Geographic Society. Mr. Franklin L. Fisher, the Chief of that Division, telling of this work, says:

"The specimens pictured represent most of the insect families to be found in North America. They were selected from the U. S. National Museum's collection of more than a million individuals through the generous cooperation of the experts of the Museum and of the Bureau of Entomology of the U. S. Department of Agriculture.

"Each specimen reproduced on the 24 full-page color plates was chosen as the most picturesque and colorful representative of its species or family. The subjects selected were placed with care in relaxing jars (a sort of humidor) to render flexible their delicate legs, wings, and antennae, so that they might be 'posed' in lifelike attitudes. After the humidor treatment, the individuals were grouped according to their scientific relation one to another, and each group was then skillfully arranged for symmetry and with appreciation of color contrasts.

"The minuteness of some of the specimens, their irreplaceable value in the Museum's collection, and the fragile nature of their anatomical members added materially to the sense of responsibility of the members of the National Geographic Society's illustrations staff and to the time required in obtaining the desired results.

"The 21 color plates of specimens, on each of which is reproduced from 6 to 21 individual insects, were arranged and photographed by Mr. Edwin L. Wisherd, of The Society's photographic staff.

"Supplementing the photographic records of the actual specimens are the three paintings showing the life history of three representative insect families—the Caddisfly (page 28), the Bumblebee (page 52), and the Japanese Beetle (page 68). These have been executed in microscopic detail by The Society's naturalist-artist, Mr. Hashime Murayama."

CHAPTER III

Man's Winged Ally, the Busy Honeybee

Modern Research Adds a New Chapter to Usefulness of the Insect Which Has Symbolized Industry Since Early Bible Times

By JAMES I. HAMBLETON

Senior Apiculturist, Bureau of Entomology and Plant Quarantine, U. S. Department of Agriculture

DOES the buzz of a bee recall an unfortunate encounter, or is it a reminder of sweet music in a blossom-decked meadow?

To a beekeeper, and there are some 800,-000 in the United States alone, no music is more welcome. Many laymen, however, have not had the pleasure of having their hands in a hive of bees, and to them every buzz is a signal of danger.

Since early Bible times the honeybee has been a symbol of industry, and honey a simile of plenty. The study of honeybees and their remarkable life history has inspired philosophers, whose writings are replete with references to them.* But modern research now enables us to pen a new chapter about them.

In the United States today these bees yield about 100,000 tons of marketable honey annually; but in helping maintain our agriculture they are of even more importance. They may be likened to the enzymes in our food, small and mysterious, but highly essential to our well-being.

EARLY EXPLORERS BROUGHT BEES

The honeybee is not a native. There were none in North America when the Spanish explorers arrived. Settlers coming in later expeditions brought them, and at first the Indians called them the "white

* See "Our Friends, the Bees," by A. I. and E. R. Root, in the NATIONAL GEOGRAPHIC MAGAZINE for July, 1911.

man's fly." Since then they have followed man in his migration and settlement of every part of the United States and Canada.

Until recently these insects' chief usefulness to man was their production of honey and beeswax—no mean service, since for centuries honey was virtually the only available sweet. But now, as pollinating agents, they perform a far more important duty.

In the pioneer stages of American agriculture, bumblebees and other native pollinating insects that fed upon nectar and pollen were plentiful everywhere. But the planting of vast areas which once were forests, prairies, and swamps with fields of grain, orchards, and gardens upset the delicate balance of Nature.

Widespread cultivation of single plants in huge acreages brought about an abnormal condition of insect population. Injurious species, afforded an enormous food supply, prospered and multiplied until now serious insect pests menace almost every important crop.

Insecticides must be used to protect farm crops, particularly fruits. Unfortunately, these materials kill not only harmful but beneficial insects. The toll includes honeybees and other wild bees, as well as the efficient bumblebees—all the insects that carry pollen from one blossom to another.

Even yet we scarcely realize the dependence of many plants upon insects to effect pollination.

The cutting of wood lots and the clean

THERE IS A RIGHT AND A WRONG WAY TO OPEN A HIVE

An expert never stands in front of a colony or moves with nervous jerks; such tactics irritate the bees. A puff or two from the smoker (foreground) disorganizes the entrance guards (see page 100) and sends all workers rushing to the honey cells. There they load up, apparently fearing fire is about to destroy their home. Then the keeper removes the cover, sends a few whiffs of smoke into the hive from above, and inspects the frames. The card tacked to the hive records the condition of the colony.

cultivation of our fields have added to the difficulty of survival of our useful insects, with the result that more and more dependence has to be placed upon the honeybee, the only pollinating insect that can be propagated and controlled.

SEX LIFE OF THE PLANTS

Some plants bear only male flowers, which produce pollen but no fruit, and female flowers in the same species occur on a separate plant. To set fruit, pollen must be carried to the female flower.

Some plants simultaneously bear both male and female flowers, but still require cross-pollination to set fruit. Then there is a third class in which both sexes occur

in the same blossom. Some of these plants can set fruit with their own pollen. But in many plants pollen from another is necessary to set a full crop of fruit or seed.

The blossom of the apple, for example, contains both sexes, but in most varieties the pollen produced is not suitable for pollinizing its own blossoms. Its flowers must be fertilized by pollen from an entirely different variety. Thus, if blossoms of the Grimes Golden are cross-pollinated from the Jonathan, a good set of fruit should result, but the pollen of the Stayman produces little or no fruit when transferred to the Grimes Golden. When all pollen except its own is excluded, the Grimes Golden produces little or no fruit.

Photograph courtesy U. S. Department of Agriculture

A LANDLORD OUSTS HIS TENANTS, BUT PROVIDES A MODERN HOME

He puffed smoke into the old hive, then broke it open. Lifting out chunks of comb and honey, he brushes off the clinging bees near the door of the new hive (right), which they occupy readily. The keeper may destroy the old hybrid queen and give the colony a prolific young Italian (see text, page 116 and page 111). The exposed brood combs are thick and black, indicating that many generations of larvae have been reared in them.

"The priests of the flowers" honeybees have been called, since they perform the marriage ceremony of the plants.

Although the honeybee is by no means domesticated, it is easily controlled. Consequently, millions already are being moved from one section of the country to another and placed in orchards and on farms. Bee men in the South even offer for sale a pollination package, a wire cage filled with bees.

The grower distributes the requisite number throughout his orchards, opens the cage, and leaves the rest to the bees. Hundreds of full colonies are rented to orchardists during the blooming period. The bee has also largely replaced the camel's-hair brush in pollinating cucumbers under glass.

Were it not for the work of the honeybee, most of our apple, pear, plum, and cherry orchards would bear poor crops, the growing of certain forage crops would be unprofitable, and the variety and quantity of our vegetables would be materially reduced.

BEE CITIZENS OF MANY LANDS

Honey and beeswax are produced over a wider geographical range than any other agricultural crop. There is scarcely a country in which honeybees are not kept. They inhabit the Tropic and Temperate Zones, they are found in the deserts, on the mountains, in the plains, and in swamps, and as far north as Alaska.

Scattered over the world are several

Photograph by Grover Mobley

A RUNAWAY SWARM BUILT THIS HONEYCOMB SKYSCRAPER

If a beekeeper is not on hand to capture a swarm as it issues, the whole group, after clustering, may make a "bee line" for a hollow tree, a vacated woodpecker nest, or even a rocky cavity in the earth (see illustration, page 96, and text, page 110). This colony chose the space between the inner and outer walls of a building in Garden City, Kansas, which they occupied until ejected by the State Bee Inspector, who stands at the right.

distinct races, such as the Italian, Carniolan, Caucasian (page 111), and Cyprian. All races, everywhere, react in almost the same manner. A skillful beekeeper can succeed in Australia as well as in Ohio, provided he keeps an eye to the weather and studies the local flora.

If honeybees are properly handled, there is no more danger in caring for them than in raising chickens. However, the belief that bees learn to know their master and will not sting him is without foundation.

During the active season the average life of a bee is six weeks. The first two weeks are lived almost exclusively within the hive (pages 102 and 109), but thereafter the bees pass most of the daylight hours in the fields when the weather is good, in search of pollen and nectar. Since the beekeeper rarely opens the hive more than once a week, there is little opportunity for the bees to become acquainted with their owner.

Some persons are so constituted that one sting may prove highly dangerous to them and require immediate medical attention, but these cases are rare. Although it may not be dangerous to most persons, a bee sting on the eyelid, the lip, or the face does not enhance a person's beauty.

THE WEDDING FLIGHT OF A QUEEN

During the active season, a normal colony contains one queen, a fully developed female; thousands of unreproductive worker bees, which are females only partly developed; and several hundred drones, or male bees (page 102). The queen is endowed with great powers of reproduction, since she can even produce male progeny without mating, but she cannot produce female bees, workers or queens, without going through the marriage ceremony. Thus, the maligned drone is indispensable to the completion of the immortal cycle of the honeybee.

Upon the wedding flight of the queen depends the subsequent development of the colony. On a bright spring day the virgin queen emerges from the hive and soars away to seek a mate from among the hundreds of drones cruising about in the warm sunshine. Blissfully, perhaps, the drone is seeking an encounter that will cost him his life but insure the perpetuation of his race.

A moment after mating, the drone dies

and the newly mated queen at once becomes a widow. But this one mating enables the queen for the rest of her life, three or four years, to perform her maternal duties.

A few days after returning to the hive, she begins egg laying, slowly at first; but at the height of her career she may lay as many as 1,500 eggs a day and maintain this rate for days at a time (page 104).

She lays two kinds of eggs. One kind is unfertilized and hatches into a drone, or male bee. Mating has no influence upon this part of her family. Her sons are not the sons of her mate or husband, and are consequently fatherless, but they can claim a grandfather.

The other type of egg is fertilized by the queen with a male cell, of which she retains an almost unlimited number in a special organ of her body. The fertilized egg hatches into a female bee, usually a worker.

Thus both workers, or neuter bees, and queens come from the same kind of egg. Yet the two show marked differences. The queen has the function of reproduction; the worker bee has not. The queen bee possesses teeth on her mandibles, or jaws; the worker bee has smooth jaws. The worker bee has pollen baskets (page 107); the queen lacks them. The worker bee has a straight, barbed, unretractable sting; the queen has a curved, smooth sting. The worker bee loses its life after stinging, but the queen does not (page 106).

A worker bee takes 21 days to develop from the egg to the adult, while a queen, who is much larger, requires only 15 or 16 days. The colony itself has the power of determining whether a fertilized egg shall develop into a queen or a worker bee.

During its normal existence, only one queen is necessary to maintain the population of a colony. Unlike the worker bee, who lives but six weeks, the queen may live two, three, or more years, but eventually she also becomes old and decrepit. Then a new queen must be raised to carry on the life of the colony.

HER MAJESTY IS FED "ROYAL JELLY"

The raising of a new queen is entrusted to the worker bees. An egg or a newly hatched larva less than three days old is selected. The cell in which the larva is

Photograph by J. C. Carter

A NEW HOUSING PROGRAM GETS UNDER WAY

Without veils or gloves, these Chinese coolies are capturing a black mass of bees clinging to the foot of a tree on the hillside. They trust the good-natured swarmers, which are gorged on honey consumed before leaving their old home. The swarm is smaller than those that issue from well-cared-for colonies.

reproduce but possesses all other maternal instincts, or one that has the function of reproduction but lacks all maternal instincts, for the queen becomes virtually an egg-laying machine.

There is no evidence that she has anything to do with the regulation of the colony. She gives no attention whatsoever to the raising of her young. She does not help feed them, nor does she gather stores, or take part in the defense of her family. These duties fall exclusively to the lot of worker bees.

From the endless flight of bees at the entrance of the hive, it would appear that most of the energy of the colony is consumed in the rather hazardous task of gathering nectar, pollen, and water (page 106). However, the work done by the corps of young bees approximates that of the field bees, since every conceivable task within the hive must be performed by the bees not yet old enough to fly.

The hum of industry within the hive continues throughout the 24 hours. Before the queen lays, each cell which is to receive an egg must be cleaned and polished until it shines. Since she lays 1,500 eggs a day, and it requires three days for the egg to hatch, there may be as many as 4,500 eggs in the hive to be cared for at one time. The number varies with the season.

Upon hatching, the young bee is a footless and blind larva and as such goes through an intensive feeding period of six days (page

deposited is broken down and enlarged and the heiress apparent is given special care and attention from this time on. For the first three days worker and drone larvae are fed royal jelly, a milky white secretion from the glands in the heads of worker bees (page 104). After the third day a coarser food, such as nectar and pollen, is given them. The queen larvae, however, are fed royal jelly exclusively throughout the larval stage, which lasts five and a half days.

The difference in diet during the two and a half days, therefore, determines whether the larva will develop into a bee that cannot

102). Thus the nurse bees are taking care of six different sets of larvae, each age group requiring special care and food. Within six days a larva will increase in weight as much as 1,500 times and therefore it requires constant feeding. After the sixth day the larva is given no more food; a porous cap is placed over the cell and it spins its cocoon. In this stage it remains for 12 days, developing from a wormlike grub into a fully matured worker bee. Thus the period from egg laying to maturity is 21 days, and there will be 12 sealed-in age groups in the hive at one time (page 102).

The nursery duties occupy only a portion of the available workers. Others build new comb from the wax which they themselves secrete. Hundreds of new cells are necessary to store incoming nectar. The bee that brings the nectar from the field does not deposit it in the cell, but gives it to a nurse bee, who, in turn, places it in that part of the hive where the process of conversion into honey will begin.

© R. O. Pearse

AFRICAN NATIVES HANG THEIR HIVES AMID THE BLOSSOMS

Modern beekeepers place their colonies near the ground, enabling heavily laden workers to enter easily. A hollow tree trunk closed at each end except for a small hole for the bees to enter serves as this hive in Kenya. To tap the sweet harvest is a messy, risky job if the bees have not been smoked to death beforehand.

THE HIVES ARE AIR-CONDITIONED

Newly gathered nectar generally contains so much water that, if it were immediately stored, it would soon ferment. The bees, therefore, removed the excess moisture, largely through a well-organized and efficient system of fanning (page 100). In the midst of a good harvest a hive may lose one-fourth as much during the night as it gained the previous day.

The temperature is regulated much more closely than in most modern homes. The bees are able, even with a range of 50 degrees outside, to keep the temperature of the brood nest within two or three degrees of normal. The warm weather of midsummer finds each colony well equipped with a cooling system composed of a corps of fanners, because the temperature for brood rearing must be maintained uniformly throughout the active season.

Transforming nectar into rich, mellow

© Kurt and Margot Lubinski

"BUY HALF A ROW OR NONE" IS THE CUSTOM IN THIS DUTCH BEE MART

Buyers and sellers once a year bargain noisily for some 2,000 skeps or straw hives (page 100), each inhabited by about 20,000 bees. Reed mats, row upon row, protect

© Kurt and Margot Lubinski

A FALL WOULD SPILL PANDEMONIUM!

Netherland country folk bring their bee skeps for miles to the Veenendaal market, where bidders lift the colonies to estimate the honey content (see illustration, opposite page). Inmates of the heavier hives are "brimstoned"—killed by sulphur fumes—and the honey is removed, while the lighter ones are kept through the winter in the hope that they will make more honey during the next season.

Photograph by Willard R. Culver

"LOOK, THERE GOES A BIG DRONE!"

The children are studying the brood nest of the glass-walled observation hive in the Smithsonian Institution, Washington, D. C. (see drawing, page 105). In the glass dome on top, bees have begun to construct the irregular honeycombs they make when unguided by frames. The fountain jar (right) contains sugar syrup, fed to the bees when nectar is scarce. Behind it slopes a long glass passageway used when the bees garner nectar outside.

99

ALERT GUARDS POUNCE UPON A HAPLESS STRANGER

Although the bumblebee is much larger and stronger than the attacking honeybees, the ferocious fighting workers make quick work of the casual visitor with their stings. Each colony has a distinctive odor, so that sentinels even recognize and pounce on invading honeybees from other hives.

Paintings by Hashime Murayama

THE AIR-CONDITIONING APPARATUS OF A BEEHIVE HUMS AT ITS DOOR

The idea of an air-cooled home is not new. A corps of firmly anchored fanners make their wings vibrate on a sill, thus causing circulation and keeping the temperature even within. This process also draws moisture from the newly gathered nectar, which is evaporated to the consistency of honey.

STOGIES AND SMOLDERING PIPES AID MECHANICAL SMOKERS

As long as seller and buyer slap hands after each other, no bystander may interfere by raising the offer, according to the rules of this Netherland bee exchange. When bees swarm in the market, the new colony is publicly sold and the proceeds donated to charity.

honey requires more than the evaporation of excess moisture. The bees add certain enzymes which convert the complex sugars of the raw nectar into simple sugars, known to the chemist as dextrose and levulose. When honey is eaten, these sugars are therefore absorbed without any preliminary digestion, that having taken place in the body of the bee.

EVERY YOUNG BEE HAS ITS TASK

The skillful bee chemists not only preserve for us the sweetness of the flowers, but the perfume, the mineral salts, and certain nitrogenous products which the plants liberate in the nectar. All these ingredients are processed in the laboratory of the hive so that we have many varieties and colors of honey (page 113), each peculiar to its flower, each with its distinctive bouquet, color, and characteristic flavor.

Young bees perform manifold duties in maintaining the colony, which, being a self-sustaining community, imposes upon each individual certain health, sanitation, and protective duties. A temperature of about 93 degrees Fahrenheit must be maintained in that part of the hive where the queen lays and where all the young bees are reared. This is a concentrated area near the center of the hive, spherical in shape, its size depending upon the population of the hive and the season of the year.

After a cell has served as a cradle for the birth of a young bee, it is thoroughly cleaned. Abnormal larvae are not permitted to mature as deformed adults, but are removed from the hive. Sick and ailing bees are also encouraged to leave and to die outside. Any bees that die while at work are immediately carried out and consigned to the winds.

When they are from a week to ten days old, the bees venture into the outside world for the first time, usually on short flights of only a few feet in front of the hive. During these so-called play flights, they learn to use their wings and no doubt also note the location of their homes. Toward the close of their duties within the hive young

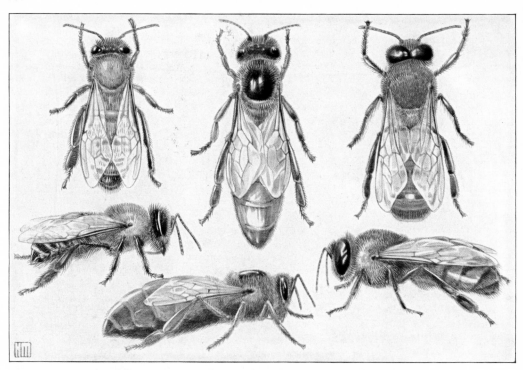

THREE KINDS OF HONEYBEES ARE FOUND IN A COLONY

The mother of all bees in a hive is the queen (center), whose long body is more graceful than that of her children, worker (left) and drone, or male (right). All figures three times life-size.

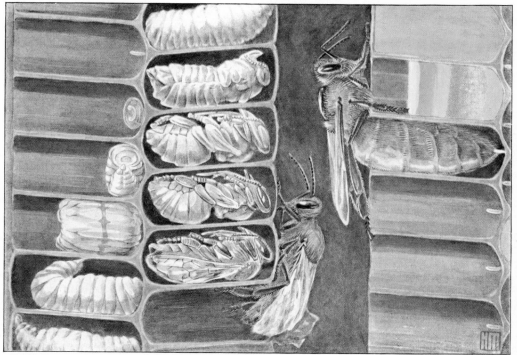

Paintings by Hashime Murayama

THE GROWTH OF A BEE FROM EGG LAYING TO BIRTH

Three days after the egg is deposited by the queen (right), a tiny grub emerges (left column, second from top). For six days the larva is fed by workers, increasing its weight 1,500 times. Then it spins a cocoon (second from bottom, left) and becomes a fully developed worker bee (bottom center).

Photograph courtesy U. S. Department of Agriculture

ALL TUCKED IN WITH FELT QUILTS FOR A LONG WINTER'S REST

Honey-filled supers, which were stacked high above these brood chambers during the summer, have been removed, leaving only enough food to last the bees through cold weather (see page 109). Queens cease egg laying as freezing weather approaches and then workers go outside only on occasional warm, sunny days. Though during the honeyflow bees may work themselves to death in six weeks, those hatched late in the fall live until spring (see text below).

bees appear more often at the entrances until they eventually take over the duty of defending the colony (page 100). Several dozen may assume this responsibility.

A SHORT AND BUSY LIFE

On their first trip to the field, young bees gather water or propolis. The latter is a resinous, gumlike material called bee glue, garnered largely from the buds of various plants and trees. It is used to close the cracks in the hives, to smooth over rough places, to cement the combs securely in place, to regulate the size of the entrances the better to guard the hive, and to control the temperature.

The next duty is that of gathering pollen and, finally, nectar. In an emergency the field bees can resume nursery duties again, but when a bee becomes old enough to work in the field it usually dies in its boots, literally working itself to death.

A newly emerged bee is covered with fluffy golden hair. After four weeks in the field it is darker, much of the hair has been worn from its body, and its wings are tattered and torn (page 111). Eventually

it will no longer be able to sustain itself in flight. Thus its life span is measured largely by the amount of work done. The bees reared late in the fall, when there is little or no work to be done in the fields, live all winter.

Whenever plants are in blossom and it is warm enough for the bees to fly, they go forth at daybreak and continue until nightfall, or until it becomes too cold or rainy to work. Drop by drop the nectar comes into the hive. The storage of more food than the colony can consume for its own needs seems an incredible task, yet in a favorable locality strong colonies have brought in as many as 25 pounds of nectar in a day.

A steady stream at the entrance continues day after day, the bees going several miles and returning unerringly to their homes. Bees have flown eight and a half miles away from the hive in search of food, although usually they forage within a mile or two of the hive, going no farther than necessary.

In gathering nectar and pollen, the bees do not fly aimlessly, as butterflies do, from

THE QUEEN'S LADIES IN WAITING KEEP HER WELL FED AND PREENED

Her diet is not honey and pollen, but "royal jelly," a secretion from head glands of her daughters.
Workers (lower right) are cleaning cells. Two baby bees are gnawing their way out.

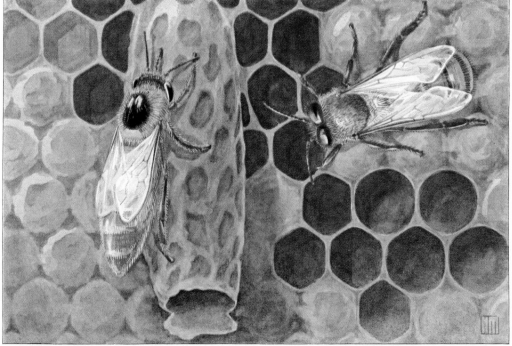

© National Geographic Society   Paintings by Hashime Murayama

THE QUEEN'S ROYAL BIRTH CHAMBER RESEMBLES A PEANUT SHELL

Although a queen is much longer than a worker or drone, she emerges from her pendulous cell only
16 days after the egg is laid, instead of the 21 days usually required for her industrious sisters. A drone
perches on a group of male cells at the right, and on the opposite side are workers' cells. Mating takes
place only on the wing outside the hive, after which the male dies.

one species of flower to another. If a bee starts working on dandelions, for example, it will continue throughout the trip to visit only dandelion blossoms, and in all likelihood it will continue working on dandelions as long as it can obtain a modicum of nectar or pollen. Another bee from the same colony may concentrate on apple blossoms, in which case it carefully avoids the blossoms of pear trees or other varieties. It may even have to fly over acres of dandelion-studded meadows before reaching another apple tree, but its instinct keeps it to a single track.

Such constancy makes the bee a dependable pollinizing agent. If it collected indiscriminately from the flowers, its work would be less effective (see text, page 92). The pollen of the apple would not bene-

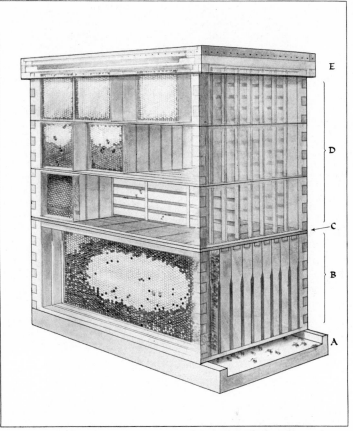

Drawing by Hashime Murayama

AN ARTIST'S VIEW OF A HONEYBEE WORKSHOP

Bees enter the "city's" guarded gateway across the bottom board (A). The queen lives in the 10-frame nursery or brood chamber (B). The patch of capped cells in the long lower comb contains the brood, not honey. Immediately above, a wire screen, or "queen excluder" (C), with spaces large enough to allow only workers to pass through, prevents Her Majesty from invading the honey storehouse above and laying eggs in (D). No larvae are found in the square honeycombs, which may some day grace a family table. The cover (E) protects the colony from rain, and contains an insulating air space.

fit the blossom of the pear, and vice versa. Changes in atmospheric conditions, or in the plants themselves, may cause a wholesale change in the work schedule.

Some plants secrete nectar only a few hours a day, while other plants may continue throughout the day; and, since bees wisely seek the richest source of nectar, they may suddenly desert one plant for another that proves more tempting. The richness of this sparkling drop of nectar, which the blossom offers to the bee in exchange for the pollen from another blossom, causes the bee to accept the highest bidder.

Although bees invariably effect pollina-

tion in the blossoms from which they obtain either nectar or pollen, the latter is so indispensable to the welfare of the colony that the bees are compelled to visit countless numbers of flowers which secrete little or no nectar but which do furnish them with pollen. Thus the bees pollinize numerous varieties of plants.

WHY A BLOSSOM WEARS "PERFUME"

The worker bee is particularly adapted to gather pollen. Almost every part of its body is covered with hair (page 107). Many of the hairs are long, lacy, and branched; spikelike hairs even grow

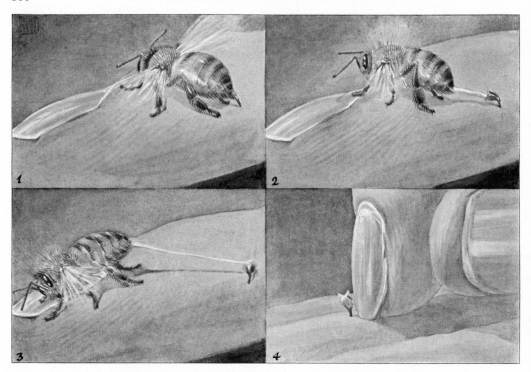

A STING IS WORSE FOR THE STINGER THAN THE STUNG

The bee inserts its tiny harpoon in the flesh (1) so firmly that when attempting to withdraw it (2 and 3) the barb is severed from its body, tearing its delicate tissues and killing the bee. After a bee stings, scrape out the still throbbing stinger (4); pulling it forces more poison into the wound.

© National Geographic Society   Paintings by Hashime Murayama

ONCE A BEE HAS DRUNK AT A POOL, IT RETURNS AGAIN AND AGAIN

Honeybees consume quantities of water, as do cows, for they must supply water and the creamy secretion called "royal jelly" on which are fed the queen and larvae during brood rearing. Honeybees always attend strictly to business while drinking, and will not attempt to sting unless molested.

A BUMBLEBEE TAPS THE HONEYSUCKLE AND WISE HONEYBEES FOLLOW BEHIND

Nectar is buried so deeply in many flowers that bees cannot insert their tongues to obtain it. Bumblebees cut holes in the lower part of the corolla with their sharp jaws and take out some nectar. The honeybee, with smooth jaws that cannot cut flower tissue, revisits the spot and obtains a sweet load.

Paintings by Hashime Murayama

BRILLIANT PORTULACA BLOSSOMS YIELD AN ABUNDANCE OF CONVENIENT POLLEN

The bee literally rolls in the yellow dust of the flower, coating its hairy body. Then, hovering over the blossom, it combs the pollen off and packs it securely in baskets on the rear legs. Usually a bee obtains only one kind on a trip, so many workers entering the hive bear differently colored loads.

Photograph by Herman H. Kreider

THIS TURKISH BEEKEEPER STACKS HIS HIVES

Boxes have no movable frames inside, honeycombs being firmly attached to the under side of the covers. Open a hive, turn the lid upside down, and the family life of the colony is disclosed. A stone wall at the rear provides protection from wind, and the reed matting over the apiary keeps out moisture and cold.

between the facets of its compound eyes (see illustration, page 114). When a bee alights on a flower that has abundant pollen, the pollen grains become entangled in its numerous hairs, and in gathering a load to carry back to the hive, the bee brushes over the stigma of the blossom, inadvertently transferring to its sticky surface grains of pollen. For this act the blossom lives and offers its alluring perfume and enticing nectar.

Shortly after pollination is effected, the blossom wilts. After thoroughly covering itself with pollen, the bee hovers above the flower for several seconds, combing the pollen from itself and packing it securely in the two pollen baskets in its hind legs (page 107). Thus it can carry two pellets, each almost as large as its head.

"BEE BREAD" IN THE HIVE'S PANTRY

Upon reaching the hive, the bee inserts its hind legs into a cell and pries off the two pellets of pollen. There a young bee, with its head, rams the pollen into a compact cake into the bottom of the cell. Pollen is not mixed with honey. It is stored in separate cells close to the brood nest, where it is readily available to the nurse bees (see text, page 97).

The pollen furnishes the fat and protein in the diet of the honeybee, while the nectar supplies the carbohydrate. The adult bee can sustain itself on a pure carbohydrate diet, but the developing bees must have the other two ingredients. Pollen stored in the hive is often referred to as "bee bread."

Early in the spring, when the alders and willows are putting forth their fuzzy catkins, the bees go forth to search for food so that the queen may start egg laying. From then on, progress depending upon the weather and the amount of food available, brood rearing continues at a constantly accelerated pace. Within a few weeks the hive becomes so populous that there is no more room where the queen can lay and no more space in which to store honey.

With food available from myriads of flowers, but with no place to store it, the bees prepare to relieve the congestion. The time has come when some must go. This

OLD-FASHIONED STRAW SKEPS GIVE WAY TO MODERN HIVES

The honey of former days, squeezed from the comb, was dark and often contained foreign matter. Whirling centrifugal machines now throw out the honey from shaved combs, yielding a cleaner, better product. A few puffs of smoke drive the guards back into the hive and make the bees more docile.

© National Geographic Society   Paintings by Hashime Murayama

AN APIARY AT THE CLOSE OF THE SEASON IS PILED HIGH WITH HONEY HARVEST

The rearing of the brood is confined to the lowest layer, the upper "supers" being reserved for marketable honey. Since usually not more than 200 colonies may be operated profitably in one yard, beekeepers owning thousands of hives may scatter their yards over several hundred miles.

Photograph from Topical Press Agency

HEAD VEILS MAY GIVE STUDENTS CONFIDENCE, BUT BEES WILL FIND A WAY

This class, which included 40 English youngsters, ranging in age from eight to 12½ years, harvested 150 pounds of honey in one season from four colonies near London.

corresponds to the time when fledglings are pushed over the rim of the nest and made to seek their own way in the world. But with the honeybee the young are left to carry on in the established home, and it is the old queen and the flying, or older, members of her family who search for other quarters and begin the labor of constructing a new home.

The first indication that swarming may be imminent appears when thousands of bees cluster at the entrances, literally loafing. The hive boils over with bees. Inspection within reveals the presence of several pendulous peanut-shaped queen cells (page 104), an almost infallible indication that the hegira is about to take place. Each queen cell holds a prospective heiress, possible successor to the old queen.

SWARMING THEIR GREAT ADVENTURE

The reigning queen and her daughters do not wait until the heiress actually arrives, however, but on the first bright warm day after the queen cells are sealed a mighty commotion heralds the issuance of the swarm. This usually takes place from 10 to 12 o'clock in the morning. Most of the

bees that have attained flying age (and this includes virtually all the field bees) rush out of the hive, tumbling over one another in their eagerness to taste the thrills of the great adventure.

Back and forth in front of the hive, in sharp straight flights, they take wing until thousands are in the air, the queen with them. Likely as not, this flying entanglement will shortly move toward some tree or fence post. A few bees settle, and then a few more, until within 10 to 15 minutes all have alighted in a tightly packed mass.

Shortly after the swarm settles, scout bees fly in all directions to search for a new abode, or, being foreminded, they may have attended to this duty several days before. If a place already has been located, the bees may take to the air again within a few minutes. Assuming a formation that looks like a hazy smoke ball 10 to 20 feet in diameter, the swarm gradually works its way through the treetops and, clearing all obstructions, seems to float like an enormous soap bubble, making a "bee line" toward its new home.

If the scouts fail to find a hollow tree or a cozy nook in someone's attic, the bees

WORKERS TAKE RINGSIDE SEATS AS TWO RIVAL QUEENS FIGHT TO A FINISH

In such struggles for supremacy, the battle is interrupted by the onlookers only when it appears both may die. Here a golden Italian queen is about to sting to death her darker adversary below, a gray Caucasian. Should their own mother be killed, bees will readily accept the new queen.

Paintings by Hashime Murayama

A WORK-WEARY FIELD BEE PASSES ITS LOAD TO A YOUNG NURSE AT THE HIVE

Wings tattered and torn, golden hair gone from its body, this aged black, but once yellow, bee is about to expire. The gray bee (right) is an immigrant from the Caucasus Mountains, the yellow ones being from Italy. Both kinds are thoroughly at home in the United States.

Photograph courtesy U. S. Department of Agriculture

A CLUSTER OF HOMESTEADERS INSPECTS A NEW HOUSE

When swarming, thousands of bees rush pell-mell from the old hive, setting up a buzz heard hundreds of feet away. The disorderly cloud usually settles first on a near-by bush or tree limb before setting out for a home of their own choice (see illustration, page 96, and text, page 110). This keeper has captured such a swarm and laid it in front of a new hive, which the bees will enter willingly. Tied trouser legs keep crawlers from exploring.

will continue to hang at their first stopping place for several hours, or even for several days. Should the scouts fail entirely in finding habitable quarters, the bees may decide to "camp out" and build their comb in the open air.

All the young bees, the brood, the honey, and the combs, including interest and good will, are left in the parent hive. Within a few days, a new queen issues from the oldest of the queen cells. Apparently aware that she is born to the royal purple, she at once seeks to clear the hive of any possible rivals. She makes a thorough search for queen cells and mutilates each by tearing a hole in its side. She may even render the occupant *hors de combat* by giving her a fatal thrust with her sting.

A few days after emergence the young virgin queen selects a day for her wedding flight (see text, page 95). She usually chooses a clear, warm, quiet day because her honeymoon is short, and she must make the most of it. Only when she leaves the hive with a swarm, probably a year hence, will she have another occasion to fly.

Mating always takes place on the wing, and if conditions are such that the queen cannot fly she will die a virgin. The strongest drone is her mate, for the queen is a good flier, and the weak are thus eliminated in this wise provision to maintain the strength and vigor of the race.

Before the queen has had time to return to the hive after the mating flight, the drone will have fallen to the earth dead. There is an old saying that the drone no sooner becomes a husband than he is a corpse, and the queen no sooner a bride than a widow.

Because of her specialized duties and the fact that she does not engage in outside work and is not subject to the hazards of weather and enemies that might prey upon her, the queen may live to the ripe old age of three or four years. When she becomes too old, or when she can no longer produce queen and worker bees, or if she becomes accidentally crippled, the bees will raise another queen to replace her, and for a while both mother and daughter may work side by side in the hive. But this arrangement

BEES BUZZ WHERE SWEET CLOVER BLOSSOMS GROW

Two hundred pounds of honey per season from one hive are not unusual in the Great Lakes region, where this drought-resistant, soil-enriching plant is grown extensively.

© National Geographic Society   Paintings by Hashime Murayama

THE MOST SKILLFUL CHEMIST HAS BEEN UNABLE TO DUPLICATE THE PRODUCT OF THE BEE

Each species of flower produces honey of a characteristic color and flavor. The honey from the yellow star thistle of Sacramento Valley is yellowish green (left). That from orange blossoms has a pronounced bouquet. White buckwheat produces very dark honey. Appalachian tulip trees yield a rich wine-red, while from the purple blossoms of alfalfa comes a light honey.

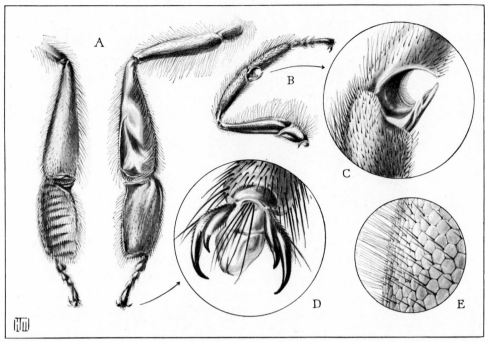

Drawing by Hashime Murayama

THE WORKER'S LEGS AND FEET ARE VERSATILE AND ITS EYES ALL-SEEING

With the broad lower segment of its hind leg (A—inside left, outside right) the honeybee brushes sticky pollen from its body and sweeps it into the basket formed by the stiff hairs on the longer joint immediately above. In an aperture on each front leg (B) is a handy and perfect comb (C—magnified) with which the worker cleans its rodlike antennae. The sharp claws on each foot (D) enable the honeybee to cling to rough surfaces, while the pad between, kept moist with a sticky liquid, serves well on hard and slippery surfaces. Some 5,000 hexagonal-shaped facets, with interspersed hairs (E), make up each of two compound eyes. In addition, the honeybee has three simple eyes.

does not last long. The old queen will shortly disappear.

A QUEEN FIGHTS ONLY A QUEEN

The marked differences between the queen and worker bee, both of whom come from the same kind of fertilized egg, have already been mentioned (see text, page 95). Their difference in behavior is even more pronounced. The worker bee is armed with a straight sting, the end of which is barbed like a harpoon (page 106 and page 115). When a worker bee stings, it cannot disengage its sting. The violent effort of tearing itself loose from the well-anchored sting so severely damages the tissue of its body that it dies within a few minutes. Normally it can sting only once, and in doing so it defends not itself but the colony.

The sting of the queen, instead of being straight and barbed, is smooth and curved. It is constructed so that it can easily be withdrawn when she uses it. The queen seemingly does not realize that she possesses this very effective weapon. She may be picked up and handled as harmlessly as a kitten. Her instinct to battle is aroused only in the presence of a rival queen.

If the queen gets into the wrong hive in returning from her mating flight, a royal battle is sure to ensue, and the two queens fight it out until death comes to the weaker. The worker bees make no attempt to protect their own mother. Here, again, is the survival of the fittest. Close observers say that when two queens in a rough-and-tumble battle get into such a position that both are apt to receive a fatal thrust, the bees separate the two and then let them come together again until one or the other has the advantage. If the mother queen is slain, the intruder, having proved her superiority, is allowed to take the place of the former queen.

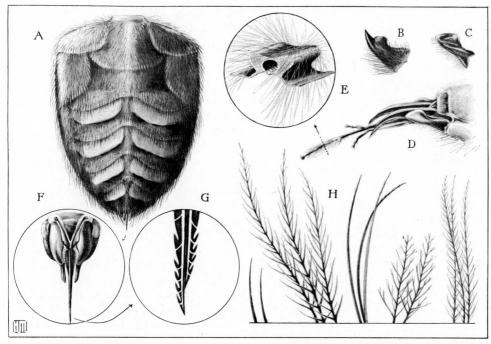

Drawing by Hashime Murayama

THE HONEYBEE'S ANATOMY VIEWED THROUGH A MICROSCOPE

The wax glands are located beneath the eight scales (A), that fit like shingles under the bee's abdomen. The circles below show enlarged details of the stinger (F), including poison sacs and the appendages that are left in the flesh. The stinger, highly magnified (G), is composed of two barbed lancets, each sharper than the finest needle. Poison flows down a central canal formed between the two lancets, which alternately work themselves deeper into the wound (see page 106). In the circle (E) is a cross section of the hollow, hairy tongue which protrudes from the mouth (D). The queen's toothed jaw (B) contrasts with the smooth mandible (C) of the worker. The various types of hair (H) that grow on a bee's body resemble certain plants.

If the queen used her sting indiscriminately, she might easily lose her life in meeting an enemy with which she could not cope. If she were being handled by her keeper and attempted to free herself by stinging him, he might instinctively retaliate by crushing her frail body. Should he do so, it would jeopardize the future life of the colony, especially if there were no larvae in the hive from which a successor could be raised. For her protection, therefore, she depends upon her own daughters or sister workers, who far outnumber her and whose sacrifice is not so fatal to the well-being of the colony.

The drone usually is regarded as a lazy individual, but, after all, he is the father and is entitled to certain respect. He gathers no food, nor does he help defend the family; he has no tools to collect sweets nor has he a sting to defend even himself. During his brief existence, however, he has certain privileges not accorded his sisters. He can safely visit neighboring colonies. Neither workers nor queens are accepted in other hives, but during the breeding season drones are allowed to come and go as they please.

When the breeding season is over, and the honeyflow comes to a close, the bees become more economical with their food supply, which must carry them through the long, cold winter. Then they drive all the drones from the hives, thus dooming them to perish soon for lack of food and shelter.

The person who can recall the names and faces of several hundred acquaintances is unusual; yet in a family of 80,000 individuals the bee instantly recognizes every member. It is evident that recognition is not through the sense of sight; instead, it is effected by the more highly developed sense of smell.

Every colony has a distinctive family

odor, different from that of every other colony. If a strange bee attempts to enter a hive, the guards at the entrance detect its alien odor and drive it away (page 100). When a colony is divided into two parts, the parts placed in separate hives and given queens that are sisters, the bees in each half develop different odors. Within a week's time they become total strangers to each other. Were the halves united again, the bees would disregard the existence of any relationship.

It sometimes happens that a beekeeper unites two or more colonies, which separately are too weak to produce a crop or to survive a hard winter. The usual method is to place one hive on top of the other, inserting a sheet of newspaper between them. The bees from both sides gnaw small holes in the paper and, in doing so, they "rub noses," but the holes at first are not large enough for the bees on either side to engage in combat. The apertures permit the mingling of the odors of the two units, so that by the time the holes are large enough for the bees to pass through, the two parts have an identical odor. Thus union takes place peacefully.

"CORONATION" OF A NEW QUEEN

If it becomes necessary to place a new queen in a colony, it is essential that she be properly "introduced." The old queen is removed at least an hour before the newcomer is "presented." In this interval the colony discovers that it is queenless and it may start constructing new queen cells.

Even though the colony desires a queen, it would not do to release the usurper, because her strange odor would antagonize the bees and endanger her life. She is placed in a wire cage to protect her from assaults. Although her new subjects would kill her were she suddenly released, they feed her by inserting their tongues through the meshes of the wire.

After the queen remains in this cage for two or three days, she will have lost much of the odor of her former hive and acquired that of her new abode. Even then her actual release must be accomplished quietly and without excitement. Her cage is provided with a plug of soft candy. Two or three days are required for the bees to tunnel through. Meantime the odors have mingled, and the queen can walk out on the combs of her new home without undue risk.

Honeybees help perpetuate their race by their insatiable desire to gather nectar. Unlike bumblebees, hornets, yellow jackets, and wasps, honeybees cannot live from hand to mouth. They must store enough food during the summer to keep the colony alive throughout the winter. Of the four other insects just mentioned, all the individuals in each colony die at the approach of winter except the young mated queens, and these simply crawl into protected places where they hibernate. During this period they require no food.

Among honeybees, only the drones die in the fall. The queen and the workers live and are semi-active throughout the winter (see text, page 115). It is important, therefore, to gather enough food during the summer to maintain the colony during seasons when insect activity largely ceases.

At the end of the swarming season, which coincides with the height of the breeding season, the queen lays fewer and fewer eggs until fall, when the rearing of the brood entirely ceases. Cold weather has overtaken the colony by this time, imposing changes in its organization to cope with low temperatures. Individual honeybees die of chill at temperatures well above freezing; in fact, they seldom fly when the temperature is lower than 45 degrees Fahrenheit. Hence the colony must maintain a life-sustaining temperature when the thermometer dips to zero or lower.

REGULATING WINTER TEMPERATURE

During the active season the bees spread over the entire interior of the hive; when winter comes, they gather in a spherical, compact cluster with the queen in the center. Those on the outside are crowded in a sort of insulating shell to prevent escape of heat. Those on the inside are in looser formation. Those in the center carry on muscular activity, which generates sufficient heat to keep the bees from chilling.

The bees do not permit the periphery of the cluster to fall below 57 degrees Fahrenheit; thus the colder the outside temperature becomes, the more muscular activity

Photograph by Wilhelm Tobien

GERMAN BEEHIVES, LIKE SCARECROWS, WEAR STRAW SKIRTS AND TIN-PAN HELMETS

The Marienwerder flower girl explains that the grotesque coverings protect the colonies from the rain and sun. Such old-fashioned hives cannot be inspected readily. Sometimes a colony becomes queenless and dies before the keeper discovers the absence of the "mother." In Europe, as in the United States, modern equipment is rapidly replacing such apiaries.

they must perform to maintain warmth. The bees composing the insulating shell change places at frequent intervals with those of the interior.

The average colony consumes from 30 to 50 pounds of honey during the winter and early spring, the quantity depending upon its size, prevailing temperatures, and the condition of the hive. A thoughtful bee-keeper packs his colonies in sawdust or other insulating material (see page 103), or places the bees in a properly constructed cellar during winter. Thus he decreases the consumption of honey and prevents the bees from aging too rapidly, insuring them sufficient vitality in the spring to renew brood-rearing activities.

The U. S. Department of Agriculture estimates that there are approximately 4,650,000 honeybee colonies in the United States. This number will require about 165 million pounds of honey for its own consumption during winter; and, to carry on brood rearing and honey production during the active season, will need double this amount. Thus honeybees in this country gather some 500 million pounds of honey to maintain themselves during the year, without a drop being available to place on our tables.

BEEKEEPING BENEFITS THE COMMUNITY

The marketable crop of honey in the United States varies widely from year to year, but a fair average is about 200 million pounds, making a grand total of approximately 700 million pounds credited to the labor of this insect. It has been estimated that if a single worker bee could gather enough nectar to make one pound of honey, she would have to work every day in the year for more than eight years, and in doing so she would travel approximately three times around the earth.

These astounding figures indicate the tremendous benefit honeybees render to our agriculture. To gather so much honey, they must visit myriads of plants in which pollination is effected. Therefore, it can be understood why honeybees are of infinitely greater value to the community in which they are kept, in producing crops of seed and fruit, than they are to their owner, who is paid in honey and beeswax.

The supposition that the keeper of bees has nothing to do but watch the honey and money roll in is fallacious. Keeping bees is a specialized job, and one must have an inherent love for them. A thorough knowledge of bee behavior, gained only through experience, is a primary requisite.

Attention must be given to a vast number of details. There are plenty of griefs in connection with the business: the loss of bees during the winter is heavy; diseases of bees take a large annual toll; and wax moths, which destroy the combs, cause further losses. The operation of an apiary requires close personal supervision. Thus the production of honey is largely a one-man affair. In favorable localities, however, honey production is as remunerative as any other branch of agriculture.

Although hundreds of plants secrete nectar, only about two dozen species furnish honey in market quantity. The layman thinks of a spacious garden as a rich haven for honeybees, but often such is not the case. All the flower gardens in the beautiful city of Washington probably would maintain not more than two dozen colonies of bees. Honey production on a commercial scale must be carried on where there are many acres of a plant from which the bees can obtain more nectar than is needed for their immediate requirements.

In most sections of the United States there is usually one particular flower from which the bees produce a surplus crop. In carrying on brood rearing, and in obtaining enough honey for their own needs, they visit flowers of endless variety. Bees freely visit apple blossoms, for example, yet apple-blossom honey is practically unknown. There are too few apple blossoms, and the blossom period is in early spring when honey requirements of the colony are so great during brood rearing that the bees consume the nectar as rapidly as it is gathered. The same is true of many flowers.

Perhaps the most concentrated honey-producing section in the United States is

that surrounding the Great Lakes, where the white Dutch clover, the common variety that grows so abundantly on our lawns, reaches the peak of perfection. There the bees also produce a surplus from alsike clover, sweet clover, basswood, buckwheat, and occasional crops from raspberry and milkweed.

Another rich area is on the Pacific coast, where the heavily scented orange groves furnish thousands of pounds of highly flavored honey. The foothills of California supply sparkling sage honey and a bountiful quota of alfalfa honey comes annually from the Imperial Valley.

The whitest honey of all, often water-white, is produced from the fireweed, which grows in the burnt-over forests of Washington and Oregon. The Intermountain States send to our eastern and foreign markets carloads of alfalfa and sweet-clover honey, heavy and flavorous. The Dakotas and the surrounding States rank high in large crops. There 100 pounds a colony from sweet clover (page 113) and alfalfa is not unusual, and crops of 200 to 250 pounds to the colony are frequent in favorable seasons.

Many kinds of honey plants occur in the Southern States, where the honeys run the gamut of the color scale. Usually the honeys from the South are dark, spicy, and highly flavored.

Probably no other food is produced over a wider area than honey. Wheat, corn, milk, and potatoes are almost universal, yet their production is restricted to areas having certain soil and climatic conditions, whereas the mountains, the swamps, the deserts, the wind-swept plains, and the Tropics all add their quotas of honey.

Surely no other food has such romantic associations. Every drop of honey has its origin in the bosom of a delicate flower, where it has been exposed to the rays of the summer sun and bathed with the morning dew. You have only to close your eyes and picture fields of clover, and fill your lungs with the perfumed air from myriad nodding blossoms; or in memory to walk again through scented orange groves to realize the origin of this incomparable food.

CHAPTER IV

Stalking Ants, Savage and Civilized

A Naturalist Braves Bites and Stings in Many Lands to Learn the Story of an Insect Whose Ways Often Parallel Those of Man

By W. M. MANN

Director, National Zoological Park, Washington, D. C.

TO WRITE the word "ant" in Japanese, you take the character for "insect" (to the left, below) and add to it "unselfishness, justice, and courtesy" (center). Then you have the character (on the right) which means "ant" and also shows the flattering Japanese opinion of it.

虫 義 蟻

This delightful compliment is most interesting and many species undoubtedly deserve it; yet there are ants as savage and ruthless as the ancient Huns or Mongols— ants that devote their lives to foraging in vast armies, destroying the nests of others, and killing all insects and animals in their way (see page 137). There are queen ants that enter a foreign colony, ingratiate themselves with the citizens, foully murder the true queen, and usurp her place. There are ants that raid the nests of their neighbors and kidnap their young as slaves (see page 124).

GROW GARDENS AND KEEP "COWS"

Some, high in the scale of ant civilization, make their own gardens and grow their own special food. There are ants that keep "cows"; others that gather and store honey in barrels made from living nest-mates; * still others that use their own young as

* See "Living Casks of Honey," Chapter V, page 139.

spools of silken thread in making nests (see page 130).

In sheer numbers, too, the ants challenge imagination. Their legions outnumber those of every other land creature in the world, except possibly some minute forms of life. So far, some 8,000 species, subspecies, and varieties have been collected and painstakingly classified—a different kind of ant for about every word of this article.

The immense amount of work devoted to studying ants in all regions of the world bears witness to their magnetic appeal to the interest of man.

Thus there have been published monographs on the ants of Madagascar and of New Caledonia; catalogues of the species which inhabit Brazil, Chile, Switzerland, Connecticut, and the peninsula of Baja California. One huge volume concerned with the ants of the Belgian Congo alone contains 1,139 pages.

Even the ants that crawled on the earth three million years ago live again in the pages of voluminous books, because their bodies happened to be entombed and preserved in the flowing resin of prehistoric pines, now known to science as the "Baltic amber."

LIKE SHIP LIFE AND HEATED HOUSES

Of these incredibly numerous and interesting creatures there are certain to be colonies on your lawns; there may be a nest or two in the rafters of your home and almost certainly some in the vicinity of the kitchen. Each colony of a species contains from a few to many thousands, even hundreds of thousands, of individuals.

The common little yellow house ant, *Monomorium pharaonis,* takes readily to life on shipboard, and so has traveled to all parts of the world (see page 126). It takes kindly, also, to heated houses, and so, although a tropical ant, it thrives in northern countries and has become a pest everywhere.

One of our lawn ants, *Lasius niger,* in its several varieties spreads itself throughout the entire Northern Hemisphere, where it damages the golf greens of Washington, D. C., as impartially as it does the temple gardens of Japan. It is one of the most abundant single species of insect (see page 126).

Some warm day, preferably after a shower, find a nice, flat stone on a sunny hillside and turn it over. There probably will be an ant nest beneath it—a series of channels leading from one cavity to another. Worker ants rush about, excited at the sudden uncovering of their home. One, very much larger than the others, is the queen, or there may be several of them if the colony is a large one. If there are males, and they are present only during the mating season, they are usually much smaller than the rest, generally dark in color and wearing large wings.

Piles of larvae and pupae, a few of them unusually big and destined to become females, will be whisked below out of sight while you are watching. If you look closely, you may see the eggs, little clusters of tiny white specks adhering together. The "ant eggs" of commerce are not eggs at all, but pupae of the large red ant. The cocoons, from which adult ants soon would emerge, are gathered in large quantities in Europe and dried and exported, to be used as food for goldfish and captive soft-billed birds. At the Zoo we sometimes put a few of them in the custard fed to the anteaters.

In our nest under the stone there may be one or more reddish beetles stalking slowly about among the ants. These are guests or parasites. Often they have a strange hold upon the affections of their hosts. They beg liquid food regurgitated from the communal crop, or storage stomach, of the ants, which sometimes so neglect their own young to pamper these insidious spongers that the colony becomes debilitated and dies out.

HONEYDEW ON ANTS' MENU

On the roots of plants in the passages there may be plant lice, or aphids and coccids, the "cows" of the ants (see illustration, page 143). As the weather gets warmer, the lice will be taken out and "pastured" on the roots of other plants, sometimes on Indian corn, where they do much damage to the farmers' crops. In this case, ants are an accessory to the fact. It is the aphid that does the harm, but the damage is greatly exaggerated by the ants' tender care.

By a stroking process similar to milking, the ants obtain from the plant lice a highly valued food substance, honeydew. This is the sweet sap of plants after it has been sucked out and passed through the bodies of the tiny insects, most of which take more than they can absorb.

As this forms the chief food of many ants, they tend and protect their cows as conscientiously as do any pastoral people. Sometimes they even build sheds of carton, a papery substance, on the trunks of trees to shelter them. At the approach of cold weather the ants sometimes gather them into their nests on plant roots, taking them out to pasture again when the danger of frost is over and their proper food plants are growing. A common sight about Washington in the spring is a troop of ants tending aphids that are feeding on the stalks of our common roadside weeds.

Examine carefully the nest under the stone on the hillside and you may find the home of another ant there, an almost microscopic yellow species (*Solenopsis molesta*), sometimes called the thief ant.

Making a nest adjoining that of a larger species, it tunnels into the larder of its neighbor and aggravatingly helps itself. The passages are so small that the big ants have no more chance of chasing their

A GOOD TEE-SHOT FROM ATOP A GIANT TERMITE HILL

Scores of natural hazards have been erected by the insects on this strange nine-hole golf course at Elisabethville, in the copper-mining region of the Belgian Congo (see illustration, page 145).

tiny tormentors than a man would have of pursuing a marauding rat into its hole. Uncovering two such nests sometimes precipitates a battle in which the larger ants get their long-sought revenge. The thieves can only cling annoyingly to their big opponents, which they do until bitten to death.

Break open a rotten log and a colony of a different kind may be revealed, with workers less excitable (see page 126). Slowly and methodically they move their young away from the disturbance.

MARVELOUS RESOURCES OF THE QUEEN

Under a deeply imbedded rock you will perhaps discover a small family of the Troglodyte ants, blind dwellers in the dark, remaining motionless to avoid detection.

All ant colonies have one point in common. The members, excepting, of course, guests, parasites, and other intruders are all children of a widow queen who has left the home nest on her nuptial flight. After mating high in the air, the male always dies, as he falls to earth far from the home nest and is helpless without workers to care for and feed him. The female, however, has marvelous resources within herself, and all alone she establishes a home and a family of her own.

After fertilization the queen creeps into some cranny beneath bark or under a stone; sometimes she constructs a small shelter of crude paper made by chewing bark from a tree. Now she lays her first eggs. During the time when she was a larva and a newly hatched female in her home nest she had been constantly cared for and even pampered by the workers of the parent colony. Special foods were given her, and she was able to lay up in her body a considerable surplus. Her wing muscles were enormously developed for just this one flight. Fat was stored in her abdomen.

From now on there is no further use for wings, so she scrapes or bites them off. The wing muscles disintegrate and add to the stored-up food which she is able to feed her first babies by regurgitation. The first hatched are runts and weaklings, but ants, nevertheless. Their instinct is fully developed and they go to work collecting

Photograph by Ernest G. Holt

TERRIBLE SCOURGES OF LEAF-CUTTING ANTS DESTROY THE LIFE-GIVING CROPS OF
SÃO GABRIEL

The legions of Brazil's insatiable saubas have raided the gardens of this lonely village on the Rio Negro so often that the natives must depend upon a few banana plants, a patch of sugar cane, and a little cassava. But for the bounty of forest and river, the inhabitants would starve. The leaves are not eaten by the ants, but are used in growing their "mushroom" food (see text, page 136).

food for their mother and for their new and constantly appearing sisters.

An ant colony has been created. The queen, her troubles over, becomes a mere egg-laying machine, carefully fed and protected by her children.

Mating flights of ants are common in the spring and midsummer, when hosts of males and females swarm into the air. Crowds of them are seen emerging from cracks in cement walks, on lawns and in gardens, and at this time of year the entomologist receives many letters asking about these "flying ants" and usually enclosing a specimen, folded and badly crushed, in the envelope.

Although practically all ant colonies are founded by a lone female, there are some extraordinary exceptions. One is Carebara, an ant of Asia and North Africa, noted for being a great enemy of the "white ants," or termites, on which it feeds (see page 133).

When the mother-to-be Carebara goes

on her honeymoon, a number of the almost microscopic workers attach themselves to her legs by their jaws, and in this way are with her to be of help when she starts the new colony.

Extraordinary and somewhat piratical methods of establishing colonies are followed by the females of some ants, usually species not physically capable of caring for their own first brood. One kind steals into the nest of a related species, hurriedly seizes and makes a pile of the pupae already there, and fiercely defends them from their rightful owners. When adult ants emerge from these pupae they are loyal to their kidnapper mother and, antlike, commence to care for her eggs and for the young hatched from them. This results in a mixed colony of two species.

A few species of Western ants of the genus *Formica* have very small females, thickly covered with soft yellow hair. Entering a colony of another, though closely

Photograph by Jacob Gayer

BRAZILIANS FIGHT ANT ENEMIES WITH SMOKE

In Belém (Pará) leaf-cutting pests are killed by pumping sulphur fumes into the nests (see page 131 and illustration, page 122). The can at the left contains a charcoal fire. It is placed over the entrances and the pump at the right does the rest.

related species, they so ingratiate themselves with the workers that they are adopted and the rightful queen is murdered by her own progeny, who devote the rest of their lives to the new queen and her young. The original inhabitants eventually die off, leaving their native nest entirely in the possession of the usurper and her brood.

THE QUEEN IS MURDERED

In North Africa a fertile queen of the "decapitating ant" (*Bothriomyrmex decapitans*) will fly to a nest of Tapinoma, a much larger ant, and loiter around the entrance until Tapinoma workers seize her. They take her into the nest, but for some reason do not eat her; whereupon she climbs onto the back of the rightful queen and saws at her neck until the head falls off. Then the Tapinoma workers adopt her and care for her eggs and young until the nest is populated only by the offspring of the regicide.

More males and females are produced;

queens fly away, find another nest of Tapinoma, and repeat the process. One wonders how the host species has persisted so long, but it may be that it will eventually be exterminated by the decapitators; then the latter must disappear also, for such a parasite cannot exist without its host.

Certain ants have gone so far in parasitic development that the worker caste has entirely disappeared, leaving only males and females incapable of caring for themselves and entirely dependent on their ability to find nests of suitable host ants. Some fifteen genera of these have been discovered.

When the Amazon queen goes out to found a colony or "queendom," she enters a nest of the common Formica and immediately pierces the head of their queen with her long, curved, and sharp-pointed jaws. She is then adopted by the Formica workers, who devote the rest of their lives to caring for her progeny.

The Amazon, with its lethal mandibles, made only for fighting, is incapable of feeding itself or performing the ordinary

(Inset, natural size)

RED AMAZONS WITH ICE-TONG JAWS DEAL DEATH IN A KIDNAPPING RAID

One drives the twin prongs through her black foeman's head. Others grapple or poise for the kill. With duller jaws, the desperate blacks (*Formica*) gnaw their enemies' legs, but some of the reds dart into the nest and bear off the booty—fat pupae from which black ants will emerge to become their slaves (see text, pages 122, 123). Without them these Amazon ants (*Polyergus*) of the United States, Europe, and Japan would die, as their weapons are so long and sharp they can neither feed themselves nor care for their young. The Geographic's staff artist peered through microscopes for months to make these remarkable action paintings.

home duties of an ant, so the supply of slaves has to be replenished from time to time by raids on neighboring Formica nests (see page 124).

The hard-working defenders, with their short, triangular mandibles, are no match for their well-armed foes and the battle is always one-sided. It is interesting to see the Amazons, sometimes in a more or less regular file, bearing home the captured pupae from which new slave ants will emerge. Later the captives occasionally help raid their old nests and enslave their own sisters.

The Amazons occur throughout the temperate regions of the Northern Hemisphere, rather rarely in eastern United States, but commonly in parts of the West. I have found them only twice in the vicinity of Washington, D. C., on the edge of Soldiers' Home Park and on Bull Run Battlefield, curiously enough.

THE "FORGOTTEN ANTS"

One feels sorry for some of the industrious species of Formica, solid citizens, but really the "forgotten ants," because they seem to be preyed upon by every sort of warrior ant and their nests are nearly always shared with various guests and parasites.

Two kinds of ants, very different from each other, sometimes live together amicably, each occupying a separate part of the same nest and contributing to the general welfare.

The little shampoo ant (*Leptothorax emersoni*), discovered by Dr. William Morton Wheeler, of Harvard,* in the peat bogs of Connecticut, lives in the nests of *Myrmica canadensis,* a much larger species. When the Leptothorax worker needs food, it approaches the Myrmica worker and proceeds to shampoo and lick it. The Myrmica obviously enjoys this, for it regurgitates food to the Leptothorax.

One day in Brazil I was investigating an ant nest consisting of a mass of earth six inches in diameter in a fork of a tree.

I tapped this nest gently with my forceps and the surface was immediately covered

* See "Notes About Ants and Their Resemblance to Man," by William Morton Wheeler in the NATIONAL GEOGRAPHIC MAGAZINE, August, 1912.

with small, reddish-brown ants of the genus *Dolichoderus.* When I gouged into the nest to find the various forms, a swarm of Odontomachus rushed out and one of them stung me. Odontomachus was a dozen times as big as the Dolichoderus and provided with strong biting jaws and a red-hot sting.

Undoubtedly the little Dolichoderus had built the nest and the Odontomachus had taken up their abode there also. Evidently a small insect alighting on such a nest would attract only the smaller inhabitants, but a severe jolt would bring out the shock troops in defense. Both of these ants were new to science and never have been found again.

THE THRILLS OF AN ANT HUNT

Often I have had as big a thrill from a successful hunt for a rare ant as I have from the capture of giraffes or wart hogs. There is about as much physical exertion involved, too, turning over thousands of stones and logs, digging into the earth, chopping hard wood, and peeling bark from innumerable dead trees.

Luck frequently plays an important part. In 1901 Father Schmitt, a Jesuit missionary, sent to the great myrmecologist, Forel, of Switzerland, a single specimen of a new and extraordinary ant from Haiti. Forel described it and named the genus after his good friend, Carol Emery, of Bologna, and the species after the Jesuit (*Emeryella schmitti*). This lone specimen was long the only representative of its kind in collections, and the species was something I especially wanted to find while in Haiti (see page 133).

At the end of a month's work I had found one solitary worker along a roadside. I had no fine-tooth comb with me, but for two months I tried every other method I knew of to discover the nest or more of the workers. Finally I reported to my teacher in zoology that, as far as I could make out, the species was now extinct and I had captured the last survivor on the island.

Then one evening I went for a stroll just before dinner and noticed on the path a millipede, or thousand-legger, moving in an unnatural way. Bending over, I saw that

"PUBLIC ENEMIES" SPOIL PUTTS, LOOT PANTRIES, STING LIKE HOT NEEDLES

The lawn ant (left, *Lasius niger americanus*) and the tiny, yellow house ant (*Monomorium pharonis*, upper right) are known to all. The tropical fire ant (lower right, *Solenopsis geminata*) carries a burning sting (see page 120).

© National Geographic Society   (Insets, natural size)

A PRIMITIVE UNITED STATES ANT "PLAYS POSSUM" WHEN ATTACKED

This sluggish dweller in rotten wood is *Proceratium croceum* (upper left). On the tomb of Haiti's black king, Christophe, Dr. Mann discovered *Camponotus cristophei* (upper right), hence its name. South America's rare *Dolichoderus spinicollis* (lower left), has horns, and the Texas harvesting ant (*Pogonomyrmex desertorum,* lower right) wears a beard in which it carries sand in nest-digging (see pages 121, 125, 128, 134).

the millipede was dead and was being carried by an ant. The ant was *Emeryella!*

It took all of my strength of character to keep from seizing both ant and prey at once, but I smoked my pipe as calmly as I could and watched the ant till it leisurely entered a small hole at one side of a flat stone.

When the stone was turned over, there was an entire colony of some sixty workers. Later, in the same locality, I found a similar colony, and specimens of these have now been distributed to all the important ant collections in museums all over the world.

There were no females in either nest; so it is not improbable that this species lacks a special female, and that one of the workers functions as an egg-layer. At night there came to lights in my quarters a reddish ant, which from its general character we assume to be the male of the species and have so described it.

I had talked about *Emeryella schmitti* so much that it became well known to the scant white population of the island under the name of "Mary Ella Schmitt," and when I finally reported its discovery there was a great celebration among my fellow Americans, railroad men vacationing at Port-au-Prince.

Another missionary priest, Père Sallé, had sent to the Museum in Paris from Haiti a curious nest of vegetable fiber, not unlike a wasp's nest.

Forel, while rummaging about among the specimens, found it and tapped it on a piece of white paper. Several dead and dried ants dropped out. They belonged to the genus *Macromischa*, the most exquisitely formed of the ants and with beautiful metallic coloration—purples, greens, and reds (see page 128). The genus is interesting, too, because it alone of the ants of the West Indies has developed into numerous species. About thirty are known from Cuba alone.

I remember one Christmas Day at the Mina Carlota, in the Sierra de Trinidad of Cuba. When I attempted to turn over a large rock to see what was living underneath, the rock split in the middle, and there, in the very center, was a half teaspoonful of brilliant green metallic ants glistening in the sunshine. They proved to be an unknown species of this genus.

FINDING A "LONG LOST"

One of the "long losts" was *Macromischa sallei,* in Haiti, and my heart was set on finding it again. Coming into Furcy one afternoon, mounted on a diminutive Haitian horse, I saw an ant walking across the road. It was *M. sallei.* I collected it and put it carefully into a vial of alcohol.

Père Plombé, most genial of hosts, greeted me and announced that dinner was nearly ready. On the little ridge where the church and priest's house stood were low bushes belonging to the genus *Baccharis.* While waiting for dinner I strolled among them and noticed an oval object on one of the bushes. I tapped it with my forceps and the next moment the thing was literally covered with ants. They were *M. sallei* swarming out to defend their home.

Other bushes contained other nests, and I shall not forget the thrill I had when I told Père Plombé, on my return to his home ten minutes later, that I had rediscovered this species and had enough specimens for all the museums in the world.

Père Plombé in his profession meets all sorts of people with all sorts of enthusiasms, but my elation over this find puzzled him a little. He gazed at me, then at the vials densely packed with ants, shook his head, and murmured to himself, "C'est curieux!"

The fire ant (*Solenopsis geminata*) is such a good traveler that one variety or another is found throughout the warmer parts of the earth (see page 126). It gets its name from the painful, burning sting it can inflict. A colony contains vast numbers of workers. They have recently been reported as doing great damage to young quail in the Southeastern States. The birds, incapable of defending themselves, are stung to death.

Fire ants nest in almost any kind of locality and are extremely prolific. Even floods cannot daunt the fire ant, for it has been reported in Brazil that when the water rises and washes out a colony, the ants form a ball, queen and brood in the middle, and this living ball floats away to a tree or to higher ground, where the ants recommence housekeeping.

THESE SLENDER BEAUTIES OFTEN WALK WITH THEIR HINDQUARTERS REVERSED

Macromischa purpurata, found by Dr. Mann in the West Indies, feeds on small insects or plant nectar, nests in hollow twigs, and works without the energetic haste often associated with ants (see page 127).

(Insets, natural size)

A BIG, HOMELY FACE MAKES A LIVING DOOR

The soldiers of *Camponotus* (*Colobopsis*), left, living throughout the world, have oversized, curiously indented heads. With these they block the round entrances to their nests in the hollow stems of sedges, as one is doing here, and open only at the proper "password"—a series of antennae strokes (see page 126). A blind, primeval Australian ant is *Eusphinctus steinelli* (right).

The tailor ant (*Oecophylla smaragdina*) and a few other ants (*Polyrhachis*) are unique among all the earth's creatures, so far as we know, in that they use their young as tools in nest construction (see page 130).

Few adult insects spin silk, but the larvae of many have this ability to enclose themselves in silken cocoons, from which they will later emerge as fully formed adults. Oecophylla utilizes this accomplishment of its young in making its nests.

I have often torn one of the leaves that formed its box-shaped nest and then watched the proceedings.

At first there is a wild sortie on the part of the ants, all in fighting mood. They cannot sting, but they bite annoyingly.

After they have given up trying to find and destroy the intruder, worker ants seize larvae in their mandibles and bring them to the damaged portions. Other workers seize the edges of the leaves and pull them together, while those with the larvae pass them back and forth, stimulating the grub to exude silk, which sticks and holds the pieces of the leaves together.

After their silk has been used for the common good, the luckless larvae have to sleep naked!

The tailor ant lives throughout the Old World Tropics and is one of the few ants that is greenish in color, though some of its varieties are red, and one, in West Africa, is brown almost to black.

COLLECTING FROM TREETOPS

In the Solomon Islands this pugnacious Oecophylla abounds. On the island of Malaupaina I had for two weeks the unusual and delightful good fortune for a naturalist of being able to collect among the tops of high trees. A plantation company was felling the original forest, clearing the land for coconuts. One enormous tree after another was felled, and as soon as it came down I would go among the upper branches and collect.

Oecophylla was abundant, and I can safely say that there was scarcely a moment of daylight during those two weeks when an ant was not biting me on the neck. I would instinctively reach up, seize the little creature, break its neck between my thumb and forefinger, and go on collecting.

But once, as I crushed one of them, I noticed that it was unusually hard. It was another ant, a Podomyrma, rare and desirable. After that it was necessary for me to seize each attacking ant and carefully examine it before destroying it, so as not to crush a valuable specimen by mistake.

Eight thousand different kinds of ants are a large order, but students have simplified their study by a classification which is one of the finest that has been done for any insect group. They have been arranged into different families, and the first and most primitive of these is the Ponerines, the ant savages. Like cavemen, they live solely by hunting. Big, strong jaws run in the family and at the other end they carry a poisonous sting. Their headquarters are the Tropics, but a few forms extend into the colder climates also. Some are minute in size, but others, the largest of the ants, attain a length of more than an inch and have antagonistic dispositions more than worthy of their bulk.

In Bolivia we found that one kind, nearly an inch long, locally called "buni," but classified as *Paraponera clavata*, would sometimes actually drive the bare-footed natives from their own corn patches.

PROMENADING IN THE FOREST

A still larger species, the "great, terrible ant" (*Dinoponera grandis*), the "tucandero" of the Brazilians, also inhabits tropical South America. At Belém (Pará) every day we could see individuals an inch in length, black and shining, walking unconcernedly along the path in the forest.

One primitive group includes the bulldog ant of Australia, which gets its name from its powerful biting jaws; also it has a sting so efficient that it inspires respect (see page 135). There are many species, and they range from a third of an inch to more than an inch in length. Some live beneath stones; others make mound nests, and they forage all over the place.

The Australians are very fond of picnicking. I remember on my first visit there, when we would go out for a day our place for luncheon was carefully selected, usually in the center of a broad

(Inset, natural size)

TAILOR ANTS, LIKE MEN, HAVE MASTERED THE USE OF TOOLS

Their own young are used as spinning machines in nest-building. While some of the long, vicious, red workers (*Oecophylla smaragdina* of the Old World Tropics) yank the edges of growing leaves together with their tusks, others pick up half-grown larvae with well-developed silk glands for spinning cocoons. Stimulating the grub with its antennae, the tailor makes it produce a silken thread which sticks to the leaves and binds them together. These ants bite so ferociously that they often leave their heads in the wound when brushed off. In India, men pound the ants to a paste which is eaten with curry. Wearing the wings of their marriage flight are the queen and the smaller male (see text, page 129).

(Small inset, natural size)

Hashime Murayama

AT NIGHT OR ON CLOUDY DAYS, SWARMS OF LEAF-CUTTING ANTS STRIP WHOLE TREES

Pieces of leaves are sheared off with their saw-edged jaws (inset, upper right) and carried home like waving banners by workers marching in wide columns and beating regular paths. Then the leaves are chewed to a paste, on which later grow the "mushrooms" that form the only food of these ants (*Atta cephalotes*, of tropical America). They do immense damage to orange groves. Large and medium ants serve as leaf gatherers or soldiers. The smallest, riding on the leaf in the center like a mahout on an elephant, acts as gardener for the fungus, or works in the nursery. Known as sauba ants in Brazil, they are fried and eaten by Indians (see text, page 136, and illustrations, pages 122, 123).

sheet of Hawkesbury sandstone, not because this rock was particularly soft, but because of its vantage as a lookout for bulldog ants.

The Ponerines usually hunt singly, but with their formidable armament they are able to subdue insects much larger than themselves. A few hunt in groups and raid nests of other ants or of termites.

In Africa I have seen such raids made by a black hunter, *Paltothyreus tarsatus*. The workers are about three-quarters of an inch long. Marching in an orderly, though hurried, column some twenty feet in length, they enter a termite nest. From the surface there is no evidence of a struggle, but after several minutes the column streams out of the ground, each worker holding a dead termite in its jaws.

Termites (see page 133) form the chief food of many of these Ponerines. Sometimes they establish their colonies in the termite nest itself, somewhat apart from the rightful owners, but still near the source of their living food supply.

In Bolivia I found in a decayed log a populous nest of termites and in the same log was a colony of red hunter ants (*Centromyrmex*). In the chambers of the ants' home I noticed on the top of each larva the body of a decapitated termite. Near by were little piles of dead termites to provide a second helping.

ARMY ANTS ARE LIKE MONGOL HORDES

If these Ponerines, living in small colonies and subsisting by hunting, may be compared to such primitive peoples as the Australian aborigines, the Ituri pygmies, or the Carapuna Indians, then the next group, the Dorylines, or army ants, may be likened to the Mongols of Genghis Khan, traveling in countless hordes (see page 137).

Blind workers of different sizes, marching in efficient, ruthless military formation, they leave a wake of death behind them. Nothing in their path is safe. Holes in the ground are entered, tall trees are climbed, and even human dwellings invaded in search of insect prey.

Some raid only the nests of other ants for the larvae and pupae on which they live; some seem especially fond of cockroaches; and I was once driven out of my forest hut by a swarm of these ants pouring up over the door-sill log like a black Niagara flowing the wrong way. I sat outside for hours, until the invaders eventually left, carrying with them what looked like pounds of dismembered cockroaches, spiders, and other late but not lamented fellow housemates of mine.

Different species of these driver, or legionary ants, inhabit all of the continents, but they are most abundant and the armies are largest in the Tropics. Our North American species, some of which range as far north as North Carolina, are small and often subterranean in habit.

EVEN THE ELEPHANTS MAKE WAY

In Africa and in South America roam the mightiest legions. It is said that even the elephant will get out of their line of march, and that the anteater itself might find them too much of a good thing. Certainly, any living creature that becomes covered with these biting, stinging demons is in a pathetic plight. As they are blind, the size of their quarry means nothing whatsoever to them.

Once, in Africa, I leaped into a stream after carelessly stepping into a file of ants. A dozen or so of the vanguard had already clamped onto my leg and kept stinging me, even under water, until I plucked them off.

The number of individuals in a big horde of these marauders cannot be estimated. The column may be an ant or two wide, or it may be over a foot or a yard wide. One army stayed in the vicinity of our camp in Bolivia for weeks, so that I came to feel well acquainted with it as a whole, though not individually.

For hours I sat alongside and watched the column flowing along, waiting for the curious parasitic beetles that live with the ants and accompany them on their march. The beetles so closely resemble the ants that it required experience to single them out in the rapidly moving procession.

When one came along at last—one that I saw—I would grab at it with my forceps. Then a terrific commotion would result. Flanking columns hurried out to find who was molesting them, so I would retreat ingloriously and wait until the column of

Hashime Murayama

FAR FIERCER THAN ITS NAMESAKE IS AUSTRALIA'S BULLDOG ANT

This ant has a sting a quarter of an inch long. These well-armed fighters—*Myrmecia formosa* and (inset, upper right) *Myrmecia nigriventris*—are among the largest of ants (see text, page 129).

(Small insets, natural size)

THE CARPENTER ANT WEAKENS HOUSES, BRIDGES, AND TREES

Like the termites (see page 133), it bores elaborate tunnels which sometimes cause beams and rafters to collapse without warning. The thick-jawed wreckers *(Camponotus herculeanus pennsylvanicus ferrugineus)* have been found frequently in the eastern United States. On a log crawl a winged male, workers, and soldiers with large heads (see text, page 120, and illustrations, 16, 143).

From the train window the traveler in the Southwest sees large ant hills dotted over the desert. These are usually nests of the bearded agricultural ants, Pogonomyrmex (see page 126). They live on the seeds of grasses which they gather and store in their nests. There is usually a large area kept carefully cleared about the nest, which makes the mound stand out prominently. Sometimes surrounding these cleared areas is a fringe of the grass that supplies the food of the ants.

From this, some observers have thought that the ants intentionally plant their own food. This is probably not so. Refuse from the nest is carried out and deposited at the edge of the clearing, and with this refuse may be some of the seeds which germinate there. It is thus by accident that a source of food supply appears adjacent to the nest.

These desert harvesters are fierce in the defense of their home, and it is said that small children have been stung to death while playing on the nest. I have been stung a number of times while collecting Pogonomyrmex and can testify that the sting leaves a dull pain which lasts for some time.

Honey ants are another example of those that look ahead to the days of famine, piling up quantities of honeydew in living containers (see text, page 139, and illustrations, pages 140 and 141).

The fungus-growing ants, chiefly inhabiting tropical America, but also extending into the Temperate Zone as far north as New Jersey, actually plant and cultivate their food. They belong to a distinct group, called the Attinae, and all they ever eat is a little mushroom which they themselves grow.

Any evening, on a walk in southern Texas or in practically any part of tropical or subtropical America, one will see files of these ants, each ant bearing a bit of leaf. For this they have been called "parasol ants" and "leaf-cutting ants" (see page 131 and illustration, page 123).

One species is a terrible pest to citrus planters in the Tropics. The colonies are enormous. Sometimes an orange tree will be stripped of leaves in a single night.

The ants carry these leaves into their nests along well-beaten trails. There they are chewed into a paste by the smaller workers. This paste is used as a stratum on which to grow the minute mushrooms on which the ants live. The smallest members of the colony serve as gardeners as well as nurses and take care of the crop. For fertilizer most of them use leaves, but some use bits of straw, and others caterpillar droppings, on which to raise the fungus.

The queen ant, before she leaves her parent nest, takes into her mouth some spores of this fungus. When she lays her first eggs she crushes them and deposits these spores upon them. The fungus starts and maintains itself there until her second crop of eggs develops into young ants, who go out at once to obtain new food for the home garden.

TERMITE IS KIN TO COCKROACHES

There is an old saying that termites are called "white ants" because they are not white and because they are not ants. A true ant is a relative of the bees and wasps; the termite is kin to the cockroaches. But these two groups, so widely different in origin, have developed somewhat similar ways of living. In termites we have the differentiation into soldiers and workers, and we have the sexual forms, males and females (see page 133).

The latter, however, pair for life; so, instead of the widowed queen that we have in the ant nest, we find in the termites a king and a queen. Their method of establishing the colony is essentially the same. There are flights when the air is filled with flying white ants, their wings dropping off much more easily than do those of the true ants.

I remember one occasion in the Solomon Islands when such a flight occurred while we were at dinner, and we hastily withdrew from the vicinity of the lights in order to keep our soup from being entirely wings. These, however, are not mating flights, as in the ants, but are distributional flights. Pairs go out, find a suitable place, and commence housekeeping together.

Like the ants, termites build various forms of houses, mounds, and tree nests, but often live in the heart of the tree itself. Their food consists almost entirely

(Inset, natural size)

AGAINST THE HUNLIKE HORDES OF ARMY ANTS NO LIVING THING CAN STAND

Even men flee as the mighty column writhes through the jungle, wiping out all insect and animal life in its path. Like generals, colonels, and captains at intervals in this line of destroyers *(Eciton hamatum)* march the biggest ants with such long, sharp-pointed hooks for jaws that they have to hold their heads up. With the army come camp followers—guests and parasites superficially resembling ants. Just this side of the twig that serves as a bridge is a beetle. Nearer, in line with the head of the caterpillar, which has been bitten and stung to death, creeps a masquerading wasp. The hovering fly is believed to lay eggs and larvae on the heads of ants, the grubs then killing the hosts (see page 132).

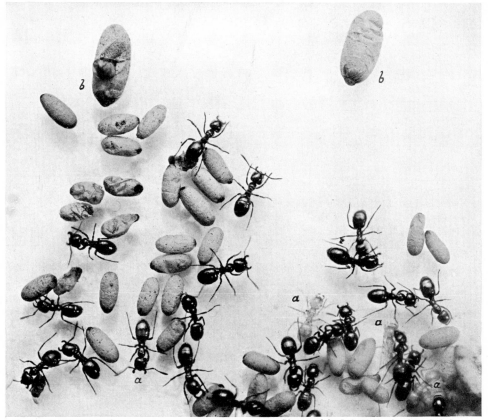

Courtesy Dr. W. M. Wheeler   Photograph by J. G. Hubbard and Dr. O. S. Strong

EXCITED ANTS DASH ABOUT AT A COMING-OUT PARTY

A new generation is making its début. Pale, callow workers, (a) have just emerged. In the two large cocoons (b) are future queens. The smaller casings will yield workers. These common ants of the Northern States, *Lasius (Acanthomyops) claviger,* keep herds of plant lice (see illustration, page 143).

of wood, which they chew up and swallow, but some of them raise fungus, reminding one of the fungus-growing ants.

With one or two exceptions, they are denizens of the dark. Exposure to heat causes the death of most species immediately.

They are much more injurious than ants. In certain tropical countries the termites' habit of destroying books makes it difficult to maintain libraries. Even as far north as Washington, D. C., it has been necessary to replace floors in the National Museum and other public buildings on account of the depredations these insects have committed.

Ants, like man, live in complicated societies. They recognize fellow citizens only by their odor, and any that do not smell the same are enemies.

Ants have an intense patriotism, evinced

by their willingness to fight and die for the home nest; and a touching devotion to their mother and to the babies in the nest. They are, for the most part, hard workers, and each individual does its utmost to contribute to the general welfare. They build complicated homes, and they show a wise providence in the storage and preservation of food.

The joker may say, also, that the ant has attained complete perfection in one field: the women do all the work.

On the other hand, there are among ants morons, paupers, and other parasites; thieves, ingrates, murderers, and kidnappers.

So, in reply to a question which has been asked me in all seriousness:

"Which is the more intelligent, man or the ant?" I feel inclined to reply:

"It depends on the man—and the ant!"

CHAPTER V

Living Casks of Honey

By JENNIE E. HARRIS

EACH year thousands of people visit the Garden of the Gods, in Colorado. They stand in awe before fiery-red pinnacles etched against blue sky. They marvel at those fantastic rock formations—the gods of mythology, with their human shapes, some of their hats, most of their spears, and a few of their cathedral spires, towering about them in red sandstone; and they are unaware, these interested sight-seers, of an ancient, dramatic *"civilization"* living under their feet.

Yet here, in the sandstone ridges, dwell creatures who might themselves have stepped from living myths—creatures with yellow heads and large, inflated, translucent bodies—who are, perhaps, the most self-sacrificing beings known.

In fairy tales boys and girls are fattened by witches, so that they may later be eaten with gusto. In this race, dwelling in darkness in the Garden of the Gods, children are fed enormously, so that a few may become overcapacious and hang in underground cellars for months, for years, as living casks of honey.

This would be terrifying were these creatures human. Instead, they are honey ants.

Honey ants are unhuman and unlike any other insect in their translation of themselves into honeypots.

They gather a honey not unlike that of bees and store it in round, thin casks that let the beautiful amber of honey shine through. But the casks possess living trunks, living heads, living legs. They hang by living claws to the cellar roof, and open a living spigot when an imbiber comes to drink (see illustrations, pages 140 and 141). For this, children are fed to enormous size and chambered in eternal darkness.

Here and there, across the tufts of grama grass and wild sunflower heads, gleam little mounds of red sandstone and bright-colored quartz—craters cut into rock. The red, loose stones roll out on all sides to a diameter of about thirty inches, with each mound rising to three or four inches, pierced by a large central entrance hole.

Outside, all looks simple; but inside, a descending shaft runs vertically for a while before carrying off sharply to a long gallery and other shafts, forming galleries under galleries, all running in the same direction. Then, seldom far from the surface, usually up or down a few steps from a main gallery, single or in suites, are the wine cellars, the honey chambers, the forever-homes of the swollen members of the race.

It would take a Gustave Doré to portray adequately the drama of honey ants.

The honey chambers where they hang are virtually death chambers, except that life flows from them freely. The severed casks of honey in the burial grounds form a nightmare thing, cask rolled beside cask. But beauty exists in the ants' refusal to touch a honey cask after its owner has died. The little crammed honeypots stand idle and untouched, once they are rolled into the cemeteries.

VISITING THE ANTS' HOME

Be an Alice in Wonderland in such a home, if you will. Come down that wide central stair, having ducked into the rabbit hole, passed sentinels at the gate, and given the essential salute. All is dusky dim; only that glimmering round of daylight above. You turn left down a long, narrow passage, which leads into deeper and deeper darkness; but the floor glints up with a firm polish—the floor deliberately made smooth, not merely worn smooth by the passing of innumerable feet. And the walls are smooth and straight, a sort of guide in the dark.

Drawing by Murayama, after H. C. McCook

THE PASSWORD GIVEN, A HONEY CASK OPENS THE FAUCET

Hungry workers flock around their balloonlike sister and swallow the sweet liquid regurgitated from her huge community stomach. By this unique storage system the honey ants *(Myrmecocystus hortideorum)* of Colorado's Garden of the Gods tide over the season when food is scarce (see illustration, opposite page).

Little feet rustle by—ants laden with earth, excavating a new room far at the end of the passage. All that mound above was formed by similar excavations; each pebble, each shining bit of quartz, was carried along galleries up the main stairs and out.

"Um-m-m!" An ant licks her mandibles, giving off a vague sweet scent. Honey! Somewhere near is a honey cellar. The ant has paused in working to take a good stiff drink. A shaft descends darkly to the left; cautiously down, down, to a great vaulted, globe-lighted room.

The vaulted roof is clustered with enormous hanging lamps. No, not lamps; pale amber spheres, hanging about midway into the room, occupying half the cellar space. The globes glow with the light that lives in honey; their pale-gold color is the richness of honey; that scent rising from them is the warm flavor of honey. Each globe is a living jewel, the distended body of a living ant, filled almost to bursting with limpid honey, clutched to the roof by its claws.

They crowd the arched ceiling; stir restlessly; twist their yellow heads, squirm their shoulders, but do not loosen hold. Below them the clean walls slope to the level floor, which is swept, polished, made smooth. But the roof is gritty, purposely left rough, for the claws to maintain perch.

The roof arches half again the height of the walls; a cellar made deliberately for honey casks, to allow free passage beneath, space for keeping the honey casks clean and the cellar free from mold.

SPIGOT MOUTHS OF LIVING HONEYPOTS

There are little soft sounds, as the great globes stir, shift an arm or foot, sway a little nearer to a neighbor. "Careful! Don't dare lean. You might break me!" And one turns a pointed yellow head toward another's. The globes are not all clear amber. Queer dark planes streak them. Their translucent part is inner skin stretched to balloon proportions, pushing apart the dark planes of the outer body, forming is-

Drawing by Murayama, after H. C. McCook

HONEY-FILLED "REPLETES" MAY CLING TO THE CEILING FOR THEIR LIFETIME

Equipped with commodious, elastic crops, the ants that are to become honey casks crawl to the vaulted roof of the storage cellar, get a good grip, and let the workers fill them almost to bursting with the sweet discharge from oak galls or living aphids (see text, page 146). Then they function as living food reservoirs, yielding drops to hungry workers on demand.

lands on a globe map of strange world seas.

Suddenly an ant enters to drink. She looks like these hanging ants, yellow-headed, yellow-waisted, but she wears no inflated balloon. Her antennae lift inquisitively. Already the foretaste of honey is in her mouth. She stands almost erect, climbs to the hanging ant, leans to its little closed mouth. "Open, please." Obediently its mouth opens. Up comes a clear drop of honey, pushed up by some inner movement, to hang a moment, glistening, on the cask's lower mandible, before dropping into the waiting ant's mouth.

She takes one, two, even three, drops. "Thank you; you may close." She climbs down, and the little spigot mouth closes. Before the ant leaves she daintily wipes her mouth against the back of her hand, smooths down her back hair, then trots off, groomed, well fed.

Another ant enters; another, another. Each climbs to a chosen sphere; says, "Open, please," with that leaning of mouth

to mouth, and at once the mouth opens and up comes the honey drop.

But suppose they enter to deposit honey rather than receive it. What then? Painfully, slowly this time, because so laden they are almost honey casks themselves, the ants climb to the hanging casks, place mouth to mouth. "Open, please," and, with antennae held back out of the way, let drops of honey form on their mandibles to enter the obedient casks.

This new honey is almost white in its freshness. As long as drops are there to fall in, the little spigot mouth holds open. Then the emptied ant, relieved, turns away; and the globe, clinging to the roof, gleams larger, more bulbous still, with the added contents. It scarcely dares draw a full breath, move an arm, or shift a leg for fear this new weight and fullness will make it burst or fall.

Poor little doomed creatures! What determined such a fate? When young, they resembled other ants. They had the same

Photograph by Will F. Taylor

HOW MANY STORIES IN THIS TERMITE SKYSCRAPER?

The photographer made it twenty-two, but the number varies, depending on the view. Not all "white ants" are wreckers of houses (see page 133). These in Angola, Africa, are master masons, working in clay, which becomes so hard that the youngster could break it only with an ax. In other regions their architecture runs to spires, monoliths, or huge mounds (see illustration, page 145).

They have had their play of light all day, while the red mounds of the ants stayed quiet, with gates closed. Seemingly all inside were asleep; yet few ants slept, being busy, most of them, with underground tasks.

Now ants push out of that round tubular hole so fast they cover the mound. If this were daylight, no red rock would shine. Yellow ants are everywhere, by hundreds, by thousands.

A NIGHT SORTIE IN
QUEST OF HONEY

A ring of sentinels begins pacing the outer edges of the mound. Others guard the gate, their heads thrusting up, like soldiers with bayonets. Still others move about the narrow platform surrounding the gate, while one ant, then twenty, then a whole column of ants, move off over the ridge, preparing for a march. In the vales between the ridges, far, far away, low scrub oaks,

two stomachs—one private, the other for communal use. Much that entered their mouths they never tasted, for it passed at once to the communal crop, to be fed later to the queen (whose duties are like those of a queen bee); to males (resembling drones in a hive); to workers, or to baby ants. But some showed an enormous capacity for food. How they begged, their pale mouths open all the time! Now these are honey casks.

Late dusk in the Garden of the Gods. The sandstone gods are cold and dark.

in the light of the moon, thrust up their dark thick leaves. The ants know these dwarf oaks.

They move through straggly bunches of grass on a familiar path, with scant deviation, reaching the oak copse in fifteen minutes. Moonlight pierces the leaves sharply, revealing the ants straddling up the stems, clambering out over leaves, searching endlessly, sometimes fruitlessly, for new oak galls, with their tiny flashes of shining sweet.

A curious insect makes an oak gall and

stimulates that flow of oak dew. The tiny creature develops in an inner cell in the gall. When he is extremely young, the gall he lies in is bright, almost scarlet or vivid blue. When he has crawled outside his nursery and lies in the outer sphere, the gall is bright green, soft, about the size of a pea, and bits of sweet stand up about it in tiny flashing dew.

Old red galls, with holes where gallflies have escaped, the ants pass by; but the new pale-green galls, glistening with honeydew, they sniff at, lap the honeydew with delight; then move off to other fresh galls. But after a while they come back to the first gall; after another period, come back again, for new galls exude usually three series of drops in a single night.

The ants started forth at dusk. From midnight till daylight they straggle home. Some are so loaded they can scarcely wabble; others only a little filled; still others empty and unsuccessful.

Photograph by Paul Griswold Howes

AN ANT CARRIES ITS "COWS" TO PASTURE

In the herder's jaws and protruding above its head is one of the tiny plant lice, or aphids, which the ants "milk" of their honeydew and move from one plant to another (see text, page 120). On the stalk feeds the rest of the teeming drove. The caretaker in this greatly enlarged photograph is a carpenter ant, often found in the beams of houses (see pages 120, 135).

All night, while they were away, sentinels paced the outer walks. Hungry now, surely; yet surprisingly few sentinels request honey from the filled ants. They only challenge them and cross antennae with antennae in salute. Inside, workers crowd the entrance stairs, begging, relieving the bearers of weighty drops. Honeydew passes from mouth to mouth.

Some workers, amazingly huge, hitch themselves sidewise to move at all; yet they come up for more and more, clowns skirted with enormous balloons. And the honeygatherers give to them willingly, knowing here are sisters fast turning into honey casks of their own sweet will.

WILLING SACRIFICES AS HONEY VATS

Babies, too, some of them, keep their little mouths open. Their communal crops, soft and elastic, easily become habitually swollen. Then the surplus honeydew, if any remains, is carried to the dark cellars and dumped into the living honey casks.

When a bee flounders home from pillaging a fresh flower, she pours the bead of nectar into an unfilled comb, where it is fanned, cooled, its water evaporated, and stored as honey in a pale waxen cell. But honey ants, laden with a similar beneficial dew, have no power to breathe out wax from their own small bodies; cannot knead wax into cells. So they use certain members of their family as honey vats.

For months, years, their whole remaining lives, honey casks cling to the vaulted roof of the dark cellar, their bodies dilated to eight or ten times normal size, all that weight of honey suspended by the frailty of tiny claws. Thirty or more honey casks, usually, to a honey cellar; about ten honey cellars to a sizable ant home.

The little swollen things move a little, but seem to lose desire for motion. Once in a great while, one becomes sufficiently empty to be able to unhook itself from the roof, climb down, and even look out the cellar door. In the main they stay filled. If they ever feed themselves, they must open a little inner spigot to let a drop of honey pass into their personal stomach. But they are frugal in the extreme; or else, hanging there so long, so still, they seldom require food. No noticeable portion of the honey they carry is ever self-consumed. In the swelling, the small stomach is pushed far down to the base of the bubble, so that it is doubtful if a honey cask ever eats or drinks.

The power of work has been taken from them. A few clean themselves, gripping the roof by their hind legs, washing with their middle legs or arms. But a regular delegation of ants comes in to keep them clean, sweep the floor, scrub the walls, and see that the globes stay dry and sweet and sanitary.

The seasons speed; years go by. The only knowledge of time to these little swollen creatures must be that oak galls are fresh outside, for they are given honey today. Or oak galls are old, winter is on them; they must yield honey now.

WHEN DEATH COMES TO A HONEY CASK

Even honey casks cannot live forever. A slender arm becomes paralyzed through that long, tight clutching to the gritty roof.

It loses hold; the whole cask falls and strikes that hard, strange floor. It lies with its body projected up by that great ball of itself, its feet and arms waving, its head nodding from side to side. But efforts do no good. It is powerless to rise.

If it falls on something large, it may be able to assist itself back to the roof by scant inches; but usually there it lies. Ants coming in to clean or drink could easily hoist the honey cask until it could clutch the roof once more. It is in the way; ants must go around it; but they seem not to notice those frantically waving arms, that desperately bobbing head, though the honey cask would grasp gladly, even at a straw. It may lie there for two or three months and be solicitously cleaned and caressed. Its new position is a relief to strained muscles, perhaps, though decidedly uncomfortable. Finally something in its plight shortens its life.

Or, losing hold, falling, the thin cask breaks and the honey spills. There lies Humpty Dumpty, sure enough, feeling all its contents trickle out. Not all the king's horses can restore that honey to the cask. Ants hear the crash, sniff spilled honey, rush in, lap up the oozing sweet in a frenzy of delight. But they disgorge most of the honey into the hanging casks, or rush out with filled crops to feed others.

Sometimes a broken cask will grow together, mending itself, and be hoisted to the roof and filled as before.

At last, after years of holding honey, a honey cask dies. It still hangs to the roof for a day or more, the ants unaware of its death. They clean this cask and others; drink from other casks. Then one climbs to the little closed mouth. "Open, please!" It does not open. What does this mean? Disobedience, unwillingness, in a community where such things are unknown?

Several in turn climb to the tight little mouth. "Open, please!" It never opens; it stays pressed tight. Yet the honey crop is full; its body is a bright amber sphere. They can see the rich honey inside. But at last they realize. The little honey cask is dead.

It takes several ants to handle the corpse. First, the cask part must be severed from the rest of the body. The separation is

Photograph from Topical Press

A GOLFER'S NIGHTMARE IS THE "ANT HILL" COURSE IN CENTRAL AFRICA

Natural bunkers as big as houses rise on every hand. They are termite nests—120 of them— guarding the fairway like mountains in miniature. Some are even used as tees, although it takes considerable climbing ability to get to the top. The man at the right, with two black caddies near him, has sliced into one of the insect-erected hazards. American greenskeepers, bothered by the castings and sand cones of common ants (see page 126), may consider such trials as these and take heart.

easy—just a biting through that one narrow connection. Then the cask is rolled through long, dim galleries to the burial ground these ants possess. The claws are unhooked gently from the roof, and the top part of the body is lifted down and carried through the same winding passages in a silent little procession to the same cemetery.

CASKS OF THE DEAD NEVER DESECRATED

And in that gloom of the dead, under the Garden of the Gods, strange gods keep watch. These gods are round, silent casks of honey. Life still lives in them, sustenance is there, food for numerous babies, workers, males, queens. The honey is still sweet and pure. But the ants never desecrate the cask of the dead. It is as if they realize it belongs no more to themselves, but to the darkness and the stillness. In that quiet cemetery, several spheres lie side by side, glowing more and more golden as the honey within them mellows with age.

This honey is almost a pure solution of grape sugar, but it never crystallizes. Its flavor is slightly aromatic, extremely sweet. The honey is limpid, like bees' honey before thickened in the hive. It can be made to evaporate to a gummy mass, but when left in the open it absorbs moisture from the air and becomes liquid honey again.

We owe much that we know about honey ants to Dr. Henry C. McCook. He and his men spent days with chisel and hammer opening a single home, coming carefully upon the used galleries and occupied rooms, taking measurements, making sketches and plaster casts. At one time he found a queen in her room, more than 28 inches below the surface of the hill, over 72 inches from the central stair. She may have dwelt in that room habitually, or else her attendants, frightened at the strange chiseling, had carried her through hall after hall, as the sounds came nearer, till they reached this far-off circular chamber, where naked babies and some of the workers and honey-bearers had also gathered in their fear.

The gallery leading to this chamber went on sloping for ten inches, ending in a bay-room and a small upcurving hall, the lowest room in the home, almost seven feet out from the main stair, more than three feet below gate level. What depth of architecture for those tiny diggers!

At Dr. McCook's excavating, ants rushed into the cellars, helped the casks down from the roofs, pushed and tugged them to safe places, solicitous about that enormous storage of honey. A large worker would take a portion of that tightly stretched skin into her mandibles and tug and tug, backing out from the cellar into the unbroken hall, and perhaps a small worker stood on the globe and pushed vehemently, though surely she was doing little more than stealing a ride.

Honey ants that were kept in a large glass bottle died in less than three minutes, killed by the sun. Perhaps they are necessarily nocturnal, never daring to venture into daylight. They like sugar, these honey-lovers; but, surprisingly enough, care little for bee honey. At present, honey ants are found in Colorado, New Mexico, and Old Mexico.

Mexicans press out honey casks as one would grapes, and ferment the honey into an alcoholic drink. The swollen casks are really not unlike grapes, their bodies being enlarged from tiny beads to full grape size, to hang like grapes in clusters to the cellar roof.

Commercializing such honey scarcely seems possible. A thousand honey casks filled to the limit would yield barely a pound of honey.

Except for that strange honey-cask custom of theirs, honey ants are rather like other ants. The queen is surrounded by attendants, who groom, caress, and feed her. They form a circle about her as she lays her eggs, then rush these carefully to the incubating rooms, to lick them and keep them warm. Other nurses care for the little things who hatch forth, touching mouth to mouth in feeding. To bathe a baby, a nurse takes it carefully into her arms, turns it slowly while passing her mouth over it. Nurses handle the infants frequently, making sure they are warm and well.

The babies are helped in shaping the cradles they spin; are watched over while they sleep in these, to awake as ants and to be cleaned, bathed, and fed until large enough to take care of smaller babies. It is not known what determines which babies shall be princesses (who are bright yellow), which drones (also bright), which workers (pale yellow); but it seems that any worker honey ants who make up their minds can become honey casks.

HONEY ANTS MILK APHID "COWS"

One intelligent custom of honey ants is shared by other ants. They milk aphids for some of their honeydew.

When fresh wild roses scent the Garden of the Gods, honey ants trail toward these instead of toward oak galls. Aphids, those green, translucent-legged creatures who thrust their sucking beaks into roses and thrive on that inner rose dew, draw forth more sweet than they need, the surplus passing out of their backs.

Ants have found this out. Usually among several aphids lies a clever ant. She crawls behind the aphid, gently strokes her sides with first one antenna, then the other, a sort of seesaw motion much like our milking a cow, to which the aphid gratefully submits. And either the aphid's pleasure or else the quiet massaging itself causes honeydew to appear faster and faster on the aphid's rear. The ant laps the honeydew with delight and deposits it in her little inner bucket.

The aphid's body, filled with rose dew, slumps as the ant's body swells. The little green cow even lifts her back to make the milking easy and grazes farther along the rose for more honeydew for the next milker who comes along. Several ants in turn may milk the same aphid. But once in a while a stubborn aphid kicks out her leg and spurts honeydew far beyond reach of an ant's mouth; whereupon the ant probably moves to a more docile cow.

They gain about thirty drops from the same aphid in an hour, go home to empty their little buckets, and then return for further milking. The ants nurse the aphid's young as carefully as their own, and in the spring lead them out to known pastures.

CHAPTER VI

Strange Habits of Familiar Moths and Butterflies

By WILLIAM JOSEPH SHOWALTER

With Natural Color Illustrations by National Geographic Society Staff Photographers

THE order of insects made up of the butterflies and moths is one of the most fascinating of all the orders of living creatures. Its members range in size from the magnificent Swallow-tail butterflies and Cecropia moths, with wing-spreads of many inches, to the tiny leaf-mining Nepticula, measuring less than an eighth of an inch from tip to tip; in beauty, from the resplendent Peacock butterflies and Luna moths to the drab clothes-moth; in larval form, from the hairy, woolly bears and naked hickory horn devils to the grublike wood borers; in feeding habit, from the nectar-sipping Fritillaries to the aphid-eating Harvesters; in habitat, from the highest mountains and the coldest polar areas to the lowest plains and the hottest equatorial regions; and in relationship to man, from the beneficent silk-worm to the destructive cutworm and the tree-destroying Gypsy moth.

About 9,500 species of butterflies and moths are to be found in North America. Of these only 650 are butterflies.

BUTTERFLIES SERVE BEAUTY; SOME MOTHS WREAK HAVOC

Only a few species of butterflies have become pests, most of them being as harmless as they are beautiful. They are a very compact, closely knit group of insects, showing their comparatively recent origin.

On the other hand, the moths disclose a remarkable diversity of appearance, habit, and habitat. Large groups of them exact a tremendous toll of field, orchard, garden, and lawn, and levy heavy tribute upon the Nation's shade and ornamental trees.

In the orchard their caterpillars attack alike blossom, foliage, fruit, wood, and root. In the garden they prey alike upon stalk and vegetable. In the field tender shoot, growing plant, and mature grain suffer at their hands. Some invade flour mills and clothes closets, others quarter themselves in ant nests and beehives. But of the thousands of species not more than 100 are pests.

A few aberrant species have wingless females and others have clear wings, linking them closely in appearance with the bees (see page 178, figures 3 and 5) and the wasps. So thoroughly do some of the latter imitate the bees and the wasps, both in habits and in appearance, that man and bird alike usually give them that wide berth which is accorded the stinging tribe.

There are two small families, known as the Jugate moths, which form the "missing link" between the primitive insects and the full-panoplied moths and butterflies.

IN WHAT PARTICULARS MOTHS AND BUTTERFLIES DIFFER

The primitive insects had two pairs of wings equal in size and function. As they have come down through the geological ages, some of them, like the bees and wasps, have thrown the flight functions on the fore pair of wings, and others, like the locusts, crickets, and beetles, have turned the task of flight over mainly to the hind pair. A third group, the Diptera, make no use whatever of their hind pair of wings; so Nature took these away entirely. The Jugate moths carry a striking reminiscence of this change. Like the caddis flies, their two pairs of wings are tied together with a jugum.

There are many obvious differences between moths and butterflies.

BUTTERFLY AND MOTH EGGS ARE OFTEN OF STRIKING DESIGN

The eggs of butterflies are laid usually upon leaves. In most species the shells are beautiful when examined through a magnifying glass. The extreme summit is always a little rosette of the most exquisite delicacy, and the definite patterns of some eggs are such that we seem to be peering through the circular rose window of a microscopic Gothic cathedral (see text, page 159).

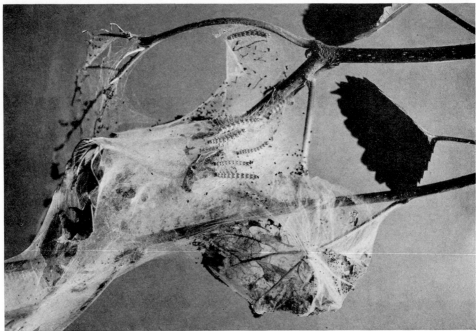

Photographs courtesy U. S. Department of Agriculture

FALL WEB-WORMS ON A MULBERRY BRANCH

The tent caterpillars are social creatures, building their houses on the community plan. The moth of the Fall Web-worm is shown in figure 17 on page 183.

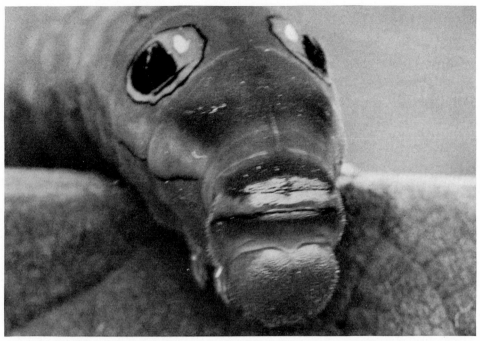

Photograph by David Fairchild

HOW A CATERPILLAR STRIKES TERROR TO A FOE

The fearsome mien of this larva of a common Swallow-tail Butterfly (greatly magnified) is only camouflage. The real head of the insect is the small semicircular segment at the bottom of the picture. The huge "eyes" are only make-believe (see text, page 158).

Photograph by Graham Fairchild

A JAVA COUSIN OF "SAMIA CECROPIA"

The antennae of moths and butterflies are believed to be the aerials through which they receive the calls of their distant mates. The photograph is greatly magnified.

THE CATERPILLAR OF THE HOG SPHINX MOTH (SEE PAGE 180, FIGURE 8)
FEEDING ON THE GRAPE

Photographs courtesy U. S. Department of Agriculture

A TOMATO CATERPILLAR VICTIM OF PARASITISM

One of the fantastic tricks in Nature encountered in the insect world is polyembryony, wherein a single egg of a parasite may produce as many as 300 larvae of the same sex. The scores of cocoons on this caterpillar's body are the offspring of such a prolific egg (see text, pages 159, 161).

THE SADDLE-BACK CATERPILLAR OF THE SOUTH IS ESPECIALLY FOND OF GREEN
CORN BLADES

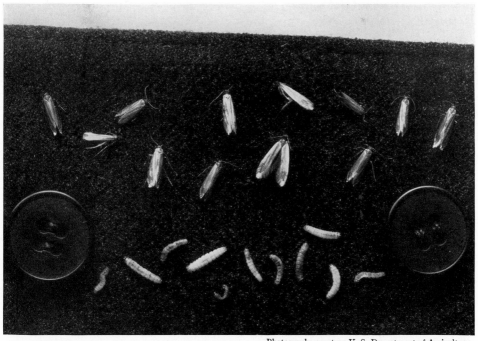

Photographs courtesy U. S. Department of Agriculture

READY TO WREAK HAVOC: WEBBING CLOTHES-MOTHS AND THEIR LARVAE

The moth itself is perfectly harmless, but the larvae that hatch from its eggs spin themselves little transparent tubes or tunnels of silk wherever they go. They feed upon the wool fabric and also use fragments of it in making their pupal cases. These larvae will riddle this coat.

Photograph from George Whittaker

AROUND, AND AROUND, AND AROUND MARCH THE PINE PROCESSIONARY CATERPILLARS

So stupid that they cannot find their way home without their guiding life line, and yet so alert to barometric changes that they make excellent prognosticators of inclement weather, these European cousins of the species that build their tents in our apple trees (see illustration, page 148) are one of the strangest contradictions in the insect world (see text, page 163).

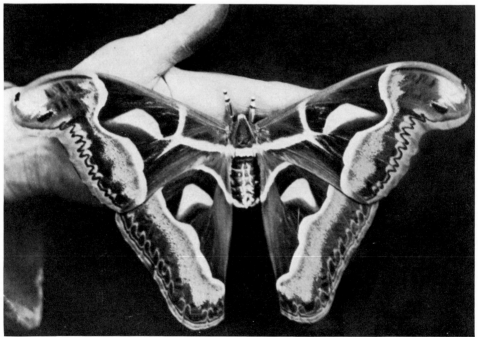

Photograph from Acme

AN ATLAS MOTH FROM THE LONDON ZOOLOGICAL GARDENS

With a wing-spread of ten inches the Atlas Moth is one of the largest of the Lepidopters. The smallest species of the order has a wing-spread of less than one-eighth of an inch.

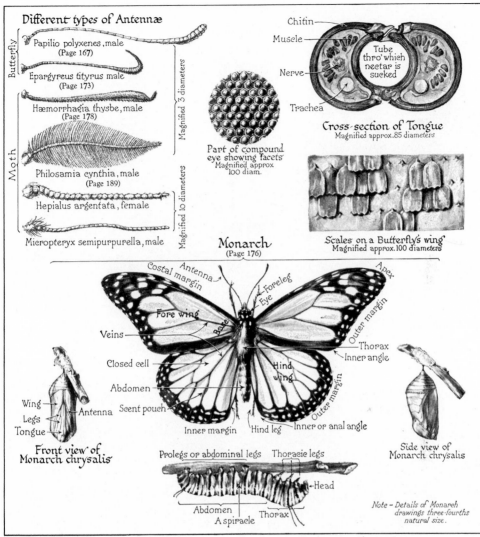

Different types of Antennæ

Butterfly

Papilio polyxenes, male
(Page 167)

Epargyreus tityrus, male
(Page 173)

Moth

Hæmorrhagia thysbe, male
(Page 178)

Magnified 3 diameters

Philosamia cynthia, male
(Page 189)

Hepialus argentata, female

Magnified 10 diameters

Micropteryx semipurpurella, male

Part of compound
eye showing facets
Magnified approx
100 diam.

Chitin

Muscle

Nerve

Trachea

Tube
thro' which
nectar is
sucked

Cross-section of Tongue
Magnified approx. 85 diameters

Monarch
(Page 176)

Scales on a Butterfly's wing
Magnified approx. 100 diameters

Costal margin
Antenna
Foreleg
Eye
Apex

Fore wing

Veins

Closed cell

Abdomen

Wing
Legs
Tongue

Antenna

Scent pouch

Base

Hind
wing

Outer margin

Thorax
Inner angle

Outer margin

Front view of
Monarch chrysalis

Inner margin

Hind leg

Inner or anal angle

Side view of
Monarch chrysalis

Prolegs or abdominal legs   Thoracic legs

Head

Abdomen   Thorax
A spiracle

Note – Details of Monarch
drawings three-fourths
natural size.

© National Geographic Society   Drawing by Hashime Murayama

THE ANATOMY OF A BUTTERFLY AND ITS CATERPILLAR

The details at the left in the upper half of the illustration show the different types of
antennae occurring among butterflies and moths. The greatly magnified section of a Monarch
butterfly's wing (right center) shows how the scales (see also lower portion of plate on page
160) are attached to the wing surface by a sort of stem to a socket. The nodules are the
sockets from which scales have been brushed away.

The butterflies wear knobs on the ends
of their antennae, while the moths with
such few exceptions that the average am-
ateur will never encounter one, lack these
knobs or possess plumed antennae (see
illustration above).

The moths make cocoons of silk, enter
the ground, or make cells in wood for their
nymphal naps, while the butterflies are
satisfied with a sort of hardened integu-

ment, or chrysalis, the pupae being otherwise unprotected.

Most of the butterflies are slender-bodied,
while most of the moths are plump.

The butterflies are day flyers, while most
of the moths prefer to take wing after the
sun has passed below the horizon.

But both moths and butterflies employ
marvelously the arts of camouflage to de-
ceive their enemies.

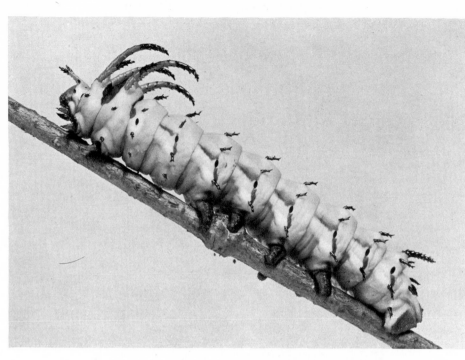

Photographs courtesy U. S. Department of Agriculture

THE HICKORY HORN DEVIL, A MATURE CATERPILLAR OF
THE ROYAL WALNUT-MOTH

The striking difference between the ugly larva and the beautiful moth is nowhere better illustrated than by contrasting this picture with figure 4 on page 185.

A CATERPILLAR OF THE ROYAL WALNUT-MOTH IN ITS
EARLY YOUTH

Contrast this illustration with that of the Hickory Horn Devil (to the right). Many caterpillars undergo similar remarkable changes on their journey from the egg to the pupal case (see page 160).

A MONARCH BUTTERFLY (SEE PAGE 176, FIGURE 12)
SIPPING SWEETS FROM A THISTLE BLOSSOM

The coiled pumping tongues of butterflies and moths are ideally fitted
for draining the nectar cups of the flowers. Moths, being, as a rule, more
hairy than butterflies, are better pollen carriers.

A LUNA MOTH WHILE AT REST (SEE, ALSO, PAGE 187,
FIGURE 4)

In the color pages accompanying this article the butterflies and moths
are shown as in flight, but this photograph reveals a Luna Moth alight,
with forewings folded over rear wings, blending into its surroundings.

Photograph courtesy U. S. Department of Agriculture

LARVAE AND PUPA (ENLARGED ONE-HALF) OF THE CODLING-
MOTH, WHICH ATTACKS VARIOUS FRUITS

The eggs are laid on the fruit and the larvae seek a convenient place
to enter—usually at the calyx cup, the stem cavity, or an injured spot.
After the fruit drops to the ground the larvae emerge and make their
cocoons as shown here.

Some of them in the caterpillar stage dress up in stinging hairs that make them unattractive to birds; others possess sharp, acrid flavors that are not pleasing to a bird's palate. Many are ornamented to resemble the leaves among which they live, striped to simulate the pine needles on which they feed or the grass on which they dwell, or colored to match the ground on which they crawl, many of them being unbelievably hard to see in their accustomed surroundings.

There are all kinds of moth and butterfly foes—birds that take the adult on the wing or in repose or eat the caterpillars; parasites that attack both the eggs and the caterpillars, and scores of other creatures which consider them fair prey.

Camouflage is often practiced in a peculiar way. For example, our colorful friend, the Viceroy (see page 162, figure 7), copies the Monarch (see page 176, figure 12) to perfection. Now, the Monarch happens to be a very distasteful creature to a bird because of its acrid blood; but a Viceroy makes a delightful titbit. The bird, because of wider experience with the Monarch, usually lets the similarly colored Viceroy severely alone.

This theory was tested on a monkey, who was given a Monarch to eat; he threw it aside in disgust. Next he was given a Viceroy, and as promptly he cast it aside. Then another Viceroy was offered, this time with the wings pulled off. It was eaten with evident relish.

Many other bird-relished species follow the practice of the Viceroy and imitate acrid varieties, thereby obtaining protection.

GAY COLORS DAZZLE THE PURSUER

Even the gay colorings of our gaudiest butterflies and moths are now thought by leading authorities to be protective, those who hold to this belief asserting that a woodpecker often loses a meal because disappearing brilliancy causes him to lose track of his quarry. As he chases a showy butterfly, his eye is full of the bright color, but when the insect alights it folds its wings above its back and, presto, the bright color disappears! Instead, it shows the drab hue of the underwing, harmonizing with its surroundings.

With the folding of its wings the insect becomes a part of its background and the thwarted woodpecker flies away, doubtless wondering how that bit of bright color escaped his hungry eye. One of the Orange Sulphurs of the Pikes Peak meadows, related to those shown on page 166, is green underneath. A brilliant flash of color while flying, it seems to vanish when it alights in the grass and closes its wings.

In the Kallima, or Dead-leaf Butterfly, this scheme is strikingly carried out. The underwing surface bears a remarkable resemblance to a leaf. It even has a hindwing projection which looks like the stem of a leaf, and a mark running across the wing appears to be a midrib. Perched on a twig, with closed wings, it perfectly simulates a dead leaf, but with outspread wings it is brilliant bait for a bird (see illustration, page 191).

Photograph courtesy U. S. Department of Agriculture

CATERPILLARS OF THE HICKORY HALISIDOTA ON APPLE TWIGS AND LEAVES

The moth of this caterpillar is a cousin of the ones shown in figures 6 and 7 on page 183. The stinging hairs of many caterpillars such as these are an effective means of defense against a large group of enemies.

In the case of the moths, which rest with folded wings instead of upright ones, as do the butterflies (see illustrations, page 155 and page 187), the brilliant color is on the rear wing, which is covered up by the somber forewing when the insect is at rest.

Studies of grasshoppers, locusts, and other winged insects show how this idea of disappearing brilliant colors runs through many families of the entire winged clan.

In collecting moths, one discovers that those which live among the birches usually have a coloration approximating the tones of birch bark, while those which are found usually on the trunks of maple trees show color schemes that make their visibility low. Figures 1 and 2 on page 182 show the contrast between the two species, which are closely related.

But the beelike moths carry the art of camouflage even further than mere passive color protection. If captured or disturbed, they act exactly like the bees they simulate, give off the familiar bee odor, and even pretend to sting, in spite of the fact that they have no stinging apparatus.

MAKING MONSTERS OF THEMSELVES TO WIN PROTECTION

The caterpillars employ many of the arts of camouflage used by the adult butterflies and moths. The measuring-worms,

Photograph by Edwin L. Wisherd

AN AILANTHUS SILK-MOTH LEAVING ITS COCOON

The cocoon of this specimen was found on a tree in the back yard of a downtown Washington residence, and the moth emerged in the offices of the National Geographic Society, where it posed for its picture.

bly effective as it pushes out its curious scent organ, which looks like a forked tongue. Birds have been observed to retreat in alarm as they suddenly came upon one of these menacing-looking, though harmless, creatures.

The Puss Moth, *Cerura,* has a caterpillar with a similar fearsome aspect, and when disturbed it displays a kind of forked tail, within which are concealed long orange-colored extensile threads that can be thrust out and waved viciously. Many other harmless species wear ugly horns, and even intelligent people cannot be induced to touch them.

Most of the Swallow-tail butterflies' caterpillars exude foul odors when disturbed, and Professor Comstock has called them the polecats of the insect world.

Even in the cocoons of some moths and the chrysalis cases of some butterflies, protective devices are employed. The Southern Live-oak Moth has a cocoon that very closely resembles a live-oak terminal bud, especially as both twigs and cocoons are covered with small bits of lichen.

As a decoy to distract the attention of its enemy, the striking Banded Purple butterfly's caterpillar loosely fastens near its feeding place a small ball of leaf scraps closely resembling itself.

larvae of the Geometrid moths, simulate in color and general appearance the twigs on which they rest. Disturbed, they stand on their hind legs and look for all the world like small projecting shoots.

Many species of caterpillars protect themselves from their enemies by assuming a terrifying aspect. For example, the caterpillar of the Tiger Swallow-tail simulates a serpent (see illustration, page 149). The rings of the body just back of the head are swollen, and on top of this protuberance are two large circular marks suggesting eyes. When at rest the creature withdraws its real head and throws up the front part of its body, so that it resembles a snake's head—an impression made dou-

PARASITES CONVERT BUTTERFLY EGGS INTO FAMILY NURSERIES

The eggs of butterflies are laid usually upon leaves. In most species the architecture of the shells is beautiful when examined through a magnifying glass. "The extreme summit is always carved by a little rosette of the most exquisite delicacy, often requiring some of the higher powers of the microscope to discern, but arranged in such definite patterns that in looking at them we seem to be peering through the circular rose window of a miniature Gothic cathedral" (see page 148).

The chances of a butterfly's egg producing a live caterpillar are surprisingly small. Ants and spiders regard these eggs as a great delicacy, and a whole group of tiny insects of the fly and bee orders, almost too small to breathe, one would think, insert their eggs into those of the butterflies. Parasites are always on the job to convert the butterfly's eggs into a nursery for their own young.

Wide World Photograph

THE BEGINNING OF A SILK DRESS

Some silk-worms are feeding on mulberry leaves, others are climbing the brushwood of the spinning hut, and still others are fast asleep in their cocoons (see text, page 165).

In the case of the Viceroy and its cousins, the female butterfly lays her eggs one at a time and, unless in a hurry to be rid of the task, only one to a bush. She lays them on the tips of the leaves, as a rule. Her eggs are covered with little hairs to protect them.

But, with all the effort to conceal her eggs and to safeguard them, Madam Viceroy is not very successful, for a large majority are found to be parasitized.

Some butterflies and moths lay their eggs in rings around twigs and cover them up with a sort of varnish. The Brown-tail Moth covers hers with hairs from her own body, her tail having a bunch of these ready for application to the eggs as soon as laid.

When the caterpillars hatch out, most of them make it their first duty to eat the shells out of which they have just emerged. In the Viceroy the larva then begins to eat the leaf, leaving the midrib.

After having a hearty meal, it retires toward the end of the stripped midrib, digests its meal in the safety of its isolation, and then comes down for another feast. It makes a little packet from bits of midrib and other refuse and uses this as a sort of insect scarecrow, always keeping it at the point on the midrib where the edge of the uneaten portion of the leaf joins it.

Parasites are the bane of the caterpillars as well as of the eggs. All sorts of fly and

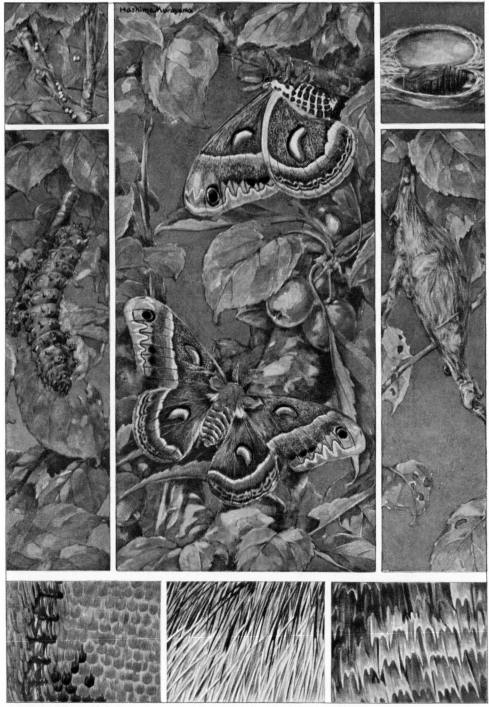

Upper Illustrations One-half Natural Size; Lower, Magnified 50 Diameters

FOUR SUCCESSIVE STAGES IN THE LIFE CYCLE OF A MOTH

Above is the Cecropia Moth, *Samia cecropia* L., a common Eastern species. Its eggs (upper left) are laid in the late spring or early summer. Upon emergence from the egg, the caterpillars are extremely small but soon outgrow their skin, which they shed. After the fourth molt the Cecropia (see panel below the eggs) spins a cocoon of silk (shown cut open at the upper right, and intact, below). From this it emerges as a full grown moth (see text, page 147). The bottom drawings show the appearance, under a microscope, of the "dust" on a butterfly's or moth's wings—actually a series of very fine scales and hairs. The drawing at the left shows the arrangement of the scales on the Gulf Fritillary Butterfly (see page 164, figure 4); the center shows the forked hairs occurring on the wings of many moths; at the right are the scales of the Cecropia around the eyelike spots on the upper wings.

bee order insects hover around watching for a chance to plant an egg on their bodies. A surprisingly large percentage of them must play unwilling host to the larvae of these foes. When the parasites' eggs hatch, their little grubs bore into the bodies of their hosts and find a fine food supply in the tissues. A single caterpillar may be unwilling host to a dozen parasites, and finally dies about the time the unwelcome guests are ready to pupate. Some parasites lay single eggs, from which as many as 300 larvae hatch (see illustration, page 150). They are all of one sex, being in reality a single individual subdivided by witchery more subtle than the art of the greatest magician of fairy story. Polyembryony (meaning many individuals from a single egg) is one of the most marvelous of all the recent discoveries in biology.

The caterpillars thrash their heads and tails about when the parasites come around, and some species, like some of the Sphinx moths, make clicking and squeaking noises.

The gamut which a caterpillar has to run to realize its ambition to reach the winged stage is shown by the researches of Slingerland and Crosby, who found that in some localities 90 per cent of the Tussock Moth caterpillars and chrysalids fell victims to parasites. Twenty different species of flies and hymenopters parasitized those studied.

But often a parasite is "hoist with his own petard," for 14 parasites were found preying on the Tussock Moth's parasites. And then these, in their turn, had parasites attacking them, reminding one of Dean Swift's famous bit of doggerel:

So naturalists observe a flea
Hath smaller fleas, that on him prey;
And these have smaller still to bite 'em,
And so proceed *ad infinitum*.

THE PSYCHE CATERPILLAR MAKES ITSELF A SUIT OF CLOTHES

Most caterpillars undergo four molts in reaching full growth, though some have been known to pass eight molts. Some change their color pattern after each molt, and most of them, preparing to molt, spin a silk web in which to entangle the legs of the old skin, so that it will remain anchored while they are escaping.

Some caterpillars roll up leaves and make themselves individual shelters. Some species occupy these shelters when not feeding, which therefore last during their full larval life; others feed upon the walls of their abode, building a new shelter when they "eat themselves out of house and home."

But there are others which make themselves suits of clothes.

Whoever has failed to read Fabre's story of the life habits of the Psyche Moth and its caterpillar's coat has missed one of the gems of entomological literature.

Commonly known as the bagworm, the Psyche caterpillar, on emerging from the egg, starts in to build a suit of clothes. Standing on its front legs and holding its tail upright, the naked creature spins a ring of silk, adding bits of wood, leaves, etc., thereto. It continues to spin, adding to the lower edge of the ring until the latter forms a sort of cone.

As the worm grows, it enlarges the bag much after the fashion that hornets enlarge their nests. When the coat gets too heavy, the worm lets it hang down, and henceforth the creature thus encumbered must crawl around on its front legs, encased in a hard, stiff, rough armor.

Finally the migratory instinct subsides and the bagworm settles down on the twig of a tree that will constitute the food of its successor. After fastening its wood-embroidered garment to the twig, the insect lines the former with heavy silk, rests awhile, casts its skin, and becomes a chrysalis.

Three weeks later the male chrysalis works himself down to the bottom of his bag, bursts the pupal skin asunder, emerges a full-fledged moth, and as soon as the glue that reinforces his wings is hardened he goes in quest of his mate.

And what a poor creature this mate is. Wingless and footless, she is doomed to die in the home she has built. She creeps down out of her chrysalis skin, welcomes her mate at the door of her house, backs into her chrysalis skin again, fills it partially with eggs, seals it up with what little is left of her body, and dies.

Most of us are familiar with the tent caterpillars of spring, summer, and fall.

Two-thirds Natural Size

THEIR FLIGHTS SPRINKLE AMERICA'S LANDSCAPES WITH COLOR

(1) Diana Fritillary, *Argynnis diana* Cram. [Male]; (2) Diana Fritillary, *Argynnis diana* Cram.
[Female]; (3) *Chlosyne lacinia* Gey.; (4) *Heterochroa bredowi* Hbn.; (5) *Euphydryas anicia* Dbldy.
and Hew.; (6) Compton Tortoise, *Aglais j-album* Bdv. and Le Con.—also known as *Vanessa
j-album;* (7) Viceroy, *Basilarchia archippus* Cram.; (8) *Melitaea neumoegeni* Skin.; (9) Portia
Butterfly, *Anaea portia* Fabr.—also known as *Pyrrhanaea portia;* (10) *Vanessa carye* Hbn. (See
pages 175, 177).

Closely related to our everyday apple tree tent caterpillar is the Pine Processionary of France, which Fabre proved to be at once the prize "bone head" and the blue ribbon weather forecaster of the insect world (see illustration, page 152).

These Processionaries live in tents. The whole tribe marches out, head to tail, single file, in quest of food. Each spins a life line to guide its footsteps back to the nest when its foraging is at an end.

The great French naturalist was able to get a foraging party of Processionary caterpillars on the rim of a huge lawn vase, and then to cut away the life line leading back to the nest. The caterpillars traveled around, came back to the point where the line was cut away, picked up the part they had laid around the vase, and marched around again.

All day long they kept following the line around and around. Night overtook them; they slept, but with the morrow's sun started marching around again.

The second night came, the third, the fourth, and the fifth; the sixth day dawned, and again they resumed the bootless march. For seven days they marched around and around, and were able to find their way back to the nest on the eighth only when one wandering caterpillar, crawling out of the procession in desperation, staked out a highway which the footsore band later decided blindly to follow.

Sight told them nothing, for nine inches away were branches laden with pine needles. Smell gave them no inkling, for almost under their noses was an abundance of their fragrant, favorite diet.

And yet, as a weather forecaster, the Pine Processionary is a marvel. It does not like to be caught out in a storm; so it always stays in its nest when storms are brewing. In its back are protuberances formed of soft, pale, hairless membrane. Of infinite sensitivity, these are supposed to be the antennae that detect the meteorological waves that tell the caterpillar of approaching bad weather. They appear and disappear at the caterpillar's will—the figurative straws that tell them how the wind blows. And Fabre reports that his caterpillars were better long-range weather forecasters than his government's meteorological station.

ANTS FEAST ON A HONEY WHICH THEY MILK FROM CATERPILLARS

The caterpillars of some butterflies appear to have entered into what human beings would call working agreements with ants. For instance, the caterpillars of the Common Blue or Spring Azure butterfly are attended by ants, who, touching their bodies, get them to exude a sweet fluid from abdominal glands, which the ants drink with relish, just as we milk cows and enjoy the milk. Some of the Hair-streaks (see page 171)—probably all of them—are attended by ants when in their caterpillar stage. Some of the caterpillars stay in the ants' nests when not out eating.

The bee moth and her larvae live in the hives of bees. When Madame Moth first enters a hive she does it by stealth, in the night, when the bee household is asleep. If she dares to do otherwise, she is stung to death. The hive odor is the countersign to those who would pass the bee's sentries, and the moth which cannot outwit sleeping sentinels is sure to get a reception that is warm, to say the least.

There are scores of burrowing caterpillars which creep up into the stems and down into the roots of briers, small shrubs, vines, and even trees. The straight wood borers, which grub their way through the hardest oak and locust wood and spend three and four years in the heart of the tree, always come to the surface to make a pupating chamber, which has just enough curtain over the window to keep a woodpecker from looking in.

Though spending three or four years as grubs in the tree and having mouths that can masticate hard wood, the emerging moths have neither mouths nor tongues. Their eating has been done for them by their larvae. They have a very few hours to live—just long enough for a chance to find a mate and die.

Most of the butterflies pupate without spinning cocoons, while many of the moths have cocoons. Some pupate on the ground, some in the grass, some under the ground, some in grain. A thousand plans are

Two-thirds Natural Size

THE DAPPER BUCKEYE AND THE STATELY REGAL FRITILLARY ARE FAMILIAR FRIENDS

(1) Leto Fritillary, *Argynnis leto* Behr. [Male]; (2) Leto Fritillary, *Argynnis leto* Behr. [Female]; (3) Red Admiral, *Vanessa atalanta* L.; (4) Gulf Fritillary, *Dione vanillae* L.; (5) Buckeye, *Junonia coenia* Hbn., (6) Delila, *Colaenis delila* Fabr.; (7) Mourning-cloak, *Aglais antiopa* L.—also known as *Vanessa antiopa;* (8) Wandering Comma, *Polygonia satyrus* Edw.; (9) Regal Fritillary, *Argynnis idalia* Dru.; (10) Crimson-patch, *Synchloe janais* Dru. (see page 177).

followed. Some species of American Saturnids (see page 189) spin such excellent cocoons that they would probably be utilized in this country in the production of silk if labor were as cheap and living as hard as in China and Japan.

MAN HAS DOMESTICATED ONLY TWO INSECTS

The silk-worm, whose cocoon China taught the world the art of using in the fashioning of the world's finest textiles, shares with the honeybee the distinction of being the only domesticated insects in the world.

The statistics of sericulture show that the world production of the silk-worm's thread amounts, exclusive of the undetermined quantity produced and used in the interior of China, to nearly 90,000,000 pounds a year.

As there are more than 900 miles of silk fiber in each pound, one may gain some conception of the enormous industry of these larvae of the silk-worm moth, *Bombyx mori,* and related species, the latter producing only a small share of the total.

40,000 SILK-WORM EGGS TO THE OUNCE

The eggs are laid once a year, in the summer, and are so small that 40,000 of them weigh only an ounce. They hatch the following spring. In about six weeks and after four molts the caterpillars are full grown and are about three inches long. They then are ready to pupate.

After a restless search the silk-worm finds a small twig, produces from the spinneret, a tiny orifice in the lower lip, a bit of sticky, viscid fibroin, which quickly dries and adheres to the twig. By a series of waving motions with its head and a circular motion with its body, it draws out the fibroin in the shape of a minute double thread, slightly twisted, and with it a silk gum that cements the two threads together (see illustration, page 159).

The worm seldom stops until its cocoon is complete, and produces from 500 to 1,300 yards of silk thread for the task. Those cocoons that are wanted for silk are usually subjected to heat and the insects

killed; but where particularly brilliant silks are desired, the fiber is reeled from the cocoon while the worm is still alive.

Those cocoons selected for "seed" are kept, and in from 20 to 40 days the moth emerges—a poor, bedraggled creature, with mouth incapable of eating anything and with wings too weak for flight. After mating, the female lays her eggs and dies—a melancholy victim of centuries of domestication and specialization in silk production.

Transcontinental silk trains, moving without schedule and having the right of way over even the crack limited expresses, rush from Vancouver to New York with the product of billions of these little laborers of the Orient that produce the raw material for the sheerest of hose and the heaviest of brocades.

THE SILK-WORM'S RIGHT TO A NICHE IN THE HALL OF FAME

The silk-worm deserves a niche in the Hall of Fame for another reason besides its gift of the world's most prized textile: it was the story that the sick silk-worms of France told the great Pasteur which led him from his beloved crystals into the study of contagious disease and the science of bacteriology, with a resultant marvelous saving of human life.

Chrysalids range from the beautiful to the ugly. The Milkweed Butterfly has a charming green house with golden nails; the Violet-tip possesses one colored like dead leaves, marked with a Roman nose, and studded with silver or gold spots.

During its nymphal slumber great changes take place in the chrysalis. Practically the entire structure of the caterpillar is torn down. Its organs, its muscles, its entire being, except a few nerve centers, are thrown into the caldron of change and reduced to a sort of milky chyle.

But certain buds, which may be detected in the caterpillar at the beginning of the pupating process, begin to take form, becoming wings, tongues, compound eyes, etc.

In due course, sometimes in a few weeks, at others after the passing of a winter, the inert mass concealed within

Two-thirds Natural Size

THE IMMIGRANT CABBAGE BUTTERFLY AND SOME OF ITS YELLOW AND SULPHUR
RELATIVES

(1) Orange Sulphur, *Eurymus eurytheme* Bdv. [Male]; (2) Orange Sulphur, *Eurymus eurytheme* Bdv. [Female]; (3) Orange Sulphur, *Eurymus eurytheme* Bdv. [Female]; (4) Cloudless Sulphur, *Catopsilia eubule* L..[Male]; (5) Cloudless Sulphur, *Catopsilia eubule* L. [Female]; (6) Orange-tip, *Anthocharis sara* Bdv.; (7) Large Orange Sulphur, *Catopsilia agarithe* Bdv.; (8) Cabbage Butterfly, *Pieris rapae* L.; (9) Dog's-head Butterfly, *Zerene caesonia* Stoll.—also known as *Meganostoma caesonia;* (10) Zerene Dog's-head Butterfly, *Zerene eurydice* Bdv. [Male]; (11) Clouded Sulphur, *Eurymus philodice* Godt.; (12) *Eurema proterpia* Fabr.; (13) Zerene Dog's-head Butterfly, *Zerene eurydice* Bdv. [Female]. (See text, pages 177, 179.)

Two-thirds Natural Size

THE SWALLOW-TAILS VIE WITH THE FRITILLARIES FOR HONORS IN THE
BEAUTY CONTEST OF THE BUTTERFLY WORLD

(1) Blue Swallow-tail, *Papilio philenor* L.; (2) Zebra Swallow-tail, *Papilio marcellus* Cram.—
also known as *Iphidicles ajax marcellus;* (3) Black Swallow-tail, *Papilio polyxenes* Fabr. form
americus Koll.; (4) Giant Swallow-tail, *Papilio cresphontes* Cram.; (5) Black Swallow-tail, *Papilio
polyxenes* Fabr. form *asterius* Cram. [Male]; (6) Black Swallow-tail, *Papilio polyxenes* Fabr. form
asterius Cram. [Female].   (See text, page 179.)

and cemented to the outer integument of the pupal cast awakens to life, and there emerges, in the words of Scudder, "like well-clad Minerva from the head of Jove, a creature of no apparent kinship either with the case that enwrapped it or the lowly worm that preceded it; a creature with a soft, elastic body, buoyant as the air in which it floats, with spreading feelers and broad spanned wings, clothed with jeweled dust and silken hair, which reflect the colors of the rainbow and in their delicate combinations defy the painter's palette."

THE BIRTH OF A BUTTERFLY

Creeping out of its pupal case, the butterfly rests with its back downward and its wings limp. With a violent pumping of its abdomen, it forces a liquid glue out through the hollow veins of the wings, between the upper and lower membranes, and even into the scales themselves. When this glue hardens, the veins become solid struts instead of hollow tubes, the upper and lower membranes become permanently bound together, the scales assume color and shape, and the insect becomes a new-blown, full-grown butterfly, ready to fly away into the romance of adult existence.

The scales that arrange themselves in such marvelous patterns on the wings of moths and butterflies are modified hairs. Under the microscope one sees every gradation from a thoroughly orthodox, elongated hair to the broad, corrugated, serrated scale. As will be noted in the microscopic section at the bottom of page 160 and the drawing, page 153, one may see the whole series on the wings of a moth and butterfly.

The tongues of butterflies and moths are marvelous adaptations to their needs as nectar sippers. Some, as in the case of several of the Sphinx moths, may be as much as six inches long, two or three times the length of the insects' bodies (see page 178, figure 7). When not in use, they coil up like the hairsprings of watches and are concealed under little hairy tippets projecting on either side of the coil.

The tongue consists of two sections, so joined together that the groove on the inner side of each forms one-half of the hollow tube they jointly make. Through this the insect draws the nectar out of the flower much as we draw medicine out of a bottle with an eye-dropper.

SOME MOTHS AND BUTTERFLIES NEVER EAT

In many cases these tongues are so long that in the pupal cases special coverings are provided for them. The natives of the South, noting the similarity of these tongue cases to wind instruments, call the pupae bearing them "horn-blowers."

The mouth parts of the scaly-wing order range from this high specialization on down to the simple biting kind, such as are possessed by locusts and beetles.

In some of the butterflies and moths, like the silk-worm moth, the period of adult existence is so short that they never eat. Consequently, their mouth parts have completely atrophied and starvation would be their inevitable fate if early death in other forms did not sooner supervene.

It is an interesting fact that, with but rare exceptions, the lowest forms of scaly-wing life fly by night, the middle forms by twilight, and the highest forms by day. It is likewise to be noted that, with only a few exceptions, the lowest forms are the most nearly colorless, and the highest forms the most colorful.

BUTTERFLY BROTHERS AND SISTERS DIFFER RADICALLY

Some butterflies have a single generation a year, others produce two broods, and still others three broods. In some cases the different broods are so different that they long were thought to be of different species. For instance, the familiar Cabbage Butterfly (see page 166, figure 8) is smaller and of a duller white in the spring brood than in later ones, and possesses broader black markings on the tip and middle of the wings.

In the American Copper spring individuals are of a more fiery red and have broader orange bands on the surface of the the hind wings than later broods. Likewise,

Two-thirds Natural Size

THE TIGER SWALLOW-TAIL (2) HAS MATES OF TWO DISTINCT COLORS (3 AND 5)

(1) *Papilio mylotes* Bates. [Male]; (2) Tiger Swallow-tail, *Papilio glaucus* L. [Male]; (3) Tiger Swallow-tail, *Papilio glaucus* L. form *glaucus* [Female]; (4) Parnassian Butterfly, *Parnassius smintheus* Dbldy. and Hew. [Female]; (5) Tiger Swallow-tail, *Papilio glaucus* L. form *turnus* [Female]; (6) *Papilio mylotes* Bates. [Female]. (See text, page 179.)

the Pearl Crescent of spring is so different from that of midsummer that the two broods passed for different species until the observant Edwards proved the contrary.

The second type of dimorphism is illustrated in the Violet-tip, where there are two forms arising from the same brood, differing alike in the brightness and variegation of their colors and in the form of the wing itself. The Blue-eyed Grayling is another which has two forms that were long able to masquerade as different species.

Then there comes a third type of dimorphism that is a mixture of both. The Zebra Swallow-tail (see page 167, figure 2) is an example of this type. It appears in three forms—*Papilio marcellus*, the *Iphidicles ajax marcellus* of the field books, emerging in early spring, with tails three-fourths of an inch long and tipped with white; *Iphidicles ajax telamonides*, appearing in late spring, with tails a little longer and bordered with white on either side for half the length or more; and the simple *Iphidicles ajax*. *Marcellus* and *telamonides* come from a single brood, *marcellus* hatching earlier. *Ajax* comes from the eggs of *marcellus* and *telamonides* alike. Its eggs in turn produce *marcellus* and *telamonides* in the spring.

In the case of the Pearl Crescent, which has both spring and summer forms, the summer form may be made to take the coloring of the spring form simply by chilling the chrysalis, which indicates the rôle played by winter in producing the spring form.

SPRING AZURE HAS MANY COLOR VARIATIONS

The Spring Azure is an example of a widely distributed species which takes on color variations, from its southernmost to its most northerly range, some broods in the South approximating the Northern forms and others widely varying.

Finally, there is sexual color variation. In the Tiger Swallow-tail one type of female is colored like the male; another type is black (see page 169, figures 2, 3, and 5); but not a black female can be found in the northern range of this species.

The Dusky Skipper, likewise, has a normally colored female and a black one, and Scudder played a joke on the male of this twin-wife species by christening him the Mormon.

Some species have white or albinic females in addition to the orthodox ones, such as the Clouded Sulphur. And still other species show all the males with one color scheme and all the females with another. The Goatweed Emperor, the Spring Beauty, the Diana Fritillary (see page 162), and the Black Swallow-tail are all examples of this type of color variation.

Both butterflies and moths survive the winter in the egg, as caterpillars, as pupae, and as adults. Some species pass it in egg form, these eggs usually being covered with a varnish to protect them. Most Swallow-tails pass it as chrysalids, most Angle-wings as adults.

About half the species hibernate as caterpillars, varying from the newly hatched Fritillaries and Graylings, whose only food has been the shells from which they emerged, to the full-grown caterpillars, which pupate in the spring without a mouthful to break their long fast.

Many of the caterpillars construct for themselves highly deceptive and thoroughly ingenious little retreats in which to rest when not eating or in which to spend the winter. For instance, the beautiful Banded Purple inhabits birch trees. Its caterpillar takes a small shoot on a budding birch, makes a shelter from it, and ensconces itself therein. Ichneumon flies buzz about, exploring the tree in search of caterpillars which they can convert into animated larders for their own young.

But the Banded Purple's caterpillar does not need to worry a great deal, for its snug little nest looks so like the birch bud that the flies usually fail to penetrate the camouflage.

THE AVERAGE BUTTERFLY'S SPAN OF LIFE IS FOUR OR FIVE WEEKS

How long do butterflies and moths live? is a question often asked. In those species which have atrophied or rudimentary mouth parts it may be assumed that their

Natural Size

A FEW OF THE COPPERS AND THEIR KIN

(1) *Heodes cupreus* Edw.; (2) Atala, *Eumaeus atala* Poey; (3) Wanderer, *Feniseca tarquinius* Fabr.; (4) Great Purple Hair-streak, *Atlides halesus* Hbn.—also known as *Thecla halesus;* (5) *Hypaurotis crysalus* Edw.; (6) *Philotes sonorensis* Feld.; (7) Bronze Copper, *Heodes thoe* Bdv. [Male]—also known as *Chrysophanus thoe;* (8) *Glaucopsyche lygdamus* Dbldy.; (9) Bronze Copper, *Heodes thoe* Bdv. [Female]—see No. 7; (10) Bronze Copper, *Heodes thoe* Bdv. [Underside]—see No. 7; (11) *Strymon martialis* H. S.; (12) American Copper, *Heodes hypophlaeas* Bdv.; (13) *Strymon acis* Dru. [Underside]. (See text, page 181.)

span of life is necessarily brief. Others live many weeks, and some, it is believed, as much as ten months; but the average life is believed by Scudder to be around four or five weeks.

Some species live long enough even to "follow the swallow" in pursuit of spring. The autumn brood of the Monarch (see page 176, figure 12), for instance, gather in hordes in the Northeastern States, and, their numbers swelling by recruits as they fly onward, finally reach the far south, to winter in lands of sunshine.

Dr. Frank Lutz says that great clouds of Painted Lady butterflies have been seen to land on the Bermuda Islands from the northwest, having covered 600 miles of ocean.

The Mourning-cloak (see page 164, figure 7) and some of the Tortoise-shells have also been observed as immigrants at times.

There are a thousand and one wonder stories that might be written about butterflies and moths. That master of butterfly habits, the late S. H. Scudder, wrote a whole volume about the Milkweed Butterflies alone, and yet he admitted that much had been left untold. Perhaps each of the 9,500 species of the scaly-winged order could instruct us as interestingly and to as great length as the Monarchs.

If we should journey to the top of Mount Washington, New Hampshire, we might find a dainty little Fritillary, *Brenthis montinus,* or that other cheery little satyr, *Oeneis semidea* (see page 176, figure 2), imprisoned on the heights because the weather is too warm below. Both came down out of the Arctic on the crest of the great Ice Age, and when the ice finally receded they were left, Robinson Crusoe fashion, on an island of cold in a sea of warm air.

O. semidea occupies only that section of the mountain above 5,000 feet. It is also found on some of the high peaks of Colorado, whence it came out of the Arctic under conditions similar to those which brought it to Mount Washington. *B. montinus* lives below the forest line in the White Mountains, as *O. semidea* lives above; but

it, too, is segregated on an island of cold. These frail little creatures demand for their existence weather so harsh and stormy that even man finds it hard to face.

BUTTERFLIES HAVE PSYCHOLOGICAL PECULIARITIES

Or we might turn aside and note with Scudder the psychological peculiarities of butterflies (he tells us that when he first prepared to write an essay on that subject his friends thought he was "spoofing" them); of butterflies in the Swiss Alps which have no fear of human beings; of Red Admirals (see page 164, figure 3) that seem to delight in barely keeping out of the way of the hunter's net; of combative species, like the American Copper and the Buckeye, that will dart madly, like bees and hornets, at a hat or other object thrown into the air; of other species that play in the air as lambs gambol on the green, with every evidence "of mirth and jocund din."

Again, we might pause to note the tendency of male butterflies to carry sachet bags in their wings to dandify themselves for courting hours; to observe how butterflies are botanists, recognizing the close relatives of their favorite food plants with unerring accuracy; to consider the inexplicable manifestations of instinct that makes the butterfly know the food plants on which its caterpillars feed, although it itself sips nectar from other honey wells.

Then there are such fascinating stories as that of the female Yucca moths, related to our Clothes-moth, upon whom the various species of Yucca are almost entirely dependent for fertilization. These moths not only render an accidental service in transferring pollen from the stamens of one flower to the pistils of another, as do most insects in their nectar-sipping expeditions, but they deliberately, as Professor Riley has demonstrated, collect the pollen in their mouths, which are particularly modified for this task, carry it to the stigma of a flower, and "apply it thereto with infinitely better care than could be done by the most skillful horticulturist,

Natural Size

BEAUTY PRIZE-WINNERS OF THE SKIPPER TRIBE, SO CALLED FROM A PECULIARITY IN FLIGHT

(1) *Atalopedes campestris* Bdv.; (2) Arctic Skipper, *Carterocephalus palaemon* Pall.—also known as *Pamphila palaemon* and *Pamphila mandan;* (3) Silver-spotted Skipper, *Epargyreus tityrus* Fabr.; (4) Tessellated Skipper, *Pyrgus tessellata* Scud.—also known as *Hesperia tessellata* and *Hesperia montivaga;* (5) *Eurycides urania* W. and H.; (6) Least Skipper, *Ancyloxypha numitor* Fabr.; (7) *Megathymus neumoegeni* Edw.; (8) Hobomok Skipper, *Poanes hobomok* Harris—also known as *Atrytone zabulon;* (9) Brazilian Skipper, *Calpodes ethlius* Cram.; (10) Long-tailed Skipper, *Goniurus proteus* L.—also known as *Eudamus proteus* (see text, page 181).

even though he might use the most delicate human appliances."

After this task is finished the moth lays her egg in the seed capsule, upon whose tissues her young will feed.

THE ROMANCE OF BUTTERFLY HUNTING

The story of butterfly and moth hunting is filled with romance. Scientists have climbed the mountains and penetrated the jungles of the earth in their quest of these elusive winged rainbows. Numerous lepidopterists have gone to the Tropics to chase innumerable species and to classify and name them.

At home, too, there have been all kinds of adventures. Holland, who has done so much to stimulate interest in the scaly-winged order, tells us of the time when, as a bashful, barefoot boy, he spied his first Diana Fritillary and gave chase.

Up by a boarding school the fluttering creature led him. At every window was a girlish face, and he the most bashful of boys. But his desire to possess the graceful insect was greater than his dread of feminine eyes, and even though the village wag cried after him that the butterfly would not let such a homely boy catch her, he did not relent until he had captured his quarry.

WIDE FIELD FOR AMATEUR RESEARCH

Two young women, wanting to know something more about moths, converted one of their rooms into a "crawlery," where they could watch microscopic caterpillars hatch out of tiny eggs, grow, molt, make cocoons, and finally emerge therefrom as beautiful moths. And from these observations resulted one of the most delightful books in the whole field of natural history.

While tremendous progress has been made in the study of moths and butterflies, there is still opportunity for careful, accurate observation of hundreds of species that dwell in every community, and there remain many gaps to be filled before the story is complete.

The great museums of the world have gathered large collections and individual collectors possess many notable ones.

Occasionally one of these collections goes upon the market for one reason or another, but usually when they pass out of private hands they are presented to such institutions as the United States National Museum, the American Museum of Natural History, and the British Museum; for the creators of these fine individual collections usually are too devoted to their specimens to place a money value upon them. One collector I know is a worker in one of America's greatest museums. He wears cotton socks bought at the 10-cent store, so that he may save money with which to buy specimens for the museum for which public funds are not available.

CHAPTER VII

Where Our Moths and Butterflies Roam

THE reproductions of the 16 butterfly and moth plates in four colors, by the National Geographic Society, were made possible through the cooperation of the United States National Museum and the late Dr. Harrison G. Dyar, whose work in the classification of Lepidoptera was an outstanding achievement in the activities of that great institution.

The photographic staff of the National Geographic Society worked out an entirely new system of furnishing the engraver with the color values of the specimens, through which one entire stage in color reproduction was eliminated and consequent loss of color value overcome.

The butterflies and moths here reproduced were selected to show at once the wide range of beautiful color patterns and to aid the everyday reader in becoming better acquainted with the fragile creatures of the air about us. These illustrations present a cross section of the lepidopterous life of North America, with a few touches of the brilliant tropical life that is always a challenge to color reproduction.

In technical nomenclature the most recent practice has been to subdivide the butterflies into 13 families. Most of the popular field and reference books, however, still adhere to an older classification of five or six families. Lutz and Holland group them into five, and Kellogg into six. Holland and Lutz put the Whites, Sulphurs, and Orange-tips into the family of the Papilionidae with the Swallow-tails, while Kellogg places them in a separate family, called the Pieridae.

Among the moths there are many families—43, according to Holland—but those most frequently observed are the Sphingidae, the Noctuidae, the Arctiidae, the Lithosiidae, the Ceratocampidae, and the Saturniidae. Here, again, different authorities assign various groups to different families.

In these pages the classifications of Lutz and Holland have been followed, as typical of the field books available to the lay reader who wishes to learn something at first hand about the fascinating folk of the moth and butterfly world.

Diana Fritillary (*Argynnis diana* Cram., page 162, figures 1 and 2).—This well-known species belongs to the southern Appalachian region, with a range extending from Virginia and West Virginia to Georgia and South Carolina and westward to the Ozarks, being found in small numbers in Southern Ohio and Indiana. The males and females have different markings, as the plate shows.

Chlosyne lacinia Gey. (page 162, figure 3).—This species is found occasionally in Texas, Arizona, and Mexico. It belongs to the same general group as the Buckeyes, Wandering Commas, and Crimson-patches.

Heterochroa bredowi Hbn. (page 162, figure 4).—The range of this species is southern California and Arizona. It is closely related to some of the European butterflies. The larvae feed on oak.

Euphydryas anicia Dbldy. and Hew. (page 162, figure 5).—This butterfly, which lacks a common name, is found in the Rocky Mountains and the Pacific States. It is a close relative of our Eastern species, the Baltimore.

Compton Tortoise (*Aglais j-album* Bdv. and Le Con.—also known as *Vanessa j-album*. Page 162, figure 6).—This fair representative of the Tortoise-shell group of butterflies is found from Pennsylvania to Labrador in the East and to Alaska in the Northwest. Its larvae feed upon willows.

Viceroy (*Basilarchia archippus* Cram., page 162, figure 7).—The Viceroy gets its everyday name from the fact that it imitates the Monarch. It is found all over the United States as far west as the Sierra Nevada, and sparingly even to the north Pacific coast. The species has two families a year in the northern part of its range. The caterpillar of the autumn brood, when half grown, rolls a leaf, ties it fast to a twig with silk, and then makes a silk couch therein, in which it spends the winter. It feeds on the willow, poplar, aspen,

Two-thirds Natural Size

ANIMATED GEMS RANGING FROM SATYR TO MONARCH (SEE PAGES 184, 186)

(1) *Gyrocheilus patrobas* Hew.; (2) White Mountain Butterfly, *Oeneis semidea* Say; (3) Alaskan Alpine, *Erebia disa* Thun.; (4) Ochre Ringlet, *Coenonympha ochracea* Edw.; (5) Grayling, *Cercyonis alope* Fabr.; (6) Ridings' Satyr, *Neominois ridingsi* Edw.; (7) *Oeneis nevadensis* Feld. [Female]; (8) Little Wood-satyr, *Cissia eurytus* Fabr.; (9) *Oeneis nevadensis* Feld. [Male]; (10) *Lycorea cleobaea* Godt.; (11) Queen, *Anosia berenice* Cram.; (12) Monarch, *Anosia plexippus* L.

and cotton wood. The Viceroy's mimicry of the Monarch, *Anosia plexippus* (see page 176, figure 12), affords a striking example of protection by imitation.

Melitaea neumoegeni Skin. (page 162, figure 8).—This butterfly is found in the mountains of southern California and in the Death Valley region. It belongs to the Checker-spot tribe, and its coloring departs from that of its closer relatives, which inhabit more colorful areas, and is as drab as the region it frequents.

Portia Butterfly (*Anaea portia* Fabr.—also known as *Pyrrhanaea portia*. Page 162, figure 9).—This essentially tropical species occasionally wanders into the southern part of Florida. It is closely related to the Goat-weed Butterfly.

Vanessa carye Hbn. (page 162, figure 10).— This is a Pacific coast butterfly of the Tortoise-shell group. Its caterpillars live upon malva, hollyhocks, and low ground plants.

Leto Fritillary (*Argynnis leto* Behr., page 164, figures 1 and 2).—The males and females of this beautiful species have different markings and range the Pacific slope. The Leto is closely related to the Great Spangled Fritillary of the East. The larvae feed on violets.

Red Admiral (*Vanessa atalanta* L., page 164, figure 3).—A thoroughgoing cosmopolite, the Red Admiral is found alike in Europe, Asia, and North America, reaching as far south as Cuba and Guatemala. Its food plants include the nettle and the hop. This butterfly winters both as a chrysalis and as an adult, and the frayed, worn appearance of the latter is in painful contrast to the spick-and-span aspect of that which spends the winter as a chrysalid.

Gulf Fritillary (*Dione vanillae* L., page 164, figure 4).—The range of this species is from southern Virginia south and westward to Florida and California. Its food plant is the passion-flower. It has a wing-spread of about three inches.

Buckeye (*Junonia coenia* Hbn., page 164, figure 5).—The Buckeye appears to be the only species of its genus which ventures outside the Tropics; its range extends from Cuba to Massachusetts and westward to the Pacific coast. In warmer areas there are three to four generations a year; in New England only one, and this hibernates as a butterfly. It loves the open fields, and its larvae feed mainly on plantains and members of the figwort family. It is rather saucy and impudent to other butterflies.

Delila (*Colaenis delila* Fabr., page 164, figure 6).—The Delila Butterfly is a tropical species which has ventured as far north as southern Texas.

Mourning-cloak (*Aglais antiopa* L.—also known as *Vanessa antiopa*. Page 164, figure 7).— This species is known to nearly every lover of the out-of-doors in the North Temperate Zone. In England its popular name is the Camberwell Beauty. It is the largest of our butterflies which hibernate as adults. When the midwinter thaws occur, one is likely to see in open glades several dark-colored butterflies flitting from tree to tree or resting with expanded wings in sunny spots. These are Mourning-cloaks which have ventured out of their winter retreats, perhaps to die victims of the ensuing cold weather. The eggs are laid in masses circling the twigs of elms, willows, and poplars in late spring, and hatch in about two weeks.

Wandering Comma (*Polygonia satyrus* Edw., page 164, figure 8).—This species deserves its name as a wanderer. It is found in the Rocky Mountains as far south as New Mexico, and westward to the Pacific from Santa Clara County, California, to Vancouver, British Columbia. It has also been found in Canada—in Ontario, around Montreal and Ottawa—and in Lewis County, New York. Its larvae feed on stinging nettles.

Regal Fritillary (*Argynnis idalia* Dru., page 164, figure 9).—Fresh from its pupal case, this lovely member of the Fritillary tribe shows a brilliant sheen of iridescence. It possesses a rather plump body and a wing-spread of about three inches. Having only one generation a year, each stage from egg to adult is more than usually long. Its range is from New England to Nebraska, in the belt characterized by 50° Fahrenheit as the mean annual temperature. The eggs are laid on the under side of violet leaves, upon which its caterpillars feed, although the butterfly itself is partial to the nectar of joe-pye-weed, boneset, goldenrod, ironweed, and swamp milkweed.

Crimson-patch (*Synchloe janais* Dru., page 164, figure 10).—This species is largely a tropical one. The northern limits of its habitat reach no farther than Texas, and it is more abundant in Mexico and Central America.

Orange Sulphur (*Eurymus eurytheme* Bdv., page 166, figures 1, 2, and 3).—The Orange Sulphur is essentially western in its habitat, though it has been noted in the region of Vancouver in the West, and the valley of the St. Lawrence in the East. The southern limits of its range extend from southern California to Mississippi. It is one of the butterflies which has females of two different types, as shown on page 166.

Cloudless Sulphur (*Catopsilia eubule* L., page 166, figures 4 and 5).—The range of this species is from New England and Wisconsin to Patagonia. The region of its greatest abundance is tropical America, where it congregates in great

Two-thirds Natural Size

GIANT SPHINX MOTH COMMANDS ATTENTION FOR ITS TONGUE (SEE PAGE 186)

(1) Striped Morning Sphinx, *Celerio lineata* Fabr.; (2) Blinded Sphinx, *Paonias excaecata* A. and S.—also known as *Calasymbolus excaecatus;* (3) Snowberry Clear-wing, *Haemorrhagia diffinis* Bdv.; (4) *Cautethia noctuiformis* Walk.; (5) Humming-bird Clear-wing, *Haemorrhagia thysbe* Fabr.; (6) Clark's Day-sphinx, *Proserpinus clarkiae* Bdv.; (7) Giant Sphinx, *Cocytius antaeus* Dru.; (8) Tersa Sphinx, *Xylophanes tersa* L.; (9) Abbot's Sphinx, *Sphecodina abbotii* Swains.; (10) Satellite Sphinx, *Pholus satellitia* Dru.; (11) Achemon Sphinx, *Pholus achemon* Dru.

swarms along streams. Other favorite haunts are the orange groves of Florida and Latin America. It will be noted that in the Cloudless Sulphur the female has different markings from the male.

Orange-tip (*Anthocharis sara* Bdv., page 166, figure 6).—A true Westerner is this species, belonging to the Mountain States of the Pacific coast. Its early stages appear still to be unknown.

Large Orange Sulphur (*Catopsilia agarithe* Bdv., page 166, figure 7).—This species occurs along the shores of the Gulf of Mexico and throughout tropical America. It is closely related to the more familiar Cloudless Sulphur (see figures 4 and 5).

Cabbage Butterfly (*Pieris rapae* L., page 166, figure 8).—This species is an imported pest. It appears to have been first introduced into Quebec about 1860 and around New York about 1868. Within 30 years of the time of its introduction it has established itself all over the United States and Canada. Its coming has led to the practical extinction of two native species, the Gray-veined White and the Checkered White, both of which formerly fed on cabbage.

Dog's-head Butterfly (*Zerene caesonia* Stoll. —also known as *Meganostoma caesonia*. Page 166, figure 9).—This is another species belonging to the tribe of the Yellows. It gets its name from the markings on its wings, which are supposed to resemble a dog's head, although some insist that it looks more like a duck. The range of the species is from Pennsylvania and southern Wisconsin to the Gulf States and Central America, and the food plants of its caterpillars are false-indigo and clover.

Zerene Dog's-head Butterfly (*Zerene eurydice* Bdv., page 166, figures 10 and 13).—This is a Pacific coast species whose habits are essentially the same as those of the species immediately preceding.

Clouded Sulphur (*Eurymus philodice* Godt., page 166, figure 11).—Everybody knows this species, since no eye is so unobservant as not to have noticed great groups of them holding their little banquets around mud puddles in the road. If one examines the border of the puddle carefully after the butterflies have flown, he will discover the mud full of pinholes where the thirsty creatures have thrust their tongues. The Clouded Sulphur loves the sun. If heavy clouds obscure it, the thousands of butterflies hasten to hide beneath clover or down in the grasses in which they spend the night. Its range is from the mouth of the St. Lawrence River to South Carolina and westward to the Rocky Mountains. There are two forms of the female, the one substituting white where the other wears yellow.

Eurema proterpia Fabr. (page 166, figure 12). —Mexico is the usual habitat of this butterfly, though it occasionally crosses the Rio Grande into Texas.

Blue Swallow-tail (*Papilio philenor* L., page 167, figure 1).—During the summer months this butterfly is found in the Middle Atlantic States. It ranges from Massachusetts to Arizona and southward into Mexico. The caterpillar feeds upon the leaves of the Dutchmans-pipe and Virginia snakeroot.

Zebra Swallow-tail (*Papilio marcellus* Cram. —also known as *Iphidicles ajax marcellus*. Page 167, figure 2).—This early spring form is found almost everywhere in the eastern part of the United States, where its caterpillars can find their favorite food, the papaw. It ranges as far north as southern Michigan and in the South passes down to Florida.

Black Swallow-tail (*Papilo polyxenes* Fabr., form *americus* Koll. Page 167, figure 3; form *asterius* Cram., figures 5 and 6).—This butterfly is the adult of the well-known striped parsnip worm and is found generally throughout the eastern United States. The male and female are different in coloration. The form *americus* is a local race from Arizona and Mexico in which the yellow markings are broader.

Giant Swallow-tail (*Papilio cresphontes* Cram., page 167, figure 4).—While a native of the South, this species is now spreading northward and has been found in Ontario. The orange growers of Florida consider its caterpillar a pest and complain of its ravages upon their trees. The larva is called the "orange dog."

Papilio mylotes Bates (page 169, figures 1 and 6).—This species belongs to a large group of brilliant butterflies the center of whose habitat is the Amazon Valley. Occasionally members of the species wander as far north as our Gulf coast.

Tiger Swallow-tail (*Papilio glaucus* L., page 169, figure 2; form *glaucus*, figure 3; form *turnus*, figure 5).—On the basis of its wide distribution, the Tiger Swallow-tail would make a lively candidate for our national butterfly. Although its metropolis appears to be in the wooded forests of the Appalachian Mountains, its range extends from Canada to Key West and the Rio Grande. It affords an example of that form of dimorphism in which females hatched from the same lot of eggs take different colors, although the males always adhere to the one form. The caterpillars, having heads resembling those of serpents (see text, page 158), are found on a great variety of trees and shrubs, including tulip trees, birches, wild cherries, apples, poplars, and ashes.

Parnassian Butterfly (*Parnassius smintheus* Dbldy. and Hew., page 169, figure 4).—The

Two-thirds Natural Size

THE HAWKMOTHS COMPRISE A BRILLIANT WINGED FAMILY

(1) Five-spotted Hawkmoth, *Protoparce quinquemaculata* Haw.; (2) Big Poplar Sphinx, *Pachy-sphinx modesta* Harr.; (3) Hydrangea Sphinx, *Ampeloeca versicolor* Harr.—also known as *Darapsa versicolor;* (4) Lettered Sphinx, *Deidamia inscripta* Harr.; (5) *Pholus typhon* Klug.; (6) Nessus Sphinx, *Amphion nessus* Cram.; (7) *Erinnyis caicus* Cram.; (8) Hog Sphinx, *Ampeloeca myron* Cram.—also known as *Darapsa myron;* (9) Alope Sphinx, *Erinnyis alope* Dru.; (10) Lesser Vine Sphinx, *Pholus fasciatus* Sulz. (see text, pages 186, 188).

Parnassians are Alpine or Arctic in habitat. *P. smintheus* is found in the high mountain regions from New Mexico to Montana and thence to the Pacific coast. The caterpillars resemble those of *Papilios,* but are darkly colored and are found wandering on the ground amid the scanty vegetation of their Alpine abode.

Heodes cupreus Edw. (page 171, figure 1).— This species is found in dry country, its favorite habitat being eastern Oregon and Wyoming.

Atala (*Eumaeus atala* Poey., page 171, figure 2).—This Southern form is found only sparingly in Florida and Cuba. The larva feeds on zamia, one of the few remaining cycads of the Coal Age. The butterflies are all tame and may be hand picked from flowers with a little care.

Wanderer (*Feniseca tarquinius* Fabr., page 171, figure 3).—This little Copper is found all over the Atlantic States from Nova Scotia to the Carolinas. It also inhabits the Mississippi Valley. There is but the one species of this genus known. The larva feeds on the masses of white bark-lice found on alder bushes, greatly reducing the numbers of the lice. This is our only carnivorous butterfly.

Great Purple Hair-streak (*Atlides halesus* Hbn.—also known as *Thecla halesus.* Page 171, figure 4).—The Great Purple Hair-streak is our largest Hair-streak species. It is very common in Central America and Mexico. Although a tropical form, it extends from California to Florida and occasionally occurs as far north as southern Illinois. Its larvae feed on the mistletoe growing on oaks.

Hypaurotis crysalus Edw. (page 171, figure 5).—This is a Western butterfly. It is found generally in California, Utah, and Arizona.

Philotes sonorensis Feld. (page 171, figure 6).—This is a Southern butterfly whose range includes southern California and Mexico. It is prized for the curious red markings, so exceptional in one of the Blues.

Bronze Copper (*Heodes thoe* Bdv.—also known as *Chrysophanus thoe.* Page 171, figures 7, 9, and 10).—This is a rare insect although it occurs in northern Illinois, Nebraska, Iowa, and the upper Mississippi Valley. It has two families a year, and winters as an egg. It finds both goldenrod and Canada thistle much to its liking.

Glaucopsyche lygdamus Dbldy. (page 171, figure 8).—Although the exact range of this silvery blue butterfly is not known, it has been found in the Atlantic States from the upper waters of the Susquehanna to Georgia. In its northern range it reaches westward to Ohio, Michigan, and Wisconsin.

Strymon martialis H. S. (page 171, figure 11).—The range of this butterfly is very limited; it is found only in southern Florida and the Antilles.

American Copper (*Heodes hypophlaeas* Bdv., page 171, figure 12).—These little butterflies are found in the Atlantic States. In the northern part of their range they are double-brooded, and in the southern part triple-brooded. It winters as a chrysalis. It is sorrel in color, matching the sorrel on which it feeds.

Strymon acis Dru. (page 171, figure 13).— Southern Florida is the favorite haunt of this butterfly.

Atalopedes campestris Bdv. (page 173, figure 1).—This butterfly was first found by Boisduval in California. Some authorities have considered it identical with, or at least a variety of, the Sachem or Velvet-spotted Skipper, *Atalopedes huron,* but Scudder declared that the specimens he examined would not permit of such a conclusion. At any rate, it is a very close relative of the Sachem, which ranges from the Catskills of New York to Florida and westward. Its larvae feed on Bermuda grass, fastening together a number of blades and spinning in the cylindrical cavity thus formed silken webs which serve as retreats, from which they emerge only when feeding.

Arctic Skipper (*Carterocephalus palaemon* Pall.; also known as *Pamphila palaemon* and *Pamphila mandan,* page 173, figure 2).—The range of this butterfly extends from southern Labrador south to the White Mountains and the Adirondacks, and thence westward to the summits of the Sierras in northern California and to southeastern Alaska. Its caterpillars feed on grasses.

Silver-spotted Skipper (*Epargyreus tityrus* Fabr., page 173, figure 3).—The range of the Silver-spotted Skipper reaches from Quebec to Vancouver and as far south as the Isthmus of Panama. It has one generation annually in the North, and is double- or even triple-brooded in the South and within the Tropics. The caterpillar feeds on leguminous plants and is especially fond of wisteria and the locust tree.

Tessellated Skipper (*Pyrgus tessellata* Scud., also known as *Hesperia tessellata* and *Hesperia montivaga,* page 173, figure 4).—This, one of the commonest of the southern Hesperids, claims the whole of the United States for its range. Its caterpillars feed on hollyhocks, Indian mallows, and related plants.

Eurycides urania W. and H. (page 173, figure 5).—This beautiful butterfly is a tropical species, but on rare occasions individuals have been found within the southern borders of the United States.

Two-thirds Natural Size

THE MOTH'S CONCEALED BEAUTY IS REVEALED TO THE COLLECTOR

(1) White Birch Under-wing, *Catocala relicta* Wlk.; (2) Darling Under-wing, *Catocala cara* Gn.; (3) *Cirrhobolina mexicana* Behr.; (4) *Chalcopasta koebelei* Riley; (5) *Basilodes pepita* Gn.; (6) *Syneda hastingsi* Edw.; (7) *Stiria rugifrons* Grt.; (8) *Erebus odora* L. [Female]; (9) *Thurberiphaga diffusa* Barn.; (10) *Momophana comstocki* Grt.; (11) *Cirrhophanus triangulifer* Grt.; (12) Ultronia Under-wing, *Catocala ultronia* Hbn.; (13) Variegated Cutworm Moth, *Peridroma margaritosa* Haw.; (14) Clouded Locust Under-wing, *Euparthenos nubilis* Hbn. (see text, pages 157, 188, 190).

Two-thirds Natural Size

THIS GROUP OF MOTHS RUNS THE GAMUT FROM THE TIGER TO THE WEB-WORM

(1) Mexican Tiger-moth, *Apantesis proxima* Guer.; (2) Leopard-moth, *Ecpantheria deflorata* Fabr.; (3) Beautiful Utetheisa, *Utetheisa bella* L.; (4) Acraea Moth, *Estigmene acraea* Dru. [Female]; (5) Colona Moth, *Haploa colona* Hbn.; (6) Big Halisidota, *Halisidota ingens* H. Edw.; (7) Spotted Halisidota, *Halisidota maculata* Harr.; (8) St. Lawrence Tiger-moth, *Hyphoraia parthenos* Harr.; (9) Acraea Moth, *Estigmene acraea* Dru. [Male]; (10) Painted Arachnis, *Arachnis picta* Pack.; (11) Virgin Tiger-moth, *Apantesis virgo* L.; (12) Showy Holomelina, *Eubaphe ostenta* Hy. Edw.—also known as *Holomelina ostenta;* (13) Isabella Tiger-moth, *Isia isabella* A. and S.; (14) Crimson-bodied Lichen-moth, *Lerina incarnata* Bdv.; (15) Milk-weed Moth, *Euchaetias egle* Dru.; (16) Ranchman's Tiger-moth, *Platyprepia virginalis* Bdv.; (17) Fall Web-worm Moth, *Hyphantria cunea* Dru.; (18) *Arctia americana* Harr. (see text, pages 190, 192).

Least Skipper (*Ancyloxypha numitor* Fabr., page 173, figure 6).—The smallest of the Skippers is different both in habit and structure from its cousins of the tribe. It is slender-bodied where they are plump and when resting it has a manner of twirling in opposite directions alternately its two antennae. The eggs are laid in the grass and the butterfly usually floats slowly just above the herbage in sunny places in wet meadows and along the open margins of brooks and marshes. The range of the species extends from Quebec to Florida and westward to the Rocky Mountains.

Megathymus neumoegeni Edw. (page 173, figure 7).—This species has been found in Arizona and Mexico. It is closely related to *M. yuccae,* which is found rather generally distributed in the Southern States. The larvae bore into the roots and stems of yucca.

Hobomok Skipper (*Poanes hobomok* Harris; also known as *Atrytone zabulon,* page 173, figure 8).—This species ranges from New England to Georgia and westward to the Great Plains, being very common in Pennsylvania and Virginia and along the Ohio River.

Brazilian Skipper (*Calpodes ethlius* Cram., page 173, figure 9).—The Brazilian Skipper might be called a guest from the Tropics, as its southern range reaches to Argentina. It occurs as far north as South Carolina, is abundant around the Gulf of Mexico, and there is a record that one individual was taken some years ago in New York State. Almost every year we find some of the larvae on the ornamental cannas in Washington, D. C. Its powers of flight must be considerable, as it is killed off every winter in the North.

Long-tailed Skipper (*Goniurus proteus* L.; also known as *Eudamus proteus,* page 173, figure 10).—This is another tropical species which has ventured into the temperate regions and is found occasionally as far north as New York City. Its caterpillar feeds on wisteria and the butterfly-pea, beans, etc., cutting a flap out of the corner of a leaf which it folds over and fastens with a few strands of silk.

Gyrocheilus patrobas Hew. (page 176, figure 1).—This species is found in Mexico and Arizona. It is a close relative of the Arizona Blackamoor, *G. tritonia,* which has the same general range.

White Mountain Butterfly (*Oeneis semidea* Say, page 176, figure 2).—As pointed out in the text on page 172, this butterfly has a remarkably restricted habitat in the United States, appearing only on the summit of Mount Washington. It is a survival of the Ice Age in those regions, and reaches the lower areas only in Labrador and the Far North. Another colony has been left on Mount Katahdin, Maine, differing a little in color from those on Mount Washington.

Alaskan Alpine (*Erebia disa* Thun., page 176, figure 3).—The Alaskan Alpine is found in Alaska and on the mountains of British Columbia. Its larval stage has not been discovered.

Ochre Ringlet (*Coenonympha ochracea* Edw., page 176, figure 4).—The Ochre Ringlet has a range extending from British Columbia to Arizona and reaching as far east as Kansas. Although a small butterfly, it belongs to a genus that is widely distributed throughout the temperate regions of both the New and the Old World. It is often seen flying in dry herbage, which its colors simulate.

Grayling (*Cercyonis alope* Fabr., page 176, figure 5).—This species occurs from the Atlantic to the Pacific and has several varieties, among them the Blue-eyed, the Dull-eyed, the Hybrid, and the Sea-coast Graylings. The blue-eyed variety is a lover of lonely lanes and bramble-covered walls and fences as well as of the open woods. It visits the hardhacks in the East and the tickseed on the plains of the West. Its caterpillar hibernates without eating after hatching. The dull-eyed variety is simply a Northern variation of the blue-eyed. Comstock describes the Hybrid Graylings as the progeny of the yellow-banded beauty of the South and the sad-colored Puritan of the North.

Ridings' Satyr (*Neominois ridingsi* Edw., page 176, figure 6).—Ridings' Satyr is found in the Mountain States of the Pacific coast. Its eggs are somewhat barrel-shaped, broader at the base than at the top, and with a rounded summit.

Oeneis nevadensis Feld. (page 176, figures 7 and 9).—This species occurs in the Pacific States, the male and female differing somewhat in appearance, as is shown in the illustration. It is an inhabitant of the higher hills.

Little Wood-satyr (*Cissia eurytus* Fabr., page 176, figure 8).—The Little Wood-satyr is one of the most vivacious species of the genus to which it belongs. It loves the shades of thickets and groves. A peculiar thing about its eye spots is that when looked at directly from above they seem solid, but when looked at from an angle they show double pupils of metallic sheen. The species is single-brooded and puts in an early spring appearance. Its caterpillars feed by night and hide during the day among the roots and bases of grass.

Lycorea cleobaea Godt. (page 176, figure 10).—This species is essentially a tropical one which occasionally reaches as far north as southern Florida. Its brilliant colors are mimicked in the Tropics by the delicate Heliconias.

Queen (*Anosia berenice* Cram., page 176, figure 11).—*Anosia berenice* is a Southern species with a range that includes the Gulf States, New Mexico, and Arizona. The Viceroine imitates the

Two-thirds Natural Size

THE ROYAL WALNUT-MOTH, THE IMPERIAL MOTH, AND SOME OF THEIR SMALL COUSINS

(1) *Adelocephala isias* Bdv.; (2) White-lined Syssphinx, *Adelocephala albolineata* G. and R.—also known as Syssphinx albolineata; (3) Honey-locust Moth, *Adelocephala bicolor* Harr.; (4) Royal Walnut-moth, *Citheronia regalis* Fabr.; (5) Rosy Maple-moth, *Anisota rubicunda* Fabr. [Male]; (6) Orange-striped Oak-worm Moth, *Anisota senatoria* A. and S.; (7) Rosy Maple-moth, *Anisota rubicunda* Fabr. [Female]; (8) Imperial Moth, *Eacles imperialis* Dru.—also known as *Basilona imperialis;* (9) Heiligbrodt's Syssphinx, *Adelocephala heiligbrodti* Harv.—also known as *Syssphinx heiligbrodti;* (10) Stigma Moth, *Anisota stigma* Fabr. [Male]; (11) Stigma Moth, *Anisota stigma* Fabr. [Female]. (See text, pages 192, 193, 194.)

Queen just as the Viceroy copies the Monarch. The caterpillars are found on a climbing milkweed.

Monarch (*Anosia plexippus* L., page 176, figure 12).—The Monarch is one of the world's greatest butterfly travelers. With the advent of spring it presses northward from the Far South until it reaches the latitude of lower Canada. In the fall the northern clans gather and press southward, calling millions of recruits to their standards as they go, until the swarming hosts literally cover the trees upon which they rest during the night. It has crossed the seas, following the trade routes, and has succeeded in establishing itself in Australia, Java, Sumatra, and the Philippines. Likewise, it has gained a foothold in England and the Cape Verde Islands. It has traveled across the seas probably as a stowaway in the chrysalis stage, in packing material. The larva is the common striped milkweed caterpillar with its shaking black horns.

Striped Morning Sphinx (*Celerio lineata* Fabr., page 178, figure 1).—The range of the Striped Morning Sphinx, which is probably the commonest of all the North American sphinx moths, extends from southern Canada to Cuba and Central America. The moth flies in the sunshine and is frequently found swarming around electric street lights in the evening. The caterpillars feed upon the various species of the purslane family, including the flame flower, the Virginia springbeauty, and the ordinary purslane of the garden. The moths visit the blossoms of thistles and of the soapwart in their search for nectar.

Blinded Sphinx (*Paonias excaecata* A. and S.; also known as *Calasymbolus excaecatus*, page 178, figure 2).—The range of this species extends from southern Canada to Florida and westward to the Great Plains. Its caterpillars feed upon the willow, hazel, ironwood, and other allied trees and shrubs.

Snowberry Clear-wing (*Haemorrhagia diffinis* Bdv., page 178, figure 3).—This species has a range that extends from New England to Georgia and westward to the Dakotas and Oklahoma. It occurs in three forms, one in the spring and two in the summer. Its caterpillars feed upon snowberries, honeysuckles, and the like.

Cautethia noctuiformis Walk. (page 178, figure 4).—This is a tropical species, and although it has been seen in southern Florida, it only occasionally comes farther north than Cuba.

Humming-bird Clear-wing (*Haemorrhagia thysbe* Fabr., page 178, figure 5).—The Humming-bird Clear-wing is the largest and commonest species of the genus to which it belongs. Its caterpillars feed upon viburnum and kindred plants, and the insect's range reaches from Nova Scotia and Canada to Florida and the Mississippi River.

Clark's Day-sphinx (*Proserpinus clarkiae* Bdv., page 178, figure 6).—Clark's Day-sphinx has a range that extends from Utah and Montana northward into northern California and Oregon.

Giant Sphinx (*Cocytius antaeus* Dru., page 178, figure 7).—The Giant Sphinx, famous for its magnificent tongue, has a range that extends from Florida into southern Brazil. The larvae are large green worms with a horn near the tail, feeding upon plants of the custard-apple family.

Tersa Sphinx (*Xylophanes tersa* L., page 178, figure 8).—This species is a common and easily recognized one, possessing a range that extends from southern Canada to northern Argentina. Its peculiar tapering body gives it a graceful appearance.

Abbot's Sphinx (*Sphecodina abbotii* Swains., page 178, figure 9).—This, one of the beauties of the Hawkmoth group, has a range that extends throughout the Eastern States and southern Canada and as far westward as Iowa and Kansas. The larvae occur in two forms, one with large green moon-shaped spots, the other plain brown, and are found on woodbine and grape.

Satellite Sphinx (*Pholus satellitia* Dru., page 178, figure 10).—The Satellite Sphinx is widely distributed throughout the eastern United States and southern Canada. During the first several molts the caterpillar is green. In the later stages of development it frequently becomes dark brown. The genus to which the Satellite belongs embraces 19 species. The caterpillars have the body large in front, into which they can draw the head. They are red or green, with white spots on the sides, and occur on the woodbine and grape.

Achemon Sphinx (*Pholus achemon* Dru., page 178, figure 11).—The Achemon Sphinx has a range that includes all of the United States, southern Canada, and the northern part of Mexico. Its caterpillars feed upon vines and show a special fondness for grapes. The Virginia creeper is another of its food plants. It is very much like the caterpillar of the Satellite Sphinx, except that the white spots on the sides are of another shape.

Five-spotted Hawkmoth (*Protoparce quinquemaculata* Haw., page 180, figure 1).—This species is very common, particularly in the South, where, because of its larva's attack upon the tobacco plant, it has long been known as the tobacco fly. Many species of the potato family are to the liking of its larvae. The green caterpillars with a horn near the tail are easily recognized.

Big Poplar Sphinx (*Pachysphinx modesta* Harr., page 180, figure 2).—The Big Poplar Sphinx is one of the noblest of the Hawkmoths. It ranges over the entire United States and its caterpillars feed on poplars, willows, and kindred trees. There are several varieties of this species, the Western one being paler than that which

Two-thirds Natural Size

THE NIGHT-FLYING LUNA (4) IS THE PREMIER BEAUTY OF THE MOTH WORLD

(1) Mendocino Silk-moth, *Saturnia mendocino* Behr.; (2) Pamina Moth, *Hyperchiria pamina* Neum.—also known as *Automeris pamina;* (3) Range Caterpillar Moth, *Hemileuca oliviae* Ckll.; (4) Luna Moth, *Actias luna* L.; (5) Buck-moth, *Hemileuca maia* Dru.; (6) Pandora Moth, *Coloradia pandora* Blake; (7) *Pseudohazis eglanterina* Bdv.; (8) Io Moth, *Hyperchiria io* Fabr. [Male]—also known as *Automeris io;* (9) Io Moth, *Hyperchiria io* Fabr. [Female]—also known as *Automeris io* (see text, pages 194, 195).

dwells in the East, to match better the lighter colors of the dry western plains.

Hydrangea Sphinx (*Ampeloeca versicolor* Harr.; also known as *Darapsa versicolor,* page 180, figure 3).—There are few lovelier moths than this beautiful species, which ranges from New England to South Carolina and westward toward the Mississippi River. Its caterpillars feed upon the wild hydrangea, which is found in deep, wooded glens, along the margins of small streams.

Lettered Sphinx (*Deidamia inscripta* Harr., page 180, figure 4).—This "learned" member of the Sphinx family is a common species in western Pennsylvania, but is not often encountered in the remainder of its range, which extends from Canada to Virginia and westward to the Mississippi. Its caterpillar feeds upon the wild grapevine and woodbine.

Pholus typhon Klug. (page 180, figure 5).— This species has a limited distribution, being reported only from Arizona and Mexico. It is a close relative of the Satellite Sphinx (see page 178).

Nessus Sphinx (*Amphion nessus* Cram., page 180, figure 6).—Ranging from Canada to Georgia and thence westward to the Rocky Mountains, this Sphinx is a day flyer. The wild grape is one of its favorite food plants.

Erinnyis caicus Cram. (page 180, figure 7).— This is a tropical species which occurs occasionally in Florida. It is marked like its close cousin, the Ello Sphinx, which is the commonest of all the Hawkmoths of the American Tropics and has straggled as far north as Canada.

Hog Sphinx (*Ampeloeca myron* Cram.; also known as *Darapsa myron,* page 180, figure 8).— The Hog Sphinx is a resident of the Atlantic States, but its range extends as far west as Kansas and Iowa. Its caterpillars feed upon wild and domestic grapevines and the Virginia creeper; but they never become sufficiently numerous to do serious damage, since certain species of ichneumon flies employ them as larders for their own young. The female flies deposit their eggs upon the skin of the young caterpillar. When these hatch the larvae penetrate the skin of the host, and before the latter has reached maturity are ready to pupate themselves, which they do by weaving little white cocoons on the backs of the caterpillars. Those which escape this parasitization make themselves loose cocoons of closely woven threads of silk, spun under leaves at the surface of the ground, which is the orthodox method of many Hawkmoths.

Alope Sphinx (*Erinnyis alope* Dru., page 180, figure 9).—This is another tropical species which occurs in southern Florida and possesses typical Hawkmoth attributes.

Lesser Vine Sphinx (*Pholus fasciatus* Sulz., page 180, figure 10).—The Lesser Vine Sphinx is quite common in the Gulf States, though more abundant in tropical Latin America. Stragglers of the species have been taken as far north as Massachusetts.

White Birch Under-wing (*Catocala relicta* Wlk., page 182, figure 1).—This is one of the Under-wing moths, which have bright colors on the hind wings that do not appear when the insect is at rest. This species frequents the birch trees, and its folded wings perfectly simulate the markings of the birch bark. Its range includes most of the northern Atlantic States area.

Darling Under-wing (*Catocala cara* Gn., page 182, figure 2).—The Darling Under-wing is a native of the Appalachian area. Frequenting the maples as *C. relicta* frequents the birches, its forewings are shaded to give it protective coloration when resting on the maple.

Cirrhobolina mexicana Behr. (page 182, figure 3).—This species has a range extending from Colorado and Texas into Arizona and the plateaus of Mexico. It belongs to that same family of moths, the *Noctuidae,* which gives us so many of our army worms and cutworms.

Chalcopasta koebelei Riley (page 182, figure 4).—This species is an inhabitant of the arid Southwest, Death Valley being included in its range.

Basilodes pepita Gn. (page 182, figure 5).— This is another of the family of *Noctuidae,* whose range extends from Pennsylvania to Florida and westward to Colorado.

Syneda hastingsi Edw. (page 182, figure 6).— This member of the family of Noctuids is found in California and Oregon. The moths fly about in the day, alighting on the ground when the brilliant colors of the hind wings are hidden and they resemble the dust on which they rest.

Stiria rugifrons Grt. (page 182, figure 7).— This species has been found in southern Indiana, Kansas, and Colorado. Little is known about the various stages of its existence.

Erebus odora L. (page 182, figure 8).—Compared with many of the lesser Noctuids, this magnificent species, the only one of the genus appearing in the United States, is a charming insect. It occurs quite abundantly in the warm areas around the Gulf of Mexico and is sometimes found as a straggler even as far north as Canada. It is widely distributed throughout tropical America. It does not breed in the United States, our examples all being visitants.

Thurberiphaga diffusa Barn. (page 182, figure 9).—This is a rare species found in Arizona and New Mexico. The moth flies about the time the wild cotton is in bloom and hides in the flower when resting.

Two-thirds Natural Size

THE AILANTHUS SILK-MOTH (2) IS AN EMIGRANT FROM ASIA

(1) *Hemileuca electra* Wright; (2) Ailanthus Silk-moth, *Samia cynthia* Dru.—also known as *Philosamia cynthia;* (3) *Agapema anona* Ottol.; (4) Tricolor Buck-moth, *Hemileuca tricolor* Pack.; (5) Polyphemus Moth, *Telea polyphemus* Cram.; (6) Nevada Buck-moth, *Hemileuca nevadensis* Stretch; (7) *Rothschildia jorulla* West.; (8) Spice-bush Silk-moth, *Callosamia promethea* Dru. (see text, pages 195, 196).

Momophana comstocki Grt. (page 182, figure 10).—This is a rare species. All of the specimens that have been taken have been found in New York and Canada, but these have been so few that the species is missing from many museums.

Cirrhophanus triangulifer Grt. (page 182, figure 11).—This member of the Noctuid family is found in the Southern States and also as far north as Pennsylvania.

Ultronia Under-wing (*Catocala ultronia* Hbn., page 182, figure 12).—This species possesses a number of forms, the one shown being perhaps the commonest. It occurs from Canada to Florida and westward to the Great Plains. The moths alight on tree trunks, which the colors of their upper wings resemble.

Variegated Cutworm Moth (*Peridroma margaritosa* Haw., page 182, figure 13).—This species is one of about a dozen of the genus found in the United States. It is the moth of the common variegated cutworm, so destructive to grass and low vegetation.

Clouded Locust Under-wing (*Euparthenos nubilis* Hbn., page 182, figure 14).—This is a somewhat rare species which occurs from the northern Atlantic States to Arizona. The caterpillars frequent the locust trees and are colored like the bark on which they rest.

Mexican Tiger-moth (*Apantesis proxima* Guer., page 183, figure 1).—The Mexican Tiger-moth occurs in southern California, Arizona, Mexico, and Central America. The genus to which it belongs is essentially an American one, there being only two species attributed to it in the Old World. Its family, the *Arctiidae,* includes more than 2,000 species, being represented in North American life by 38 genera, subdivided into about 120 species.

Leopard-moth (*Ecpantheria deflorata* Fabr., page 183, figure 2).—This species ranges from southern New England into Mexico, being rare in its northern territory and abundant in the southern part of its range. The big black red-banded caterpillar covered with coarse black bristles is very striking but not often found.

Beautiful Utetheisa (*Utetheisa bella* L., page 183, figure 3).—A visitor to the blossoms of the goldenrod, *U. bella* is seen in the late summer and fall in the States of the Atlantic seaboard. The only other member of the genus to which it belongs found within the United States is *U. ornatrix,* which occurs in southern Florida. The larvae live in open webs, resembling spiders' webs, on wild-indigo and similar plants.

Acraea Moth (*Estigmene acraea* Dru., page 183, figures 4 and 9).—This moth is one of the most frequently occurring in the Middle Atlantic States. There are several varieties and the two sexes wear different clothes. The larvae are the brown "woolly bears" so often seen in lawn and garden.

Colona Moth (*Haploa colona* Hbn., page 183, figure 5).—The Colona Moth is the largest species of its genus. Although found occasionally in the North Atlantic States and more frequently in the South Atlantic group, it is most abundant in the region of which Texas is the center. It occurs in local colonies, abundant where found, absent elsewhere. The species of its genus are noted for their lack of consistency in color reproduction, it being somewhat difficult to find a group of individuals possessed of uniform markings. Heredity clearly has not yet set their colors.

Big Halisidota (*Halisidota ingens* H. Edw., page 183, figure 6).—This species is found in the Rocky Mountains and in Arizona. It belongs to an extensive genus well represented in Central and South America and containing about a dozen species within the territory of the United States. It belongs to a group of species the larvae of which feed on spruce and hemlock.

Spotted Halisidota (*Halisidota maculata* Harr., page 183, figure 7).—The Spotted Halisidota has a range that covers the northern part of the United States. The black and yellow tufted caterpillars are often seen on willow and alder in the fall.

St. Lawrence Tiger-moth (*Hyphoraia parthenos* Harr., page 183, figure 8).—The St. Lawrence Tiger-moth belongs to a subarctic genus which is distributed in the subarctic areas of North America, Asia, and Europe. The present species occurs most frequently in the St. Lawrence Valley, northern New England and westward to Manitoba. Occasionally it is found in the Catskills.

Painted Arachnis (*Arachnis picta* Pack., page 183, figure 10).—This species is found in Colorado, southern California, and northern Mexico. The food plants of its caterpillars are the lupines and their relatives, though they are rather general feeders on low plants. The caterpillars are black covered with dense spiny hairs.

Virgin Tiger-moth (*Apantesis virgo* L., page 183, figure 11).—The Virgin Tiger-moth is a resident of the northern Atlantic States and Canada. The cream-colored stripes on the black wings made the pioneer American entomologist, T. W. Harris, think of a horse's leather harness, and he named one species of the genus *phalerata* "harnessed."

Showy Holomelina (*Eubaphe ostenta* Hy. Edw.—also known as *Holomelina ostenta,* page 183, figure 12).—As its name implies, the Showy Holomelina is a splendidly colored insect. It has been found in Colorado, New Mexico, Arizona, and across the Rio Grande. Little is known of its life history.

Photograph from International Newsreel

A KALLIMA BUTTERFLY ON THE WING AND AT REST

Note how this native of India when alight simulates a leaf on a twig (see text, page 157).

Photograph by Charles Martin

WHERE THE NATIONAL MUSEUM PRESERVES ITS MOTHS AND BUTTERFLIES

There are many insect foes of museum specimens which must be constantly guarded against by the use of naphthalene preparations.

Photograph courtesy U. S. Department of Agriculture

ONE OF THE SPHINX MOTHS, SHOWING HOW THOROUGHLY
IT BLENDS WITH ITS SURROUNDINGS

When moths alight they, as a rule, fold their somber-hued forewings over their brighter underwings, and the former frequently so merge into the color and apparent texture of their environment as to escape the sharp eyes of their foes. This is known as "protective coloration" in biology, but armies call it "camouflage" in war.

Isabella Tiger-moth (*Isia isabella* A. and S., page 183, figure 13).—The Isabella Tiger-moth is the adult of the clipped woolly bear, the fore part of whose body is covered with black hairs, as is also the tail, but the third quarter of which wears a beautiful surcingle of red, all the hairs of the same length. Lutz says that experiments made by him indicated that those which appear after wet spells wear more black than those which follow dry weather, but this surmise is doubtful.

Crimson-bodied Lichen-moth (*Lerina incarnata* Bdv., page 183, figure 14).—This species is a resident of Arizona and Mexico and is so different from all other species that a special genus was set up by classifiers for its accommodation.

Milk-weed Moth (*Euchaetias egle* Dru., page 183, figure 15).—The Milk-weed Moth claims most of the United States east of the Rocky Mountains

as its territory. Its pretty caterpillars are tufted with black, white, and orange, and may be found, many together, on the backs of milkweed leaves, their favorite food. Be careful when you turn the leaf or they will all drop off.

Ranchman's Tiger-moth (*Platyprepia virginalis* Bdv., page 183, figure 16).—Occupying what was formerly the cowboy country of the West, this species came by its name of Ranchman's Tiger-moth quite naturally. It is common in Colorado, Wyoming, and Montana, and is found in the latitude of these States to the Pacific coast. The larvae are found in grass and garden. They look like our "woolly bears," but the hair is softer.

Fall Web-worm Moth (*Hyphantria cunea* Dru., page 183, figure 17).—The range of the Fall Web-worm Moth extends from southern New England to Texas and westward. Its larvae spin great webs in the foliage of almost all kinds of deciduous trees in the summer and fall, and do much damage to shade trees in nurseries and orchards, the apple and the ash being among its favorites. There is a considerable variation in the markings of both larvae and adults. The pupa weaves a loose cocoon and hibernates in crevices of brick, porous soil, etc. The eggs are laid in flat masses on the under side of leaves.

Arctia americana Harr. (page 183, figure 18).—This species occurs in Canada, New England, and northern New York, the caterpillars much resembling those of the Ranchman's Tiger-moth. It is closely allied to its European representative, *Arctia caja* of Linnaeus.

Adelocephala isias Bdv. (page 185, figure 1).—This species is found in northern Mexico and southern Texas. The food plant of its caterpillar is the mesquite.

White-lined Syssphinx (*Adelocephala albolineata* G. and R.—also known as *Syssphinx albo-*

lineata, page 185, figure 2).—The White-lined Syssphinx is a native of Mexico and Central America which is occasionally encountered in the region immediately north of the Rio Grande.

Honey-locust Moth (*Adelocephala bicolor* Harr., page 185, figure 3). —The Honey-locust Moth has a range that embraces the area from the Great Lakes southward to Georgia and Kansas. Its caterpillars find the honey-locust and the Kentucky coffeetree especially to their taste. They are green, with silver and red thornlike horns.

Royal Walnut-moth (*Citheronia regalis* Fabr., page 185, figure 4).—The Royal Walnut-moth is one of the most attractive of our larger scaly wings. Its caterpillar, on the other hand, wears such an aspect that it has been called the "hickory horn devil" (see illustration, page 154). In the mature caterpillar these horns are reddish, tipped with black. Forbidding as they appear to be, they are quite harmless, as is their owner. These caterpillars feed on the foliage of such trees as walnut, hickory, butternut, ash, persimmon, sweetgum, and sumac. This moth is not uncommon in the Atlantic States.

Rosy Maple-moth (*Anisota rubicunda* Fabr., page 185, figures 5 and 7).—The Rosy Maple-moth ranges from Canada to the Carolinas and westward to Kansas. Its striped caterpillar is a pest of silver maple trees. One scientific observer reports that this moth, once abundant in the Pittsburgh region, is now very scarce there, and attributes its disappearance to a group of adverse conditions, including odors from natural gas wells, flames from many chimneys which attract and destroy millions of adult insects, and the abundance of English sparrows.

Orange-striped Oak-worm Moth (*Anisota senatoria* A. and S., page 185, figure 6).—The Orange-striped Oak-worm Moth is one of five species of its genus found in the United States.

Photograph courtesy U. S. Department of Agriculture

THE MOTH OF ONE OF THE WOOLLY BEAR TRIBE IS ATTACKED BY A SPINED TREE-BUG

In the insect world "every individual's hand is against every other's," and between the parasitic gnats and mites that lay their eggs on the bodies of the caterpillars and the hundreds of insects, birds, and other foes which prey upon the adults, the Lepidopters have a perilous existence at best.

It is an Eastern species, closely related alike to the Stigma Moth and the Virginian Anisota. The hard, striped, horny larvae are so stiff that they can be picked up and held by the tail.

Imperial Moth (*Eacles imperialis* Dru.—also known as *Basilona imperialis,* page 185, figure 8).—The Imperial Moth has a rather wide range, and its caterpillars feed upon such a large variety of trees that they find relished pastures wherever they go. Like the Royal Walnut-moth, it has a wing-spread of five inches. The caterpillars of both of these species burrow into the ground to pupate, spending the winter as rough, brown, naked chrysalids.

Heiligbrodt's Syssphinx (*Adelocephala heiligbrodti* Harv.—also known as *Syssphinx heiligbrodti,* page 185, figure 9).—This species is found in some sections of the Southwest, particularly in

EGGS OF THE ORANGE-STRIPED OAK-WORM MOTH ON AN OAK LEAF

The species of moth that laid these eggs is shown in figure 6 on page 185. Some moths lay only one egg to a leaf or even to an entire bush, while others lay great masses of them. In some cases they lay more than their entire body weight of eggs in a few days.

Arizona. Its caterpillars feed on greasewood bushes.

Stigma Moth (*Anisota stigma* Fabr., page 185, figures 10 and 11).—The Stigma Moth's range extends from Canada to the Carolinas and westward to the Rocky Mountains. Its caterpillars feed upon various species of oak, principally the white oaks, whereas *A. senatoria* favors the black and red oaks.

Mendocino Silk-moth (*Saturnia mendocino* Behr., page 187, figure 1).—The Mendocino Silk-moth is found mainly in northern California. Its caterpillars feed upon manzanita.

Pamina Moth (*Hyperchiria pamina* Neum.— also known as *Automeris pamina,* page 187, figure 2).—This moth is found in Arizona. It is closely related to the more familiar Io Moth (see figures 8 and 9). Its pastures have been devastated by sheep herders and it is now extremely rare, if not extinct.

Range Caterpillar Moth (*Hemileuca oliviae* Ckll., page 187, figure 3).—This is another of the many species of tropical moths which is sparsely found along the southern borders of our South-

west. The caterpillars feed on grass and may destroy miles of grazing land, so that cattle starve.

Luna Moth (*Actias luna* L., page 187, figure 4).—The Luna Moth is found from Canada to Florida, and thence westward to Texas and Mexico. It is noted for its delicate green tinting and exquisite wing symmetry. The caterpillars feed on hickory, walnut, and other forest trees and pupate in thin, but compact, cocoons made of silk and leaves, on the ground.

Buck-moth (*Hemileuca maia* Dru., page 187, figure 5).—The Buck-moth is a day flyer and wanders abroad in the mellow and warm noon-days of the autumn, when the leaves are falling. It frequents the oak and other plants, where it deposits its eggs in clusters. The range of the Buck-moth extends from Nova Scotia to Florida and westward to Kansas. The black, spiny caterpillars feed together in companies until large, following each other in single file down the stems.

Pandora Moth (*Coloradia pandora* Blake, plate 187, figure 6).—The Pandora Moth is a resident of the mountains of the West from Montana and Washington southward to Mexico. The larvae

Photograph courtesy U. S. Department of Agriculture

WOOD-TRIMMED COCOONS OF THE PSYCHE MOTH, COMMONLY CALLED THE BAGWORM

The caterpillar of this moth makes a shell of silk and twigs to protect its tender body, only the head and forelegs remaining exposed. When the time to pupate arrives, the larva merely attaches its house (now a cocoon) securely to a branch, and backs into it and sheds to become a pupa (see text, page 161).

are found on pine trees and are considered a great delicacy by the Indians, who make a, to us, disgusting soup of their bodies.

Pseudohazis eglanterina Bdv. (page 187, figure 7).—This species occupies the Rocky Mountain area and is characteristic of the country of open timber. It is largely a day flyer, darting about through the woods without apparent object. The adults take no food, the mouth parts being aborted. The larvae feed on wild rose and other bushes.

Io Moth (*Hyperchiria io* Fabr.—also known as *Automeris io,* page 187, figures 8 and 9).—The fair Io Moth ranges from Canada to Florida and westward to Texas and Mexico. It has a versatile taste, so that its caterpillars find "skittles and beer" in a large number of species of trees and shrubs, low plants, and even clover. The caterpillars, with their clusters of branching spines, might be called the "curly poodles" of the insect world. The spines are covered with stings, which produce a sensation like nettle when coming in contact with the back of the hand or arm.

Hemileuca electra Wright (page 189, figure 1).—This is a relative of the Buck-moth previously

described (see page 187, figure 5). It is found in southern California.

Ailanthus Silk-moth (*Samia cynthia* Dru.— also known as *Philosamia cynthia,* page 189, figure 2).—The Ailanthus Silk-moth is an immigrant to America. It was imported from eastern Asia and became thoroughly adapted to the eastern seaboard region of the United States. Its importation was for the purpose of founding a silk industry in the United States; but, although it is possible to make a good grade of coarse silk from it by process of carding, no profitable method of reeling the cocoons has been found, and therefore its importation has served no useful purpose. It feeds on the imported ailanthus tree and is a delight to every embryo naturalist.

Agapema anona Ottol. (page 189, figure 3).— This species is found in Mexico and rarely in Arizona. It is a pretty species, but little is known of its habits.

Tricolor Buck-moth (*Hemileuca tricolor* Pack., page 189, figure 4).—Arizona and New Mexico constitute the range of the Tricolor Buck-moth in the United States. Like most of their

REELING SILK IN JAPAN

While the silk of commerce is made from cocoons whose chrysalids have first been killed by heat, the fine old silks of rarer sheen in China were usually woven from strands reeled from live cocoons (see text, page 165).

relatives, its caterpillars feed on the foliage of greasewood.

Polyphemus Moth (*Telea polyphemus* Cram., page 189, figure 5).—This species is widely distributed over the United States and feeds upon a number of trees. Fruitless efforts have been made to reel its silk. The green worms are plaited like an accordion and studded with little red buttons.

Nevada Buck-moth (*Hemileuca nevadensis* Stretch, page 189, figure 6).—This species resembles *H. maia* so much that some authorities class it as only a variety of the latter. Its range extends from the Rocky Mountains to the Pacific.

Rothschildia jorulla West. (page 189, figure 7).—This moth occurs in Arizona, but is more

common in Mexico. The genus to which it belongs is distinctly a neotropical one. These large moths with clear windows in their wings are very striking, being American representatives of the famed Atlas Moth of the East.

Spice-bush Silk-moth (*Callosamia promethea* Dru., page 189, figure 8).—The Spice-bush Silkmoth is found in the entire eastern part of the United States. The spicebush and sassafras are its favorite food plants. In pupating the larvae usually rolls a leaf, tying it with silk, and then spins his cocoon therein, fastening the cocoon to the twig by a band of silk along the leaf stem. Though the fiber of the silk this species makes is rather tough, it is not spun with sufficient system by the present methods to make it available for use, either through carding or reeling.

CHAPTER VIII

Afield with the Spiders

Web Hunting in the Marshlands and Woodlands and Along the Lanes

By HENRY E. EWING

Entomologist, United States Department of Agriculture

FOR the spider enthusiast sojourning in the country, whether in the United States or in any other land of temperate climate, the dawn of a late mid-summer day in a marsh meadow holds promise of delight. It is spider season, the time when the fairy spinners are to be observed at their best, when small, dainty webs, usually overlooked, stand out in perfect design against the green of leaf and grass, the filmy silk glistening with dew.

Webs, webs everywhere—hundreds of them, thousands of them—billow a gossamer sea in the morning light!

There are funnel webs, sheet webs, hammock webs, webs of indescribable shapes, and, finest of all, near the edge of the woods, the beautiful orb webs, bejeweled in their radiant symmetry.

Spiders are marvelous spinners. From the many microscopic spigots at the tips of their heavy abdomens they conjure several kinds of silk with which to construct webs of exquisite design and beauty. They make snares for their prey, sacs for their eggs, shelters for protection from enemies, draglines for security in movement, balloons for navigating the skies, and many other things for service in their varied and romantic lives.

FAMILY STYLES IN WEBS

Although the silken webs are of many different designs, the finery of the individual spider does not change with the passing seasons. Each species has its own style of web, to which all its members adhere so long as

environment remains unaltered by geologic progress.

Students believe the first web, a simple tube, evolved from the draglines used by the spider in going in and out of a hole in the ground, its first retreat. These threads of silk finally lined the nest and radiated from the entrance. Striking against the lines, victims would be detected and seized by the watchful spider.

By extending the sheet about the entrance to the tube and bringing the latter out of the ground, the spider developed the funnel web. The axis of the web was shifted in the course of this change until the tube of the funnel became almost horizontal, and later the lower part was expanded into a net. These changes give us the typical funnel web, such as is spun by the common grass spider, *Agelena naevia* (see illustration, page 217).

Inside the tube of the funnel, especially when this tube leads backward among tangled blades of grasses, the spider still has protection from its enemies. The placing of the web above the ground and the expansion of the lower part of it into a sheet increased its efficiency as an insect snare.

INCREASING THE INSECT CATCH

The tube, which leads away from the sheet part of a funnel web, becomes an inconvenience when webs are placed in exposed positions above the ground; hence the sheet-web weavers leave it out. By spinning the sheet in exposed positions, they are able to increase their catch of flying insects.

Photograph by Lynwood M. Chace

THE GOLDEN GARDEN SPIDER WEAVES A SHROUD

An unwary grasshopper has stepped into the perilous parlor of *Miranda aurantia* (see page 207, lower left), and his hostess quickly spins a winding sheet about him. Although still alive, the victim cannot move a leg (see text, page 219).

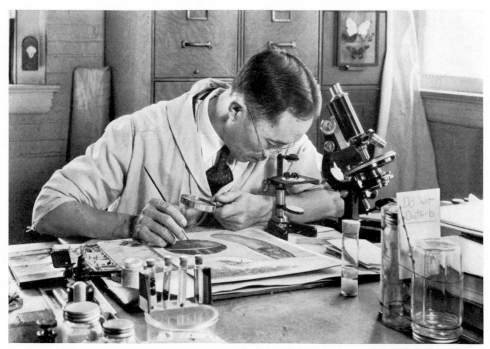

Photograph by Clifton Adams

HASHIME MURAYAMA PAINTS THE FRONTISPIECE FOR THE SPIDER COLOR SERIES

Working with an array of scientific instruments, a versatile artist of the National Geographic Society staff records in water colors the most minute details in the appearance of his subjects. He studied live specimens, kept in the jars at the right, and fed flies and other common insects.

Such closely woven sheets, however, offer dangerous resistance to the wind.

Spiders commonly modify sheet webs in two ways: They may bring the sides of the sheet upward to produce a hammock or bowl (see illustration, page 217), or downward to form a dome (see illustration, page 221).

The advantage of the bowl type is easily noted by observing our bowl and doily spider, *Linyphia communis*. It places its hammocklike web well below the tops of small shrubs or large herbaceous plants and directly under the favorite feeding places of such insects as plant lice and leaf-hoppers. Naturally every disturbance of the twigs and leaves shakes a shower of titbits into the snare.

The dome-shaped web is better suited for catching insects rising from the ground in flight, as many do about dusk or in the morning.

Irregular net webs, haphazard tangles of threads of all lengths, are spun by that annoyer of housewives in all temperate cli-

mates, the common house spider, *Theridion tepidariorum* (see page 206), and by many other species. Once considered primitive, such webs now are regarded as degenerate. They probably represent an evolution from the sheet type, altered to decrease resistance to the wind and to facilitate mending. As fly-traps, they are effective and, in addition, usually serve well for rearing the brood of spiderlings.

Like human fishermen, many spider species have found that a plane net of two dimensions is not only economical of weight and materials but ideal for landing a catch. The orb web, built on this principle, may be put in exposed places, where prey is most plentiful, since with its open construction it offers little resistance to the wind.

Suspended from a framework of stout base lines and carefully spaced to permit freedom of movement in spinning, its threads form a wheellike design of maximum strength with a minimum of material. The spider sits at the hub, ready instantly to

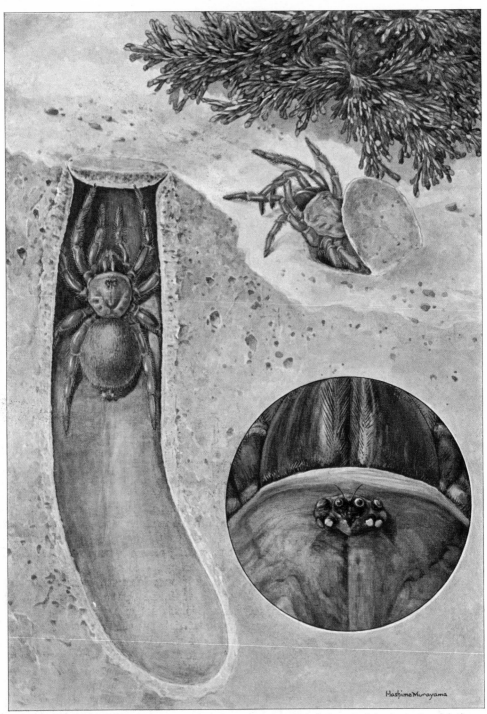

Main figures natural size, inset enlarged six times

ONE KIND OF SPIDER LIVES IN HER OWN CELLAR

This trapdoor species, *Pachylomerus audouini,* common in South Atlantic States, closes her bottlelike basement home with a wafer-type lid, which she operates with her legs. Her California cousin, described in Chapter IX, page 229, makes a cork-type covering and opens it or holds it shut with her fangs and legs. The ocular turret of an eastern specimen is shown in the inset at the right (see text, page 214).

detect a snared victim and pounce upon it. In the net-snare method of catching prey the orb web is the spider's last word. Few, if any, other animals, human or subhuman, have equaled it.

Although the most symmetrical web ever made by a spider is not really perfect, according to human standards, scientists marvel at the accuracy with which angles and distances are "measured."

SPIDER "GEOMETRY" IS INGENIOUS

The spider starts her geometrical web with perimeter lines connecting objects around a space large enough for her purpose. From these lines she suspends a few threads which converge at the center of the future web. Now begins the process of spacing the radii. She attaches the end of a new radius at the center and runs along a spoke already laid down, spinning out the silk for the new one as she goes. When she reaches the perimeter line, she takes a fixed number of steps along it and attaches the new thread. This process is repeated until all the desired radii are in place.

If the foundation lines should chance to form a wheel rim accurately circular, the distances between spokes would be equal; but, since the perimeter is usually an irregular quadrangle and never a circle, the spacing varies somewhat.

The spiral turns of silk, which complete the net, are more accurately spaced than the radii, since the spinner lays down each new turn with her foreleg touching the last one. Thus the length of the forelegs and the size of the spider determine these distances.

"Scout stepping" and use of the "leg ruler" are instinctive in spiders. Even when isolated from its kind from the moment of its birth, a spiderling will produce exactly the same web design as its mother and in exactly the same manner.

THE WORLD'S LOFTIEST DWELLERS

Spiders constitute a large clan of some 25,000 described species. Although most abundant and diversified in the Tropics, they range far into the Arctic regions, and are found almost everywhere that earthly conditions will sustain life.

Far up on Mount Everest, above the highest plant life, at an elevation of 22,000 feet, spiders have been found living among the wind- and snow-swept rocks. Thus they are the loftiest permanent inhabitants of the earth.

Some spiders, such as the trapdoor makers, occupy only a restricted area, while others, such as our common house spider, *Theridion tepidariorum,* are found in many lands and all the continents.

The largest spiders are the American tarantulas, and of these the South American species, *Theraphosa leblondi,* with a body three and a half inches long, is the giant. Its bulk is more than 100,000 times that of the smallest spider known.

In Central America is found its closest rival in size, *Sericopelma communis* (see page 202). South America produces both the Brobdingnagians and the Lilliputians of spiders, one of the latter, *Ogulnius obtectus,* being barely one-twenty-fifth of an inch in length.

Far from typifying masculine strength, aggressiveness, and dominance, the males of many spider species are much smaller than the females, and are such poor spinners that it is difficult for them to procure their own food. Some of them either use snares previously built by females or literally live on the "crumbs from the tables" of their mates. Males, however, are inclined to be more active than females and may be of roving disposition.

In a few species such as the brush-legged spider (see page 209, B), the male, less than one-hundredth the size of the female, is little more than a fertilizing mechanism to insure the perpetuity of the species.

NEW CLOTHES FOR OLD

To allow for the expansion of the soft parts of the body during growth, spiders periodically cast their skins (see page 202), new coats and new claws replacing the old. When tarantulas are exhibited singly, in cages, the sudden appearance of a cast skin, seemingly intact, may cause astonishment on the part of a keeper, who takes it to be another spider. The old skin splits along the sides of the body just above the bases

Approximately one-half natural size

OUR COMMON WESTERN TARANTULA CRAWLS NEATLY OUT OF HIS SKIN

Though fearsome looking, with sharp fangs (lower inset) and large fuzzy body (upper inset), this adult male merits the friendship of his human neighbors in Southwestern States, for he feeds on grasshoppers and roaches. The bite is painful but not poisonous to man (see page 212).

© National Geographic Society   Approximately one-half natural size

MEMBERS OF ONLY ONE SPECIES EXCEED THIS GIANT IN SIZE

The Central American tarantula, *Sericopelma communis,* of which the specimen here shown is an adult male, catches and kills birds, but it is smaller than the *Theraphosa leblondi* of South America. Though extremely painful, its bite does not cause death (see text, pages 201, 203, 205).

of the legs. The suture passes from one side to the other in front, but does not pass around the rear of the body. In an insect, the old skin usually splits down the middle of the back.

The spider, does not, like the caterpillar, spin a cocoon about herself. How, then, does she place her egg mass in the silken sac? The problem puzzled me for years, until a common house spider solved it by a performance before my eyes.

First she spun a cone, or cap-shaped, base (see page 206). She did this by holding her weight with the first and second pairs of legs, rotating the structure with the third pair, and laying on the silk with the back pair.

After completing the base, she forced the egg mass out of the vulva (see page 206). The eggs, covered with a sticky substance, clung together in a ball, which she fixed in place by pushing it upward while she pulled the opposite margin of the silken base down and under it. This accomplished, she more leisurely completed the outline of the sac, thickened it by laying on much more silk, and finally finished it by tamping down the protruding loops with her mouth parts. The whole process of egg-laying and sac-making took about one hour.

SPIDER AVIATORS BUILD AIRSHIPS

Although wingless, spiders can take to the air and reach distant places. Nature has endowed them with the capacity of "balloon" building and given them such remarkable instincts for using these airships that few winged creatures can surpass their flying feats!

Spiders were navigating the skies just as they do today millions of years before man invented the gas-filled silk bag with which he first soared above the earth.

The spider's balloon, like man's, is of silk; but, much simpler, it needs no gas. When its filmy threads are let out they catch the upward currents of air, and thus carry away the tiny aviator. Some spiders, by taking advantage of trade winds, have floated out over oceans and reached islands hundreds of miles from any continental shore.

Spiders may balloon at any time of the year, but it is in October or November, when harvests have been gathered and the golden haze of Indian summer tinges upland and lowland, that the season is at its height for the flight of baby spiderlings. Breaking from the prison walls of their cocoons, they scatter quickly, as if impelled by wanderlust.

Each climbs to the top of some elevated object, and during the heat of the day lets out many filmy strands of silk. As these float upward and away they lift the spinner's abdomen. Then more silk is spun.

Out and out it goes, until finally the spiderling is seen clinging to his perch only by the tips of his legs, so strong is the pull of the silken balloon. Now a little more silk and away goes the aviator, over fields and meadows, over pastures and woodlands, to his future home.

THE ORIGIN OF THE TARANTELLA

Late in the Middle Ages southern Europeans became obsessed by an unreasoning and unreasonable fear of spiders. They dreaded particularly the European tarantula, a medium-sized wolf spider, *Lycosa tarantula,* the bite of which was supposed to cause dizziness and nausea, followed by depressing melancholy and eventually death.

Popular superstition held that only the "medical" choreographers could save *tarantati* (bitten persons). If only the right tune could be found, music and the dance would do the trick. The choreographers professed ability to select suitable music for any "patient."

Skipping and cavorting "with great vigor and variety of steps" made the patient perspire freely, and supposedly the deadly poison left the body with the perspiration. In the wild antics devised to shake off the dread tarantism originated a charming dance, the tarantella.

Superstition and quackery gave way slowly before scientific experiments that proved the tarantulas of Europe really rather harmless. But meanwhile the white settlers of America had come in contact with much larger and more ferocious-looking spiders. The American spiders would

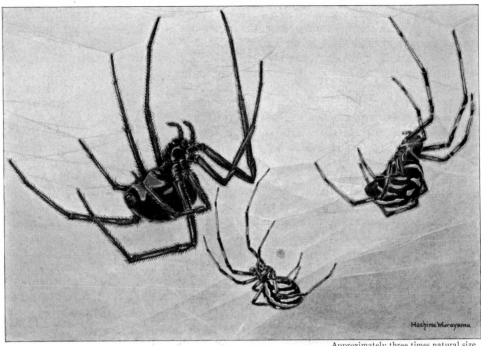

Approximately three times natural size

BEWARE THE BLACK WIDOW, MOST VENOMOUS SPIDER IN THE UNITED STATES

Beautiful but dangerous, *Latrodectus mactans* should be shunned. The adult female (left) measures almost a half inch in length, twice as large as her mate (below). The daughter (right) until mature resembles the father. The species is rare in the North (see text, page 205).

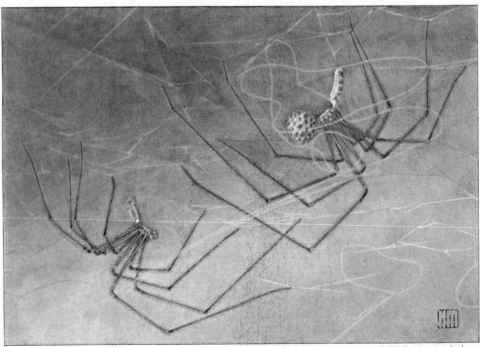

© National Geographic Society   Approximately one and one-half times natural size

NOT DADDY LONGLEGS, BUT SPIDERS

Around back doors or in basements in the warmer countries, pairs of *Pholcus phalangioides* build their irregular webs. The female (right) carries her egg mass in her jaws and feeds little till the young are hatched. The male can take care of himself (see text, page 214).

Photograph by Lynwood M. Chace

MATERNAL INSTINCT IS STRONG AMONG THE SPIDERS

That precious sac—not for one moment will the mother part with it. Females of some species place their eggs on the webs and stand guard over them. Others constantly carry the silk-encased masses in their jaws or tied to the tips of the abdomens. This member of the Dolomedes clan holds her burden with her palpi.

kill little snakes, or toads, or even birds. Naturally these fearsome creatures, though actually Aviculariidae, were called tarantulas and made the object of the same fears and superstitions that had held in Europe.

We know today that there is little justification for fear of our true tarantulas. One member of this group, however, the giant *Sericopelma communis* of Central America (see page 202), appears to be an exception in regard to its venomous nature.

ONE VENOMOUS CLAN IS HEADED BY THE
BLACK WIDOW

Although science has exploded most of the exaggerated fears of spiders in general, it has convicted as dangerously venomous one small group, the genus *Latrodectus*, found throughout most of the warmer countries of the world.

The best-known representative of the clan in the United States is the black widow, *Latrodectus mactans* (see page 204), somewhat common in the South, rare in the North.

These spiders are rather closely related to the common house spider, *Theridion tepidariorum* (see page 206), belonging, as they do, to the same family, the Theridiidae; but they have greatly enlarged poison sacs, and the venom they inject is more potent than that of a rattlesnake!

Fatal cases affecting man are rare; yet numerous fatal cases of *Latrodectus* bite affecting domestic animals have been recorded recently in foreign countries.

Black widows occur in Nature under old logs, about the bases of tree trunks, under loose bark, and in other dark places near the ground. About human habitations they more commonly are found in stables, outhouses, and basements.

The bite of the female (the male is not known to bite man) is followed by a sharp pain. A small white spot soon appears surrounding each puncture point. Within half an hour aching pains arise in other parts of the body, frequently followed by cramped breathing. After a bitten patient

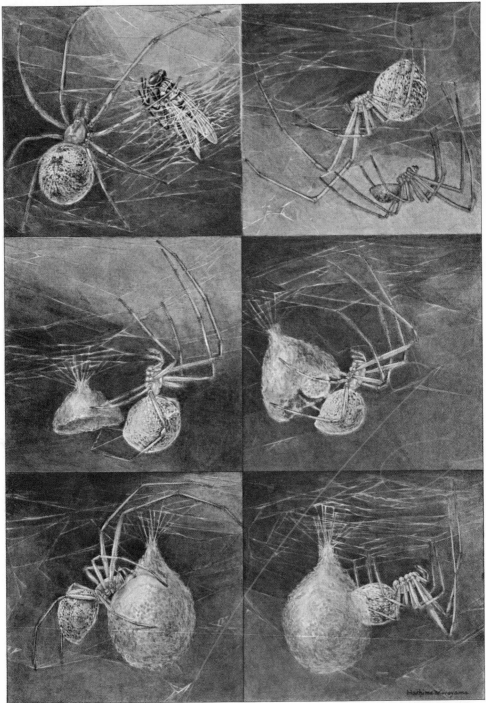

Approximately three times natural size

OUR UNWANTED GUEST, THE HOUSE SPIDER, IS AN INTERESTING NUISANCE

More than any other species, *Theridion tepidariorum* is responsible for the irregular, sticky, dust-catching cobweb; but its habits merit study. An adult female (upper left) obliged the artist by posing in the act of pouncing upon a trapped fly. Another, with her shiftless mate below her (upper right), spun some haphazard threads. A third fashioned a silken base (middle left), placed her egg mass within it (middle right), worked down the loose ends (lower left), and finally rested beside her finished cocoon (lower right). (See text, pages 199, 205, 218.)

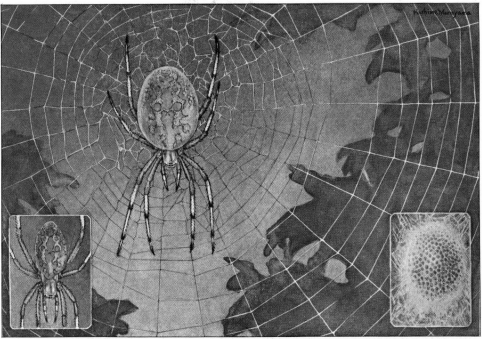

Approximately one and one-half times natural size

HEAVY WITH EGGS, THE FALSE SHAMROCK CLINGS TO HER WEB

One of the showiest of spiders, *Araneus marmoreus,* may be seen in autumn throughout most of North America and in parts of Europe. The female, after laying, becomes much smaller (left inset). She encloses her egg mass in silk (right inset) and then dies.

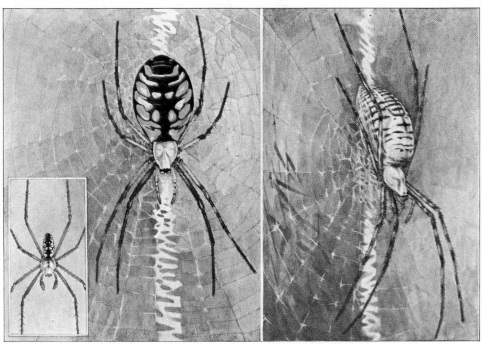

© National Geographic Society   Approximately one and one-half times natural size

GOLDEN GARDEN SPIDERS: BANDED GARDEN SPIDER

The showy specimen at the left, an adult female, *Miranda aurantia,* weaves a large geometrical net over prize blossoms; she eats plant lice. Her "husband" (inset) seems a puny dwarf. *Metargiope trifasciata* (right) is rarer than her cousin. (See text, pages 210, 219.)

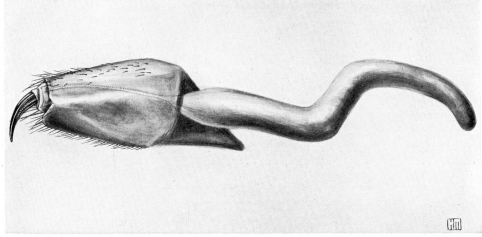

Drawn by Hashime Murayama

OVERSIZE POISON APPARATUS MAKES THE BLACK WIDOW DANGEROUS

In many species, even in the dread tarantula, the sacs which conceal the venom are contained within the jaw structure, but in *Latrodectus mactans* (see page 204) these repositories, of which each individual has two, extend far back of the jaws.

is put to bed, some fever may develop, pains become intense, and delirium ensue. Recovery is nearly always within two weeks (see illustration above).

By careful inspection, premises usually may be cleared of this spider. Not only the live individuals, but also the round, whitish egg sacs, which are placed in the irregular web of the female, should be destroyed. Close screening tends to keep them out of basements.

SPIDER SILK FOR MAN'S USE

The possibility of the utilization of spider silk in the textile industry was investigated in France more than two centuries ago by Bon, a pioneer enthusiast, who collected a large number of spider cocoons, obtained a quantity of very fine gray silk from them, and made of it some daintily colored stockings and gloves. When he exhibited his product before the Academy of Sciences of Paris, that body was so much impressed that in 1710 it commissioned the entomologist Réaumur to investigate the possibilities of utilizing spider silk as a textile.

Réaumur began his inquiry with high hope and enthusiasm, but when he had finished it he was compelled to recognize certain insurmountable difficulties.

The spider silk was inferior to that of the silk-worm; the so-called cocoons, in reality merely egg sacs, which only half of the spider population would produce, contained disappointingly little thread; and the spinners themselves were carnivorous, irritable, and belligerently opposed to crowding. It was almost impossible to provide them with enough food of the proper kind, and to isolate individuals so as to keep them from fighting.

Since Réaumur, others have taken up the problem of finding a way to utilize spider silk. Professor Wilder, stationed in South Carolina as an Army surgeon during the Civil War, became interested in the spinning ability of our brush-legged spider, *Nephila clavipes* (see page 209, B), and made extensive investigations. He sought to obtain the thread, not from the cocoons, but directly from the abdomen of the spider.

Devices for reeling the threads from spiders had already been made by others, but he improved upon them. He computed that one spider would yield at successive reelings a grain of silk, that 450 spiders would produce enough thread for one yard of silk, and that 5,400 would produce enough silk for a lady's dress.

Although spider silk proved impractical for textile use, the improvement of optical instruments brought with it a real

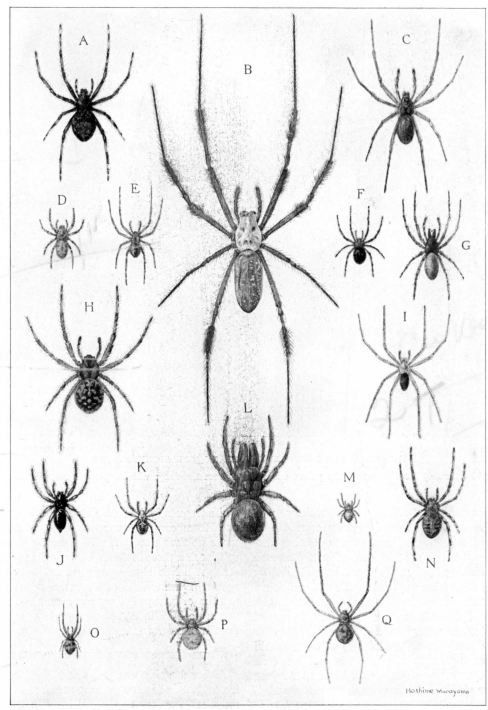

Natural size

FABRICS OF MANY DESIGNS COME FROM THESE ASSORTED SPINNERS' LOOMS

A, *Araneus benjaminus,* H, *Araneus trifolium,* K, *Araneus labyrintheus,* N, *Araneus vulgaris,* and P, *Araneus thaddeus,* make typical orb webs. B, *Nephila clavipes,* is a silk spider. C, *Filistata hibernalis,* D, *Amaurobius bennetti,* M, *Hyptiotes cavatus,* and O, *Uloborus americanus,* are hackled-band weavers. E, *Linyphia phrygiana,* spins a sheet. F, *Steatoda borealis,* produces mere cobwebs, and L, *Atypus abbotii,* fashions a tube. G, *Dysdera crocata,* I, *Loxosceles rufescens,* and Q, *Scytodes longipes,* have six eyes. J, *Zelotes ater,* is a drassid, moss spider (see pages 214, 218, 219, 224, 225).

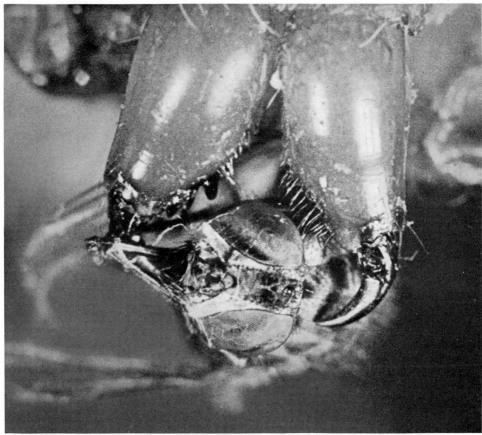

NO HOPE FOR THE FLY CAUGHT IN THE SPIDER'S JAWS

Fortunately for the victim, the poison which flows from the fangs will bring quick insensibility and death.

commercial need for the silk in making a precision device. In range finders, certain types of microscopes, and other optical instruments, it was highly desirable to have the circular field of vision precisely divided by as fine a line as possible. For this purpose a thread of spider silk was the best to be found.

Spider silk, used as cross-hairs in optical instruments, is taken in autumn either directly from the abdomen of the arachnid or from its cocoons. It is reeled out on open cards, which are filed away for future use. For this purpose orb weavers are used, three of the favorite species being *Epeira diademata, Zilla atrica,* and *Miranda aurantia* (see page 207, lower left).

When spider silk is obtained directly from the abdomen of the spider it is usually observed to be composed of several strands. Quite frequently four such strands, coming each from one of four specialized glands, make up the thread. A skilled worker can split such a thread into its four components and get a fine element for use in instruments. Spider silk retains its elasticity for months, or even years, and when cross-hairs are in position in an instrument they may remain in use for many years.

WATER SPIDERS AND SNAKE CATCHERS

Although spiders are typical air-breathing animals, a few species have acquired the remarkable ability to descend beneath the water and remain there for long periods. The diving spider takes down with it an "oxygen tank" in the form of a large air bubble, which surrounds the whole of the abdomen and much of the cephalothorax.

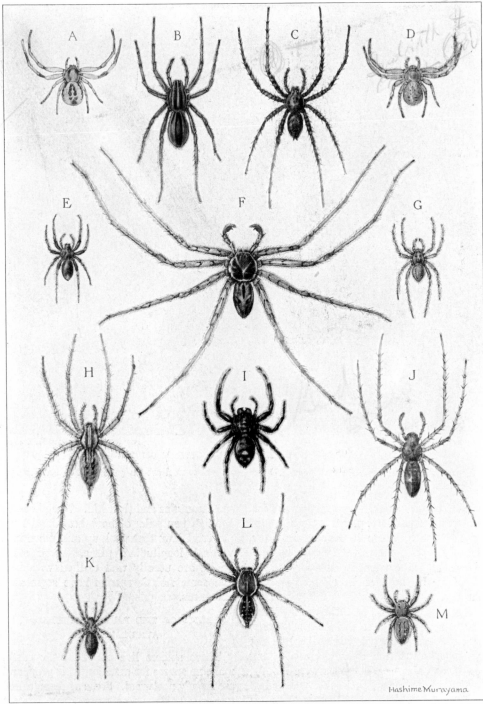

Hashime Murayama

Natural size

MENAGERIE CHARACTERS AND ATHLETES PREDOMINATE IN THIS LOT

A, *Misumenoides aleatorius,* D, *Xysticus limbatus,* and F, *Heteropoda venatoria,* are crab spiders. B, *Lycosa punctulata,* is the wolf, and J, *Peucetia viridans,* the lynx. C, *Dolomedes urinator,* and L, *Dolomedes triton,* excel as divers; and I, *Phidippus audax,* M, *Phidippus clarus,* as acrobats (jumpers). "Brush-footed" describes E, *Castaneira descripta,* and "Wandering" G, *Anahita punctulata.* H, *Agelena naevia,* and K, *Coelotes fidelis,* fall into the group of funnel weavers (see text, pages 225, 226, 227, 228).

Photograph by Lynwood M. Chace

NIGHT HANGS JEWELS IN DAINTY PATTERN ON THIS WEB

The shamrock spider (see text, page 225) weaves a symmetrical orb design that lends itself to dew adornment.

A foreign species, *Argyroneta aquatica,* builds among aquatic plants a dome-shaped air container, where it devours its prey, casts its skin, mates, and lays its eggs. Fresh air is carried to this submerged domicile in bubbles brought from the surface.

One observer reports seeing a 6-inch garter snake caught in the web of *Teutana triangulosa.* Although the snake had not yet stopped writhing, the spider was feeding on it, and the sucked tissues were bloody, soft, and pulpy. The snake weighed 8 grams, the spider only 0.0225 gram after its full meal.

The valiant arachnid had successfully caught a victim more than 350 times its own weight.

The most generalized of the spiders are the tarantulas and their kin. They breathe through two pairs of book-lungs and have powerful jaws that work up and down in a vertical, longitudinal plane. Their stout bodies are usually well clothed with hair and some Asiatic species have segmented abdomens.

RELICS OF THE PAST—LIPHISTIIDAE, AVICULARIIDAE

These spiders live on or in the earth, make no snares for catching their prey, and are largely nocturnal. Some of them, called trapdoor spiders (see page 200), protect their tunnellike nests with hinged doors.

Tarantulas occur in the warmer parts of the world. Our common Western tarantula, *Eurypelma californica* (see page 202), active at night only, passes the day in its

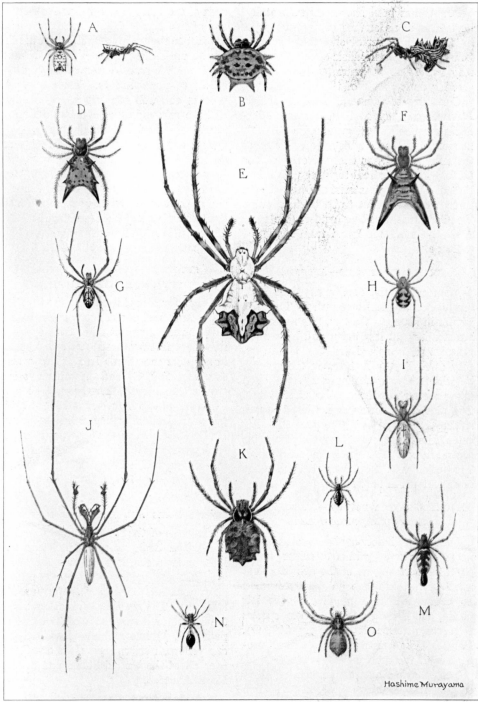

Hashime Murayama

Approximately one and one-half times natural size

PERFECTLY HARMLESS DESPITE THEIR FORMIDABLE APPEARANCE

A, *Micrathena reduviana*, B, *Gasteracantha cancriformis*, C, *Micrathena gracilis*, D, *Micrathena sagittata*, and F, *Micrathena obtusospina*, are spined spiders. E, *Argiope argentata*, is a garden spider. G, *Leucauge venusta*, and its relative M, *Leucauge lugens*, weave horizontal orb webs. H, *Teutana triangulosa*, contents itself with cobwebs. The spiny-jawed species are represented here by I, *Tetragnatha laboriosa*, and J, *Tetragnatha elongata*. Others on the page are a typical orb weaver, K, *Araneus stellatus*; a sheet-web weaver, L, *Linyphia communis*; a mimic, N, *Synemosyna formica*; and a crab spider, O, *Tmarus angulatus* (see text, pages 218, 219, 224, 225, 226, 228).

hole. As has been shown experimentally, its bite is of no serious consequence; yet its fangs are powerful enough to bring a flow of blood. Individuals of this tarantula may live 14 to 16 years, or even longer, growing during most of the time.

Our common Eastern trapdoor spider, *Pachylomerus audouini* (see page 200), digs a deep hole in the ground, lines it with fine silk, and finally adds a waferlike lid of the same material as that surrounding her home. The lid is held together with silken threads and sticky material and hinged with threads of silk. Not to be confused with the California trapdoor spider (see page 229), this species is found from Maryland to Texas.

TUBE-WEB SPIDERS—ATYPIDAE

Members of the family Atypidae have been called atypical tarantulas. They are similar in shape to the true tarantulas, but are smaller and less hairy and have more conspicuous jaws. Like the tarantulas, they dwell largely in holes in the ground, but the linings of the holes are continued above the surface of the soil as silken tubes. Our most common species, the purse-web spider, *Atypus abbotii* (see page 209, L), extends its tube upward from the ground for several inches. The species is found in isolated colonies in the Eastern States, but is more common in the South.

HACKLED-BAND WEAVERS—ULOBORIDAE, DICTYNIDAE, FILISTATIDAE

Pictures of inaction and desolation are never complete without spider webs stretched across some of the débris. That small geometrical web on the weeds near an abandoned farm building is the lair of an odd-looking spider of the species *Uloborus americanus* (see page 209, O). Her brushlike front legs are out of all proportion to the others.

The triangle-shaped web on the half-dead currant bush, looking exactly like a section of an orb web and having four radii and a complement of transverse strands, belongs to the triangle spider, *Hyptiotes cavatus* (see page 209, M).

Let us look closer at this web. Now we see a single line of thread running from the apex of the triangle to a twig. At the twig end of this line is the spider herself, holding fast to the twig, and pulling on the line of silk until there are loose folds between her legs. We soon see what she is up to—all set to throw a trap. When an insect touches the web she lets go of the line, and the rebounding web throws its sticky strands against the victim.

The old cellar walls of the ruins are decorated with silk-lined holes, each with its radiating strands or bands of silk. Our hand lens discovers three or four kinds of silk in the bands. Some of these are made by *Amaurobius bennetti* (see page 209, D). The most beautiful ones are made by *Filistata hibernalis* (see page 209, C).

SIX-EYED SPIDERS—DYSDERIDAE, SCYTODIDAE, AND OTHERS

Originally all spiders had eight eyes, but many have lost one or more pairs. A few cave species have lost all of their eyes—an important fact for those to note who believe in adaptive evolution. In *Dysdera crocata* (see page 209, G) and the other two species here mentioned, there are only six eyes. The eyes of *Dysdera crocata*, all of about the same size, are arranged in a half circle. In *Loxosceles rufescens* (see page 209, I) the eyes are arranged in three pairs. In the long-legged, subtropical *Scytodes longipes* (see page 209, Q) the six eyes are pearly white.

MOSS SPIDERS AND RELATIVES—DRASSIDAE

Members of the spider family Drassidae abound in damp woodlands, where they hide under rocks, logs, or in moss. They are eight-eyed spiders, with only two tarsal claws to a leg. The eyes are arranged in two rows. The genus *Zelotes* includes more than a hundred species. *Zelotes ater* (see page 209, J) has a shiny black abdomen and yellowish brown legs. It is distributed over all of the United States and most of North America.

SOME LONG-LEGGED SPIDERS—PHOLCIDAE

Probably the longest-legged spiders are to be found in the family Pholcidae. One very common species, *Pholcus phalangioides* (see page 204), has such long legs that it is frequently taken for a daddy longlegs.

Photograph courtesy U. S. Department of Agriculture

A EUPHORBIA PLANT NEAR KANDY, CEYLON, SUPPORTS A SILKEN COOPERATIVE
APARTMENT

Community spiders, unlike most other species of the spinners, are gregarious and enjoy close association with their fellows. They spin their webs together, often completely covering a large shrub or even a tree.

Photograph by George R. King

INSECTS SHOULD HEED THE WARNING

Not only motorists but small-winged creatures have reason to read this sign. The orb web on the left is in perfect condition; that on the right either was abandoned before completion or damaged after construction.

Photograph from Keystone-Underwood

A PAIR OF SPIDERS CONSTITUTE THEMSELVES HANGMEN

This battle was fought in a cellar at Elgin, Illinois. Probably the victim became tangled in the web accidentally as it lifted its head, and the spiders immediately bound it fast with additional threads.

216

Photographs by Henry E. Ewing

THE BOWL AND DOILY SPIDER WEAVES A DOUBLE WEB

For her filmy home *Linyphia communis* spins two sheets, one above the other. The upper, or "bowl," is concave; the lower, or "doily," is a horizontal plane (see text, pages 199, 218; also compare illustration, page 220).

THE GRASS SPIDER WEAVES A FUNNEL WEB

Though her home is usually on lower vegetation, this spinner sometimes builds in evergreen trees, as in this case. She sits near the mouth of the tube (at the arrow point), awaiting her victims (see text, pages 197, 226).

Photograph by Lynwood M. Chace

ALL SET FOR A DOWNWARD FLIGHT

Araneus needs no parachute, for she has attached to a leaf a thread of silk which, as it spins out from her abdomen, will lower her gradually. To return, she will simply reel up her line.

black widow, *Steatoda borealis* (see page 209, F), may frighten the timid or uninformed, but this near relative of the black widow, *Latrodectus mactans* (see text, page 205), is entirely harmless.

SHEET-WEB WEAVERS— LINYPHIIDAE

One summer, at my Maryland home, a bowl and doily spider, *Linyphia communis* (see page 213, L) made her web on a sweetpea vine directly in front of the porch swing. Whenever I rested in the swing that summer I had a ring-side seat for observing this dainty little sheet-web weaver. She built a snare composed of two sheets (see illustration, page 217), one above the other. The upper sheet was strongly concave and the lower flat and almost horizontal. The female clung to the underside of the "bowl," ready, when a victim was snared, to force her fangs or her entire body through the silken mesh.

A near relative of the bowl and doily spider is our hammock spider, *Linyphia phrygiana* (see page 209, E), which constructs a netted sheet more or less quadrangular and suggesting a hammock.

SPINY-JAWED SPIDERS—ARGIOPIDAE; TETRAGNATHINAE

The spiny-jawed spiders, particularly the males, are remarkable for their jaw development. The jaws are not only much enlarged, but are thrust out in front of the body and provided with conspicuous spines. Most spiny-jawed species are rather small;

No journey is necessary to see the makers of cobwebs or irregular nets. The common house spider, *Theridion tepidariorum* (see page 206), is the most easily observed representative and is present in all countries of temperate climate.

While we are studying the house spider we may find some irregular strands of silk in the lower angle of a window with a specimen of *Teutana triangulosa* (see page 213, H) on them. This spider has a strong hankering for the lower angle of a window.

Most of the makers of the irregular nets deserve our confidence and friendship, though the venomous members of the genus *Latrodectus* should be left alone. The false yet to their little victims they must appear most ferocious.

Tetragnatha laboriosa (see page 213, I) is common in meadows, where it spins an orb web. It is distributed from Alaska to the West Indies. The extreme characteristics of the spiny-jawed spiders are exhibited in *Tetragnatha elongata* (see page 213, J), a species found in damp situations throughout the United States and most of North America.

A HORIZONTAL ORB-WEB WEAVER AND ITS RELATIVES—ARGIOPIDAE; METINAE

One August morning, in a sunshiny woodland lane near the Potomac River above Great Falls, I came upon many finely spun, beautifully woven orb webs placed almost or entirely in horizontal position. Looking closely at some of these webs, I found a most exquisitely colored spider. It was a bright green with an elaborate design of silvery white, tinted with gold, and spotted below with coppery red.

This spider beauty was *Leucauge venusta* (see page 213, G), one of the most strikingly decorated of all our spiders. It has a Mexican cousin, *Leucauge lugens* (see page 213, M), in which the beauty is marred by the presence of a peculiar taillike projection at the tip of the abdomen.

SILK SPIDERS—ARGIOPIDAE; NEPHILINAE

All spiders spin silk, but members of the subfamily Nephilinae spin so much that they have been used in the attempts to

Photograph by H. H. Seaton

MORNING MIST MAKES A NECKLACE OF PEARLS

Exquisitely framed in Adirondack evergreens, this symmetrical masterpiece of the orb-weaver's spinning gleams in the sun.

establish a spider-silk industry (see text, page 208). The one well-known species found in the United States is the brush-legged spider, *Nephila clavipes* (see page 209, B). No spider is more easily recognized than this large orb weaver. Each leg, except those of the third pair, bears one or more whorls of fine setae, so arranged as to suggest a bottle brush. A foreign species of the same genus, *Nephila*, was once observed catching a bird in its web (see illustration, page 224).

GARDEN SPIDERS—ARGIOPIDAE; ARGIOPINAE

When I was a boy in the Middle West I observed a garden spider that spread its beautiful geometrical web across my mother's flower bed. The creature's size,

Photograph by W. B. Johnstone

THE SIERRA DOME SPIDER SETS ITS SNARE FOR INSECTS IN FLIGHT

Every species has its own design peculiarly adapted to its needs. *Linyphia litigiosa* spins this inverted bowl; its cousin, *Linyphia communis*, makes a similar trap right side up (see text, pages 199, 218).

Photograph by Lynwood M. Chace

FROM SETS OF SPINNERETS THE SPIDER CONJURES HER SILK

Each of the fingerlike organs (greatly magnified in the photograph) can turn out a thread. Frequently there are not five but six in each group; the one showing white at the right is a fusion of two.

EVEN THE HUGE BUMBLEBEE FALLS VICTIM

The golden garden spider quickly binds her struggling catch with silk from her spinnerets. After draining the juices from the huge carcass, she will cut the thread holding it to the net and let the empty shell fall. Her indolent mate may feed on what she leaves (see text, page 219).

Photographs by Lynwood M. Chace

SPIDERS SOMETIMES HAVE MARITAL DIFFICULTIES

"Husbands," being much the smaller, usually get the worst of it in family fights. However, stories about females luring unsuspecting swains into their webs to gratify hunger have no foundation in fact. After the mating, the male of this pair of the Araneus clan may be devoured, but more likely he will become merely a boarder in the household (see text, page 219).

© Lieut. S. E. Richardson, R. A. F.

GOSSAMER BLANKETS ENHANCE THE CHARM OF THE SILKEN EAST

In the Hangu Valley, India, spiders spread their filmy lace so thickly over large patches of low-growing vegetation as to conceal the foliage. Dew does not form here; the whiteness of the webs is due to the extraordinary multiplicity of the strands.

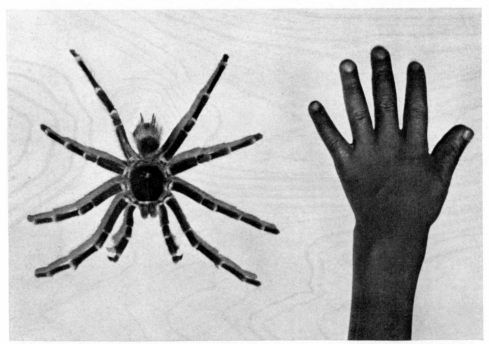

Photograph by Hugh B. Cott

WITH A SPREAD LARGER THAN A BOY'S HAND, THE MALE BRAZILIAN TARANTULA
LOOKS FORMIDABLE

His fuzzy tentacles are not so thick as at first glance they appear, the light stripes being shadows. From the sides of the jaws extend the palpi, by which mating is accomplished—two leglike projections with ends resembling feet.

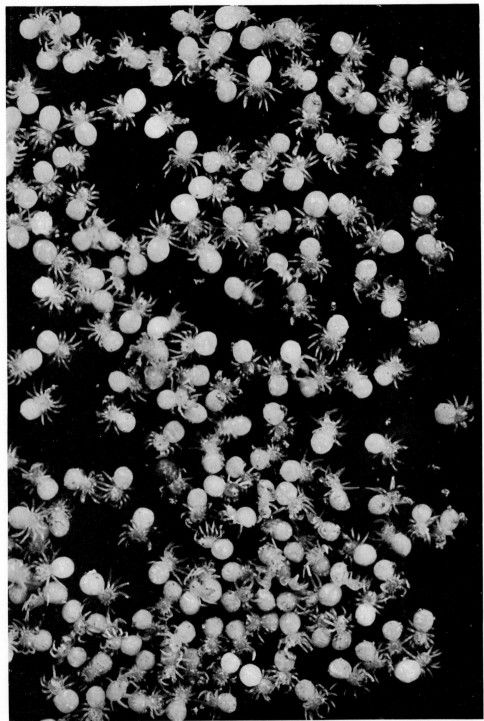

NEWLY HATCHED TRAPDOOR SPIDERS RESEMBLE PEARLS EQUIPPED WITH
WRIGGLING LEGS

The spiderlings change color as they grow older, becoming pale pink and then a darker shade. A little later, although they are no larger than grains of rice, they can spray a tiny web from their spinnerets and build a miniature nest. Few of the original 300 spiderlings live to maturity. Sometimes the mother will crush one of her offspring between her jaws, so that the other members of her family may partake of the juices. The figures are enlarged about four times.

SUCH JUNGLE TRAGEDY AS THIS, IN JAVA, IS UNUSUAL

Seldom does a snare-weaving spider catch a bird. The little flower pecker has flown into the web of a large *Nephila.*

its brilliant golden markings, and the expanse of its web compelled my attention.

Although the web was entangled among some of the most prized flowers of the garden, the spider was not disturbed, for young grasshoppers made up most of its diet.

Garden spiders build geometrical webs almost vertical in position and frequently as much as two feet in diameter. The snares, placed on low-growing vegetation, have at the center vertical zigzag bands of glistening white silk. Here the female patiently rests, head downward.

By far the most common species in the United States is the golden garden spider, *Miranda aurantia* (see page 207, below, left). The female is more than an inch long, but the male (see page 207, below, inset) is puny, being scarcely a fourth as long as the female and sometimes only a fiftieth of her weight. Less common is the banded garden spider, *Metargiope trifasciata* (see page 207, below, right), a whitish species tinged with yellow and conspicuously marked with irregular dark bands.

In the silvered garden spider, *Argiope argentata* (see page 213, E), the abdomen of the female is produced laterally into three pairs of large tuberclelike lobes.

TYPICAL ORB WEAVERS—ARGIOPIDAE; ARANEINAE

In open places and among flowers, where there are many flying insects, the typical orb weavers abound. *Araneus benjaminus* (see page 209, A) is common in Maryland and Virginia flower gardens. Its generic brother, *Araneus vulgaris* (see page 209, N), also loves the flower garden. The lattice spider, *Araneus thaddeus* (see page 209, P), builds a beautiful latticelike web, stretched across the underside of a slightly curled leaf.

As we pass along the hedges we may find the beautiful labyrinth spider, *Araneus labyrintheus* (see page 209, K), which builds two distinct types of webs situated together, thus having a composite home.

The most permanent part of this double house is an irregular net of the type built by the cobweb weavers. To this is added

A FEMALE SPIDER FIVE MINUTES AFTER SHEDDING

She appeared like a wax model and was almost transparent, as she rested by her cast-off covering at the right.

an incomplete orb. Near the central part of the irregular net the female builds a retreat and concealment nest of a few small dead leaves tied together with silk.

In a ramble in summer sunshine we may find the star spider, *Araneus stellatus* (see page 213, K), which has about a dozen spinelike tubercles around the margin of the abdomen; but to see the gorgeous shamrock spider, *Araneus trifolium* (see page 209, H), we must make a trip in the autumn. This spider frequently has a three-lobed spot, shaped like a clover leaf, on the middle of the anterior half of the abdomen.

SPINED SPIDERS—ARGIOPIDAE;
GASTERACANTHINAE

If you live in one of the Southern States, take a walk in the woods some bright summer afternoon. Suddenly you will come upon a large geometrical web stretched from one branch to another. At the very hub of the web is a black and yellow object resembling a bur. This spined object is the female of the spined spider, *Gasteracantha cancriformis* (see page 213, B).

Most of our spined spiders, however, have a longer body than this one and do not resemble a bur so closely. *Micrathena reduviana* (see page 213, A) has only two pairs of spines, both very small.

The spear-head spider, *Micrathena sagittata* (see page 213, D), has three conspicuous spines. The tropical spear-head spider, *Micrathena obtusospina* (see page 213, F), has only two pairs, but they are enormous. *Micrathena gracilis* (see page 213, C) has five pairs.

CRAB SPIDERS, LARGE AND SMALL—
THOMISIDAE AND HETEROPODIDAE

Crab spiders are so named because of their resemblance in shape to crabs. The likeness results from the flattening of the body and the assumption of a lateral direction by the legs. One species, *Misumenoides aleatorius* (see page 211, A), lives in flowers. It may be almost uniformly white or yellow or strikingly marked with reddish brown above. This spider has a tendency to take on the color of the flower it inhabits, thus becoming almost invisible.

© Lee Passmore

A TRAPDOOR SPIDER ON WATCH

A spider will remain for hours with the lid slightly raised, while she waits for her prey. When the vibrations set up by the footfalls of an approaching insect warn her, she leaps out and grasps her victim. Movement is so rapid the eye can scarcely follow.

have the legs extending laterally from the body.

The best-known member of the group is the large banana spider, *Heteropoda venatoria* (see page 211, F). This is a tropical species that frequently arrives in our northern cities on bunches of bananas and is commonly mistaken for a tarantula. Its bite is sharply painful, but not dangerous.

The female makes a flat, waferlike egg sac, which she carries about under her body by means of her mouth parts. Once I took an egg sac from a female banana spider and gave her in its place a substitute of the same size and shape which I had whittled out of pine. She readily accepted the imitation sac.

Spiders of the small family Ctenidae love to roam. One of these ramblers, *Anahita punctulata* (see page 211, G), is found in the Southern States.

The genus *Xysticus* (see page 211, D) includes about a third of all our crab spiders. Members of this genus are usually either fawn-colored or brownish. Their life is spent in seclusion, under stones or the loose bark of trees, or in other situations away from the eyes of enemies. The angulate crab spider, *Tmarus angulatus* (see page 213, O), differs decidedly from many other members of the family in having the abdomen high and pointed behind.

Related to the true crab spiders are the members of the family Heteropodidae, known as the giant crab spiders. They also

Far different in their disposition are the members of the family Clubionidae. They appear to be possessed of an inferiority complex. One of them will roll up a leaf and hide away in it as if all the world were gloomy and sinister. Another will pick out a cranny in the side of a cliff or wall. Many of the species are less retiring and some are light-colored, with conspicuous black cushions of hairs at the tips of the legs. One species, *Castaneira descripta*, is pictured on page 211, E.

Funnel-web spiders (Agelenidae) abound

in summer wherever there are moisture and vegetation. Usually they build near the ground; or, if far above the ground, in a thick growth of vegetation such as a hedge or an evergreen tree. Our common grass spider, *Agelena naevia* (see page 211, H), is the best-known funnel-web maker. It is common in many places in the United States. The tube of its web (see illustration, page 217) almost invariably leads back into a thick growth of vegetation. Thus, when the spider retreats, it is safe from its enemies.

A small cousin of the grass spider is *Coelotes fidelis* (see page 211, K), which does not spin a perfect funnel web.

DIVING SPIDERS AND THEIR RELATIVES— PISAURIDAE

Some of the members of the family Pisauridae are called diving spiders. They belong to the genus *Dolomedes* and make interesting aquaria inhabitants. I have kept several individuals of *Dolomedes triton* (see page 211, L) at different times in large aquaria jars. This species is called the six-spotted diving spider and is the most striking in color and marking.

One female kept in an aquarium, where she had been supplied vegetation above the water, lived for months and made her spherical egg sac. This she held closely in her mouth parts and only once could she be induced to drop it to feed.

Dolomedes urinator (see page 211, C) is rather somber-colored. It is found in marshy places in the eastern part of the United States.

WOLF SPIDERS—LYCOSIDAE

Spring is the time for wolf spiders. They may be found running through the grass, along woodland paths, and in many other places. They catch their prey by chasing and springing catlike upon victims.

The maternal instinct is best developed in this group. Not only do the females carry their egg sacs with them, firmly attached to the spinnerets by bundles of silken threads, but the young spiders are carried upon their mother's back for days after hatching. *Lycosa punctulata* (see page

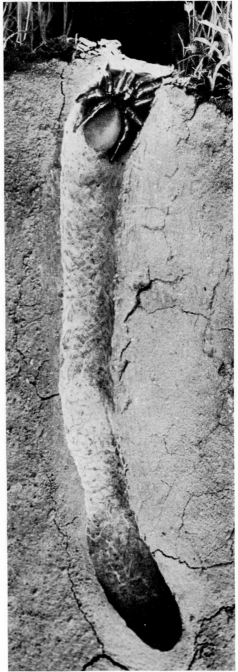

© Lee Passmore

A TRAPDOOR SPIDER IN HER LAIR

The indentations made by the spider's fangs are visible through the silken lining. The spider is in the position in which she waits under her door for her prey. The soil in which the nest was built was gray adobe. This nest is about two-thirds natural size.

211, B) is a striped species common in the eastern part of the United States.

LYNX SPIDERS—OXYOPIDAE

Members of the small family Oxyopidae chase their prey swiftly among trees and shrubs, even leaping from one branch to another. Their legs are long and each is armed with three terminal claws. The eyes are eight in number, dark in color, and unequal in size. *Peucetia viridans* (see page 211, J) is a most beautiful representative of the group. It is a large species, having a bright, transparent green as a background color and markings of red, brown, and black.

ACROBATS AND MIMICS—ATTIDAE

One warm spring morning, as I was passing along one of the drives in the Zoological Park at Washington, I saw a large specimen of the audacious jumping spider, *Phidippus audax* (see page 211, I) sitting on top of a fence post. As I reached out to collect her in my insect bottle, she followed my hand with her eyes. No matter the direction from which I approached, she always changed her position and faced my hand. Finally she was captured and I decided to make a pet of her.

On many occasions this spider attacked and captured victims twice her size. She would pay no attention to a fly until it was within a few inches. Then her eyes would be fixed on the victim, following its every movement for a few seconds. At length a well-aimed leap ended the affair.

Before a jumping spider jumps it always fastens a line of silk to its resting place. Thus, however far it may go over a precipice, it is always safe from a fall. By means of the silken line, it can regain its former position.

In *Phidippus clarus* (see page 211, M)

the female has the cephalothorax and abdomen red, and the male has only the abdomen red, the rest of the body being black.

Certain jumping spiders, as well as other kinds, have a remarkable ability to mimic ants, a fact unknown to me during my early experience as an entomologist.

This mimicry is not usually in appearance only, but frequently it is in the movements of the body as well; and it is not confined to any one family or group of spiders, but occurs in several of them.

Among the jumping spiders, or Attidae, mimicry is probably most prevalent. The mimicry may be confined to one sex or it may involve both sexes. It may be a general imitation (*i. e.*, a spider may take on an external form somewhat similar to that of many ant species), or specific aping by one spider of a single ant species.

In the case of the common ant spider, *Synemosyna formica* (see page 213, N), the antlike appearance is brought about by the unusual shape and rather small size of the cephalothorax, which in these respects resembles the ant's head; by the narrowing of the anterior part of the abdomen to suggest the ant's waist; and by attenuation of the front legs, which are held in such a manner as to suggest the antennae of an ant.

In addition to these changes in form, certain color markings aid in making the deception nearly perfect. Thus the front legs look narrower than they really are because of their white outer margins. The same thing is true of the anterior part of the abdomen.

The advantage gained by this mimicry is important where the mimicked ant species is pugnacious and unpalatable. Some tropical species repeatedly fool experienced entomologists; even a hand lens does not easily aid in the recognition of Nature's deception.

CHAPTER IX

California Trapdoor Spider Performs Engineering Marvels

By LEE PASSMORE

With Illustrations from Photographs by the Author and F. E. Beck

RETURNING one May evening from a ramble over the southern California foothills, I came across a young man busily digging in a small mossy knoll. He was so engrossed in his work that he did not become aware of my presence until my shadow fell upon the object which was attracting his attention.

With apologies for my intrusion, I asked what he was digging. He turned with a pleasant smile and replied, "Trapdoor spiders."

Then, reaching down into the hole, he handed me a strange tubular object, warning me that it was exceedingly fragile—an exceptionally fine specimen of a cork-type spider's nest.

The burrow, or nest, about ten inches long by one and a half inches wide, was built in adobe soil. Fitting neatly in its upper end was a door, hinged with tough web. The under surface of this cover and the walls of the tube were lined with smooth, silky web of lustrous, velvety appearance.

THE SPIDER HOLDS HER TRAPDOOR SHUT

I had difficulty in raising the door; the owner of the nest strenuously objected!

The spider had placed her two fangs in the holes she had made in the underside of the lid and, bracing herself, held on for dear life. Even after my superior strength had overcome hers, she allowed herself to be lifted partly out of her nest before she let go and dropped back into the dark interior. As soon as I let the door snap into place, she returned and got another grip.

This chance meeting was the beginning of my close association with Francis Beck, who for 13 years has studied the habits of the common California trapdoor spider (*Bothriocyrtum californicum*). So deeply interested was I with the specimen shown me that I gladly accepted his invitation to inspect his collection.

I found him working at his home next day under the trees, where he had placed in a natural setting the many specimens which he had brought from the neighboring hills. Here, in boxes of adobe soil, I saw big spiders, little spiders, young and old, in dozens of "transplanted" nests. There were several hundred young ones, which had been hatched during their parents' captivity from eggs contained in the nests at the time of their removal (see illustration, page 231).

Ever alert and watchful, trapdoor spiders are extremely sensitive to the vibrations of insects as they walk over the ground or moss. They seem to know the right instant to raise the door, spring out, and make a capture. Then, dropping back to the bottom of the burrow, they feast at leisure. Movement is so rapid that the insect is within the grasp of the hungry spider before the victim can escape (see illustration, page 233).

PATIENCE AND WATCHFUL WAITING REVEAL INGENIOUS NESTS

Hundreds of sow bugs and other nocturnal insects relished by the spiders are captured by Mr. Beck and guided over the ground close to the doors of the nests to provide food for his charges.

THE TREASURE IS A TRAPDOOR SPIDER'S NEST

Francis E. Beck holds a nest which he has just removed from the gray adobe soil of the southern California foothills. Numerous little mounds scattered over an area of several miles formed an ideal location for the colonies of spiders. They seemed to know the protection afforded, for no water could stand on these knolls and the slope was just enough to drain without washouts.

A trapdoor spider is careful not to let the door close behind her when she is making a capture, for the cover is difficult to reopen, once it snaps shut. The door fits so tightly in the tube that there is only a fine crack where a claw could be inserted to lift it. To forestall being locked out of her own home, the spider always leaves her hind legs and a part of her abdomen under the open door (see illustration, page 233).

Considerable patience is necessary to study the habits of trapdoor spiders. Many hours of watchful waiting and sometimes whole nights pass without even a glimpse of a wary spider. It is discouraging to sit in a cramped position for hours, with eyes concentrated on a particular trapdoor, only to discover that this is one of the nights the spider is not inclined to labor.

On many occasions we have returned home after tramping for miles over good

A HOMEMADE ZOO FOR TRAPDOOR SPIDERS

The boxes contain "transplanted" or captive spiders living in their nests within blocks of adobe earth, dug from the field. Hundreds of sow bugs are caught and fed to the spiders by placing them on the ground near the trapdoors. The spiders crouch below, and when they feel or hear an insect approach they spring out and make a capture.

spider territory without finding a single nest, so cleverly are they hidden.

Sixteen species of trapdoor spiders have been found by naturalists in the United States. Of these, eight are recorded exclusively from California. Others occur throughout the Southern and Southwestern States, with one species occurring as far north in Virginia as the Potomac (see page 200).

Trapdoor spiders prefer high, dry ground for their nests; but even then they are not present unless conditions are favorable. They have been known to vanish from their natural habitat when virgin land is opened to farming. Probably plowing and cultivating destroy the nests and kill the spiders.

Some species of these spiders, which are almost identical with those that build doors to their nests, construct a home similar to that of their relatives, but with no trapdoor.

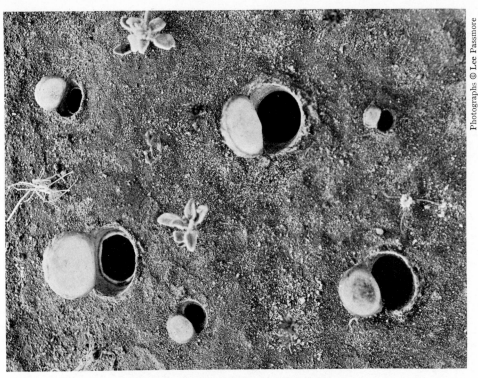

Photographs © Lee Passmore

A TRAPDOOR SPIDER COLONY WELL CAMOUFLAGED

The female spider deftly covers the top of her trapdoor with earth similar to the surrounding surface, to hide it from the view of unsuspecting sow bugs, grasshoppers, and other favorite insects. If the nest is located in mossy soil, the spider will stick the roots of living moss into the door as expertly as a true gardener. The nests vary in depth from two to nine

THESE TRAPDOORS WERE OPENED BY HAND

Female spiders living as close together as this seldom see their next-door neighbors (see illustration opposite). They never voluntarily come out of their nests and crawl around the ground. When feeding at night, the door is open only for a fraction of a second while the spider makes a capture, but always part of the body is kept in the opening of the nest to prevent

Photographs © Lee Passmore

SHE DROPS BACK INTO HER NEST WITH A VICTIM

Part of the captured sow bug protrudes above the spider. All eight of the appendages or legs radiating from the spider's cephalothorax and two of the breathing sacs on the abdomen are visible in this remarkable flash-light photograph.

A JACK-IN-THE-BOX SPIDER POUNCES ON HER PREY

The spider has just pushed back her cork-type lid and is about to sink her poison fangs into an unfortunate sow bug. The camera has caught the split-second action of a trapdoor spider feeding (see text, page 230, and illustration, opposite page).

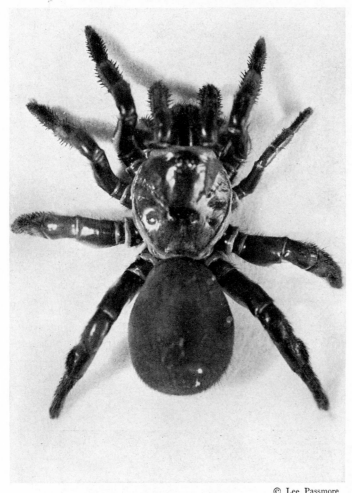

© Lee Passmore

A SPIDER AMAZON GROWS A NEW LEG

Only the lower animals are capable of replacing lost limbs, and the trapdoor spider is one. Her new leg, second on the right side, is almost fully developed (see text, page 245).

juring it, until he could lift out the entire block of earth. After cutting away the outer covering of soil, he exposed a perfect web nest of the female spider. The lady had not been harmed in any way, and, "transplanted" to Mr. Beck's nursery, she became his first specimen.

MALE PREFERS BACH-
ELOR APARTMENTS

After the first year in captivity, she raised no young, although she deposited eggs regularly. These she devoured, for she apparently knew that they were infertile.

The male spider does not inhabit the same nest with the female, so we looked elsewhere for him.

Once when we were digging out a female nest we noticed a peculiar little heap of loose earth close to the door. Curious, we dug carefully around the burrow and, upon reaching a depth of three inches, we lifted out an entire tube. It proved to be a male trapdoor spider's nest, the first we had found in ten years' search (see illustration, page 237).

Mr. Beck found his first trapdoor spider accidentally in Balboa Park, San Diego. He was attracted to an object which resembled a silver half-dollar lying on the ground. Stooping to pick it up, he discovered it was an abandoned door to a spider's nest. Beside it was a new door. Inserting his knife between the door and the inner side of the tubelike opening, he finally succeeded in lifting the lid and found the owner clinging to the under side.

The next time he went to the nest he was prepared to dig spider and home out of the ground. He trenched around the tube, keeping far enough away to avoid in-

Except for an adult specimen presented to us by the O'Rourke Institute of San Diego, the little male is the only living male trapdoor spider we ever saw. We offer our observation here only as an opinion based on our discovery, and do not make a positive claim that all male spiders build nests.

At home, we laid our captive on some earth in a box and placed over him a small glass jar, covered with a black envelope to keep out the light.

The following morning we discovered our little male spider had burrowed. Above his tube was a heap of loose earth similar to that we had seen in the field.

Two months later we opened one side of his box and found the little fellow alive and extremely active, running up and down a burrow not more than a quarter of an inch wide and three inches deep.

It appears from our evidence that the male trapdoor spider builds a nest entirely different in its surface appearance from that of the female. This nest had no hinged door.

HOW A SPIDER BUILDS ITS TRAPDOOR NEST

The female spiders seldom raise their doors in the daytime, unless the light is subdued or they are extremely hungry. We can occasionally tempt them out by imitating the tread of insects crawling near the nests, but they quickly detect the deceit and refuse to leap more than once or twice.

In order to make a series of photographs showing how the trapdoor spider builds her nest and fits it with a water-tight, cork-type door, we filled a small box with adobe soil covered with growing moss, and put upon it, in an upright position, two inches of the door end of a spider's nest containing the female.

After several hours of patient waiting, the spider raised her door and brought some moss, which she dropped over the side of the standing tube. She repeated this maneuver until all the moss had

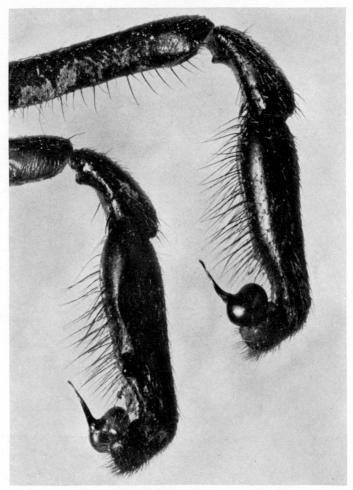

© Lee Passmore

THE CLAWLIKE FEELERS OF THE MALE TRAPDOOR SPIDER

Only the first three joints of the feelers appear, greatly enlarged. When the eggs are fertilized, the bulblike organs with sharp claws lift the covers of the sacs, exposing the eggs, and permit the semen to enter.

been cleared from the bottom of the tube.

Next, particles of earth were brought to the opening and flicked to a considerable distance with her feelers, or palpi. Upon lifting the door occasionally and peering into the tube, we could see her as she labored digging out the soil. Deeper and deeper she excavated, presently disappearing in the new burrow.

In the morning we removed the old nest and exposed the new one, but the spider by this time was down in the ground, entirely out of sight. To keep out the light during the day, we placed a tin box over this opening.

SHE HURLS A STONE HEAVIER THAN HER OWN WEIGHT

The spider shown in the photograph is bringing a large stone to the surface, holding it with her feelers. She seemed to have little difficulty.

TRAGEDY ENTERS THE BURROWS

A trapdoor spider will never allow another to enter her nest, and when two meet while excavating they fight until death.

Photographs © Lee Passmore

Photographs © Lee Passmore

A MALE TRAPDOOR SPIDER IN ITS PECULIAR BURROW

After years of search, this little fellow, uncovered accidentally, was the only male spider found by the author and his friend, Mr. F. E. Beck. They believe that the male builds a little heap of earth over his nest instead of the usual door. On three different occasions this male built a burrow exactly like the one in the photograph (see text, page 234). The male is considerably smaller than the female.

THE SPIDER BECOMES A VICTIM OF HER GUEST

The skeleton which lies at the bottom of the burrow is all that is left of the spider after a wasp larva has fed on its tissues (see illustration, page 246). The cocoon above was spun by the grub, which later will break its way out as a perfect spider wasp like its parent. Then, emerging from the burrow, the fledgling wasp flies away to look for a mate and another spider host to repeat the cycle.

237

© Lee Passmore

LIKE MOTHER LIKE DAUGHTER

The small spider, about a year old, built a tiny nest only a few inches away from that of its parent and exactly like it in every detail. As she becomes larger, she will tear the walls away, enlarge the opening, and construct a new burrow. The figures are slightly enlarged.

continued this process until the cover extended a third of the way across the opening (see illustration, page 243).

At this point we began to wonder how the little worker would manufacture a hinge for her front door, but she soon solved this problem in simple fashion. She raised the partly made door and bent it back to a vertical position. Naturally, it cracked in a straight line near the edge of the opening, but the flexible, reinforced webbing prevented separation from the side of the burrow. The fastening thus made was a hinge of amazing strength and durability.

WORKS WHILE HOLDING THE DOOR

Holding the door in a vertical position, she continued alternately to add earth and webbing to the outer edges until the door was completed.

Frequently during construction the spider would pull up tiny bunches of moss and plant it on the top of her door, carefully sticking the roots into the earth as an expert gardener might do. Today the moss is growing over the entire surface of the door and the nest is well camouflaged (see illustration, page 232).

While surfacing the underside of her door with webbing, the spider continued the process down into the tube and applied a fine silky lining to the walls of her nest. It was beautifully finished from the top to the bottom with a lustrous coating as smooth as paint.

Soon after dark she again began to bring up more earth and make preparations to build a trapdoor to her new nest. She manipulated her sharp fangs as picks, smoothing the edges of the opening and trimming away all roughness. Then she brought damp soil from the bottom and applied it to the side of the entrance, packing it down solidly with her fangs and mandibles.

After adding fresh earth each time, she would turn around, bring her spinnerets into position, and with graceful movements weave a trail of silky webbing. She

Next, the spider pressed her two sharp fangs deep into the soft earth on the underside of the door near the outer edge. She did this several times, until she seemed satisfied with the holes, or "eye-bolts."

Then, inserting her fangs again, she pulled the door shut in a succession of violent jerks. By degrees the door was drawn into the tube; and since both surfaces were soft and pliable, they soon fitted together as perfectly as a compression valve, making the nest water-tight. This last operation completed the nest. The building had consumed about sixteen hours of actual working time.

Her work finished, the little creature closed her door and no doubt found a safe and comfortable place at the bottom of her new burrow where she could rest from her labors.

We tried to lift the door next day, but found the spider was on the job. She had a good grip on the lid with her fangs.

© Lee Passmore

TRAPDOOR SPIDERS ARE HIS HOBBY

For more than ten years the author and Mr. F. E. Beck, who allows his charges to crawl over him, have been gathering these peculiar spiders and studying their solitary habits. Trapdoor spiders still remain among the least-known creatures of the animal world.

SEVENTEEN MONTHS WITH NO FOOD

Later, we obtained a photograph of this spider capturing a sow bug, the first victim to be caught from the new nest (see illustration, page 233).

Trapdoor spiders sometimes hibernate, but at no given period or season, as does the true hibernating animal. We have found on numerous occasions the nests of the spiders tightly sealed with earth just below the doors. One specimen was kept under observation for more than 17 months, the spider living in self-imposed solitary confinement during that time, with no way of procuring food. At the end of her hibernation she removed the seal and appeared fresh and clean. She had shed her outer skin.

The mother spider seals the door also when she is about to lay her eggs, for she must not be disturbed at this time. Sometimes seals are made of thin web, stretched tightly across the opening.

This we thought at first was for the purpose of keeping the young spiders in the

Photographs © Lee Passmore

THE SPIDER USES WEBBING AS A CONVEYOR BELT

When the female spider is excavating, instead of carrying small bits of earth to the surface one at a time, she spins sticky webbing over the mass, making the earth cling to the web by stirring it about. Then she pulls the webbing to the surface as a sailor would pull a coil of rope from the hold

SHE EATS HER OWN INFERTILE EGGS

In a little more than an hour the spider devoured about 300 eggs. When she had finished her repast, the spider appeared no larger than she did before commencing, even though the egg mass was the size of her abdomen. About half of the uneaten eggs had fallen from the sac and lay at the bottom of

240

Photographs © Lee Passmore

THE MOTHER STAYS CLOSE TO HER EGGS

When the spiderlings are hatched and ready to leave the sac, the mother makes an opening through which they emerge, to swarm over her body and around the walls of the nest. The door is usually sealed during incubation.

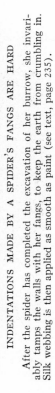

INDENTATIONS MADE BY A SPIDER'S FANGS ARE HARD

After the spider has completed the excavation of her burrow, she invariably tamps the walls with her fangs, to keep the earth from crumbling in. Silk webbing is then applied as smooth as paint (see text, page 235).

Photographs © Lee Passmore

NOT TWO SPIDERS—BUT ONE AND A DISCARDED SKIN

This spider, having shed only two days before, was too weak to move, and had to be lifted into the position shown in the photograph. Trapdoor spiders (see text, page 244) begin to shed when they are two months old.

A TRAPDOOR SPIDER LINES A JAR WITH A FILMY WEB

Placed in the jar on a dark shelf and forgotten, this lady spider tried to make a nest out of her temporary home. When found, the jar looked as if it contained milk, for web lining covered the walls but not the top.

Photographs © Lee Passmore

A PIN IS NOT ENOUGH WHEN SHE CLINGS WITH HER FANGS

Usually, when the door is shut, the spider grips with her fangs the two small holes near the top of the lid and braces her legs against the walls of the nest. A knife blade bends when attempts are made to pry open the door (see text, page 245).

A SPIDER BUILDS A TRAPDOOR

Holding the door vertical and standing on her head, the spider has brought her spinnerets into position and is applying a spray of web over the edges and the under surface. Damp earth is used for reinforcing, especially in that part where the hinge is located (see text, page 238).

243

nest, but we had to abandon the theory when we found webless nests containing young spiders. The latter seem to enjoy the warmth of the sun, for often during the day they cluster around the opening just below the door and retreat to the bottom of the tube only when the surface of the earth becomes cooler with the approach of night.

We have never found young spiders in the nests of females which have been held in captivity for more than one year. To the contrary, all nests brought from the hills unbroken and containing eggs produced the usual two or three hundred young spiders.

THE VICTIM BECOMES THE KILLER

When extreme hunger causes the spider to capture her prey in the daytime (and this often occurs), she is attracted to her door by the vibration of any insect that walks over the ground near her nest. She may even mistake for the usual sow bug a spider wasp (*Pepsis mildei*), her most deadly enemy, which, alighting by her door, she recognizes too late (see illustration, page 246).

In the struggle the wasp stings and paralyzes the spider, rendering her entirely defenseless. The door to the nest being open, the wasp enters the burrow, dragging its helpless victim to the bottom, and deposits an egg in or on the living spider.

The grub, when hatched, burrows into the body of its host and feeds on its tissues, but does not attack such vital organs as the heart. The spider lives with the grub within it, usually until nearly time for the latter's pupation. The grub then spins a silken cocoon around itself. Later it breaks its way out and appears in the form of a perfect spider wasp, which after mating finds another spider host to repeat the cycle (see illustration, page 237).

When death comes to the owner of a nest, no other trapdoor spider will take possession.

Spiders, like snakes, are the object of man's instinctive fear, and the first impulse of the average person upon encountering either is to destroy them. With few exceptions, however, spiders are harmless and will not bite if left undisturbed. The venom of a trapdoor spider acts very quickly on small insects, but it is not considered dangerous to a human being.

Since they are all carnivorous creatures and maintain themselves by preying upon insects which are real pests, the spider is far more beneficial than harmful to man.

SPIDERS ARE HELPLESS WHEN THEY SHED

The most critical periods in the life of a trapdoor spider occur when it is shedding. The hard, non-living, shell-like outer skin, becoming too small for the growing spider, is cast off.

The trapdoor spiders usually shed in July, August, and September—that is, before the rainy season. In preparation for this period, they fortify their nests to guard against possible intrusion. Seals of well-packed earth placed just below the lid fill the entrance completely.

Once, when we were watching a transplanted spider building her new nest (see illustration, page 242), we noticed that she had stopped digging for no apparent reason. Upon investigating, we found our spider was shedding.

First, the shell-like upper surface of the cephalothorax, or anterior portion of the body, separated from the lower part and the skin covering the abdomen shriveled and peeled off. Then the body of the spider appeared, heaving and pulling as she endeavored to withdraw her tender limbs from their outgrown coverings.

It required more than an hour for the spider to separate herself from the cuticle, and she remained motionless for some time after emerging, completely overcome with the exertion. She seemed to have no control of her legs.

Standing beside her was the old casing, so little disturbed that it might easily have been mistaken for another spider. The betraying characteristic of the empty shell was the abdominal portion, which was not so prominent as that of the living spider.

The spider herself resembled an almost transparent wax model, reflecting light like a piece of glass. Even the fangs were white and the mandibles quite colorless. The only parts which showed any color were the eyes, the abdomen, and the coarse hair that sparsely covered her appendages.

Three hours later the spider became darker, first a pale blue and then a greenish blue. Within two days she was quite dark. On the third day she died, presumably from exposure to the open air and light.

Occasionally we uncovered evidence of the resourcefulness of the trapdoor spider in times of emergency, such as when her home is destroyed.

When a nest is built in soft gray adobe, the hot summer sun causes the earth to crack in deep crevices around it. A heavy rainfall fills these cracks and sometimes washes away the walls of the burrow. Soon the nest fills with the loosened soil and the once cozy home with silk-lined walls is ruined.

During the deluge the spider seeks shelter beneath her door, where she remains in safety until the storm is over.

If the door and beveled edges to the opening remain in good order, she rebuilds the damaged home alongside the original. It often happens that a spider completes her new nest just as another rainstorm comes, and she must go through the whole process again. We found one nest that had been rebuilt six times, the burrows being located side by side and all under the same trapdoor.

In contrast to her size and weight, the strength of the trapdoor spider is remarkable. She is capable of resisting a lift

© Lee Passmore

SOWBUGS, BEWARE; THE DOOR IS RISING

Under the cork-type lid of her nest the California trapdoor spider awaits her prey. It is night, her hunting time, and only the flashlight reveals the widening crevice.

which we estimated at 10 pounds or more on her door. We came to this conclusion by the force we had to exert when prying upon the door with a strong knife blade. It would bend almost to the breaking point. Sometimes the web lining near the top of the burrow bears witness to her struggles to retain a hold, and the rims of the holes in the door are torn out by the pull of her fangs (see illustration, page 243).

SPIDERS MAY REPLACE LOST LIMBS

Only members of the lower orders of animals are able to reproduce lost limbs. The trapdoor spider has this peculiar

THE SPIDER WASP IS A TREACHEROUS ENEMY

Sometimes the female spider captures its prey in the daytime and instead of a harmless sow bug finds herself in deadly combat with this wasp. Usually she is stung and paralyzed by the wasp, which then carries her down into the burrow. The wasp then lays an egg in or on the spider's body. Later the egg hatches into a grub, which burrows about in the spider and eventually destroys it (see text, page 244, and illustration, page 237).

power. However, we have found only one spider, among the thousands which have come under our observation, that bore evidence of having grown a new leg. This particular specimen was full-grown, and except for the dwarfed size of the second leg on the right side, it was normal. The spider favored this smaller appendage as it walked. She would raise the small leg off the ground and carry it elevated, occasionally putting it down gently, as if it were causing her pain (see illustration, page 234).

How she lost her leg we do not know, but we believe perhaps a bird caught and tore it away from the body before the spider scuttled into the sanctuary of her burrow.

There is a remarkable difference between the palpi, or feelers, of the male and those of the female (see illustration, page 235). The female's feelers, long and strongly built, are used in building her nest. The male's feelers, however, play an important part when the eggs are fertilized.

The small, bulblike organ with a tiny claw extending from it serves to raise the cover of the reproductive organ of the female and expose the eggs for fertilization.

It is our belief that the male spider goes to the entrance of the female's home when mating occurs.

Our study of these solitary creatures continues, and we hope in time to solve many of the problems which as yet remain mysteries to us.

INDEX

ORGANIZED FOR "THE INCREASE AND DIFFUSION OF GEOGRAPHIC KNOWLEDGE"

TO carry out the purposes for which it was founded forty-seven years ago the National Geographic Society publishes this Magazine monthly. All receipts are invested in the Magazine itself or expended directly to promote geographic knowledge.

ARTICLES and photographs are desired. For material which the Magazine can use, generous remuneration is made. Contributions should be accompanied by addressed return envelope and postage.

IMMEDIATELY after the terrific eruption of the world's largest crater, Mt. Katmai, in Alaska, a National Geographic Society expedition was sent to make observations of this remarkable phenomenon. Four expeditions have followed and the extraordinary scientific data resulting given to the world. In this vicinity an eighth wonder of the world was discovered and explored—"The Valley of Ten Thousand Smokes," a vast area of steaming, spouting fissures. As a result of The Society's discoveries this area has been created a National Monument by proclamation of the President of the United States.

AT an expense of over $50,000 The Society sent a notable series of expeditions into Peru to investigate the traces of the Inca race. Their discoveries form a large share of our knowledge of a civilization waning when Pizarro first set foot in Peru.

THE Society also had the honor of subscribing a substantial sum to the expedition of Admiral Peary, who discovered the North Pole, and contributed $55,000 to Admiral Byrd's Antarctic Expedition.

NOT long ago The Society granted $25,000, and in addition $75,000 was given by individual members to the Government when the congressional appropriation for the purpose was insufficient, and the finest of the giant sequoia trees of California were thereby saved for the American people.

THE Society's notable expeditions to New Mexico have pushed back the historic horizons of the Southwestern United States to a period nearly eight centuries before Columbus crossed the Atlantic. By dating the ruins of the vast communal dwellings in that region The Society's researches have solved secrets that have puzzled historians for three hundred years. The Society is sponsoring an ornithological survey of Venezuela.

TO further the study of solar radiation in relation to long range weather forecastings, The Society has appropriated $65,000 to enable the Smithsonian Institution to establish a station for six years on Mt. Brukkaros, in South West Africa.

OTHER AUTHORITATIVE PUBLICATIONS

THE BOOK OF FISHES
By JOHN OLIVER LA GORCE and Other Authorities
Color Portraits by HASHIME MURAYAMA
92 salt- and fresh-water fishes in full color;
134 other illustrations; 243 pages
*Royal Octavo (7 x 10 in.) Dark Green Cloth
Binding, $2.*

THE BOOK OF BIRDS
By HENRY W. HENSHAW
Paintings by LOUIS AGASSIZ FUERTES
331 subjects in full color; 129 other illustrations;
252 pages
*Royal Octavo (7 x 10 in.) Orange Cloth
Binding, $2.*

THE CAPITAL OF OUR COUNTRY
By CHARLES MOORE
The late CHIEF JUSTICE WILLIAM HOWARD TAFT,
GILBERT GROSVENOR, J. R. HILDEBRAND,
and the late VISCOUNT BRYCE
16 full-page color plates, 118 black and white
engravings; 2 maps; 154 pages
Royal Octavo (7 x 10 in.) De Luxe Binding, $1.

THE BOOK OF WILD FLOWERS
By WILLIAM JOSEPH SHOWALTER and Other
Authorities
Paintings by MARY E. EATON; *Micro-paintings
by* E. J. GESKE
250 flowers and plants in exact color; 26 other
engravings; 250 flower biographies; 243 pages
*Royal Octavo (7 x 10 in.) Forest Green Cloth
Binding, $3.*

THE VALLEY OF TEN THOUSAND SMOKES
By ROBERT F. GRIGGS
*Leader, Katmai-Alaska Expeditions of the
National Geographic Society*
233 engravings and color plates; 9 special maps;
340 pages
Royal Octavo (7 x 10 in.) Blue Cloth Binding, $3.

WILD ANIMALS OF NORTH AMERICA
By EDWARD W. NELSON
Paintings by LOUIS AGASSIZ FUERTES
127 full-color portraits; 95 photographs and
track sketches; 254 pages
*Royal Octavo (7 x 10 in.) Mulberry Cloth
Binding, $2.*

THE BOOK OF DOGS
Paintings by LOUIS AGASSIZ FUERTES
102 exceptional dog portraits in color; 38 half-
tones; 109 pages
*Royal Octavo (7 x 10 in.) Brown Cloth
Binding, $1.*

HORSES OF THE WORLD
By MAJOR GENERAL WILLIAM HARDING CARTER
24 color portraits by EDWARD HERBERT MINER;
72 engravings; 118 pages
Royal Octavo (7 x 10 in.) De Luxe Binding, $1.50.

CATTLE OF THE WORLD
By DR. ALVIN HOWARD SANDERS
Editor Emeritus of the Breeder's Gazette
45 subjects in full color; 94 monochrome
illustrations; 142 pages
Royal Octavo (7 x 10 in.) De Luxe Binding, $1.50.

SCENES FROM EVERY LAND
(Fourth Series)
By GILBERT GROSVENOR
200 full-page illustrations, 23 in 4 colors; 20,000
words of text
Royal Octavo (7 x 10 in.) Gray Cloth Binding, $1.

MAPS FOR WALL AND DESK USE

The following maps in color, especially prepared by The Society's cartographers, are available on order for *50 cents each on paper, 75 cents each on linen:* Africa* (29 x 31½ inches) ; Asia* (38¼ x 31 inches) ; Europe and the Near East* (39 x 34¼ inches) ; South America (28 x 38¾ inches) ; United States* (40¾ x 26¾ inches) ; Mexico, Central America, and the West Indies* (24 x 41 inches) ; The Antarctic Regions (26½ x 19¾ inches) ; The Arctic Regions (20⅛ x 18⅞ inches) ; Islands of the Pacific (25 x 19 inches) ; George Washington's Travels (29⅛ x 20 inches). Map of North America (28 x 38¼ inches) *on paper only, 50 cents. . . .* A new World Map* (23 x 44 inches) will be available after December, 1935, for *50 cents on paper, 75 cents on linen.*
All Books and Maps postpaid in United States and Possessions.
For mailing to other countries, add 25 cents each.
*Index booklets available at 25 cents each, additional.

BOUND VOLUMES OF THE NATIONAL GEOGRAPHIC MAGAZINE

A limited number of bound volumes of THE GEOGRAPHIC, beginning with the year 1924, are available. There are six numbers to the volume, two volumes to the year. Bound in half morocco, *$5 per volume. Postpaid in United States and Possessions. For mailing to other countries, add 75 cents per volume.*

NATIONAL GEOGRAPHIC SOCIETY, WASHINGTON, D. C., U. S. A.
Illustrated catalogue describing these and other publications sent upon request.